US Army
STANDARD MILITARY
MOTOR VEHICLES

1943

GRESHAM BOOKS

First published 1943
This facsimile edition published 1979

ISBN 0 905418 46 8

Gresham Books,
Unwin Brothers Limited,
The Gresham Press,
Old Woking,
Surrey, England

Reproduced from original edition, and printed and bound in
Great Britain by A. Wheaton & Co. Ltd., Exeter.

STANDARD MILITARY MOTOR VEHICLES

Prepared under the direction of the
Chief of Ordnance

INTRODUCTION
TO THIS EDITION

TM 9-2800, of which this is a facsimile reprint, was the basic US Army Technical Manual giving data and illustrations of all the vehicles and trailers in service at the time of publication. Though there were several different editions, this September 1943 version, published at the mid-point of World War 2 is probably the most representative because it includes both early vehicles like the M3 medium tanks, and the first of the M4 medium series with the 76mm gun (page 106), the M4E6, later standardised as the M4 (76mm), etc, through the series.

It is also worth pointing out that the gun motor carriage T70 (page 70) was later standardised as the M18. Aside from from the self-explanatory classification 'standard', other equipment was classified 'limited standard', being not entirely satisfactory for universal service but suitable for issue and use when necessary. The further classification 'substitute standard' was usually given to obsolescent or expedient equipment due for early replacement which could still be issued and used pending availability of new equipment.

Fuller explanations of these terms and the terminology used in the book are given on page 4 and 5 in the original 1943 introduction.

STANDARD MILITARY MOTOR VEHICLES

CONTENTS

		Pages
Introduction and explanation of terminology		4
Classification		5
SECTION I.	Amphibians and landing vehicles	6–15
II.	Armored cars	16–23
III.	Scout cars	24–25
IV.	Cargo and personnel carriers	26–45
V.	Self-propelled artillery	46–87
VI.	Tanks	88–125
VII.	Tank transport and recovery vehicles	126–135
VIII.	Trucks	
	Truck, ¼-ton, 4 x 4 through Truck, 1½-ton, 4 x 2	136–191
	Truck, 1½-ton, 4 x 4 through Truck, 2½-ton, 6 x 4	192–237
	Truck, 2½-ton, 6 x 6 complete	238–277
	Truck, 4-ton, 4 x 4 through Truck, 10-ton, 6 x 6	278–313
IX.	Truck tractors	314–333
X.	Tractors	334–353
XI.	Ambulances	354–361
XII.	Busses	362–371
XIII.	Passenger cars	372–375
XIV.	Motorcycles	376–381
XV.	Trailers	382–459
XVI.	Semitrailers	460–527
XVII.	Dollies	528–541
XVIII.	Chart of responsibilities and index	542–552

INTRODUCTION

Data and illustrations herein are from the most reliable sources available at date of publication. Production variations and changes account for some discrepancies. It is suggested that such differences or additional pertinent information be brought to the attention of Military Publications Section, Executive Branch, Tank-Automotive Center, Detroit, Michigan, at the earliest possible moment, for use in preparation of future editions.

Information on responsibility of maintenance, storage and issue is given in section XVIII. This section also contains an index, and shows classification according to general purpose, special equipment or special purpose.

More detailed information will be found in the Technical Manuals listed for each vehicle.

EXPLANATION OF TERMINOLOGY USED

The term "maximum gradability" indicates the steepest slope the vehicle can negotiate in low gear.

Ordnance practice of determining slope in terms of percent is the same as is customary in other technical fields such as surveying and construction of roads and railroad grades.

Percent of slope is defined as the ratio between the vertical rise and the horizontal distance travelled.

Some confusion arises from the practice of measuring angles in degrees. Examples of slopes measured in terms of degree of angle and percent of slope follow:

Degree of angle	Percent of slope
0°	0%
10°	17.633%
30°	57.735%
45°	100%

SNL   Standard Nomenclature List.

6 x 4   Six wheels, four driving wheels.

Angle of approach   Angle of Departure

w/w   With winch.

wo/w   Without winch.

Net weight   Weight of vehicle in operating condition without crew or payload.

4

CLASSIFICATION

The vehicles in this manual are classified in the following manner, in accordance with Army Regulations 850-25, paragraph 13:

a. Standard Vehicles are the most advanced and satisfactory that have been adopted by the Secretary of War and are those which are preferred for procurement to meet supply demands.

b. Substitute Standard Vehicles are those which do not have as satisfactory military characteristics as standard vehicles but are usable substitutes for standard vehicles. They are not normally in use or available for issue to meet supply demands but would, when necessary, be procured to supplement the supply of standard vehicles.

c. Limited Standard Vehicles are those which do not have as satisfactory military characteristics as standard vehicles, but are usable substitutes for standard vehicles, and are either in use or available for issue to meet supply demands. Complete major units will not be reproduced but component parts and complementary articles, even though they may be limited standard articles, may be procured if necessary to maintain the complete major units in serviceable condition.

The wheeled vehicles in the manual are further classified in the following manner, in accordance with Army Regulations 850-15, paragraph 3:

a. General Purpose Vehicles are all wheeled vehicles intended for movement of personnel, supplies, ammunition, or equipment or towing of guns, trailers, or semitrailers, and which are used by more than one service.

b. Special Equipment Vehicles are wheeled vehicles, the chassis of which are basically identical to those used in general purpose vehicles, but which have a special body or special equipment mounted thereon.

c. Special Purpose Vehicles are wheeled vehicles, the chassis and body of which are designed for a special purpose. These vehicles do not incorporate body or chassis of either general purpose vehicles or special equipment vehicles.

5

TRUCK, AMPHIBIAN, ¼-TON, 4 x 4

Technical Manual: TM 10-1263

Part List: SNL G-504

Manufacturer: Ford Motor Co.

RA PD 308923

Classification: Standard

Purpose: To transport personnel on land and water.

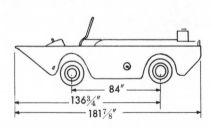

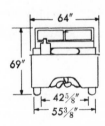

TRUCK, AMPHIBIAN, ¼-TON, 4 x 4

GENERAL DATA

Crew, operating.....2......Passenger capacity, including crew   5

Weight.................Net.......................(lb)   3,660

                       Payload.................(lb)   800

                       Gross...................(lb)   4,460

Shipping dimensions.......(cu ft)   (sq ft) 81

Tires..................Ply...6.........Size...6.00 x 16

Tread, center to center.............................(in.)   49

Ground clearance....................................(in.)   8⅞

Life preservers............Seat cushion type..............   5

Loaded waterline length..............................(in.) 165

Loaded freeboard:
    at coaming (in.)........Front 21...............Rear 19
    at deck (in.)...........Front 17..............Rear 9½

Loaded draft (in.) at front wheels 29¼.....at rear wheels 33½

Electrical system....................................(volts)   12

Capacities...............Fuel, 70 octane gasoline.....(gal)   15

                       Cooling system.............(qt)   13

                       Crankcase (refill)...........(qt)   4

Pintle height..(in.) 28¼

Brakes..Hydraulic

PERFORMANCE

Maximum gradability............................ (percent)   45

Turning radius (ft)........Land 18¼............Water 18

Angle of approach..................................(deg) 37½

Angle of departure.................................(deg)   37

Cruising range........Land.......................(miles) 250

              Water, top speed 2nd gear......(miles) 18¾

              Water, cruising speed 3rd gear..(miles)   37

Maximum allowable speed (mph):...............1st 2nd 3rd

                     Land..............24   41   60

                     Water..............   5.5 4.5

ENGINE

Manufacturer......Ford.....................Model GPW

Type.............In-line, 4 cycle.....Number of cylinders   4

Displacement.......................................(cu in.) 134

Governed speed............................Not governed

Brake horsepower....................................   60

Ignition type.......................................Battery

ADDITIONAL DATA

. . . .

TRUCK, AMPHIBIAN—2½-TON, 6 x 6

Technical Manuals: TM 9-802,   Parts List: SNL G-501
    TM 9-1802A, TM 9-1802B

Manufacturers: General Motors Truck and Coach Div. of Yellow Truck & Coach Mfg. Co.

Armament: Provision for installation of M36 truck mount for antiaircraft machine gun.

RA PD 308913

Classification: Standard

Purpose: To transport cargo and personnel on land and in water. This vehicle is popularly known as "The Duck."

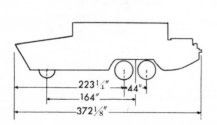

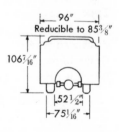

TRUCK, AMPHIBIAN, 2½-TON, 6 x 6

GENERAL DATA

Crew		2
Weight............Net.................(lb)		14,500
Payload................(lb)		5,000
Gross..................(lb)		19,850
Shipping dimensions.......(cu ft) ....(sq ft) 248		
Tires....................Ply 10.......Size 11.00 x 18		
Tread, center to center (in.).Front 63⁹⁄₁₆..........Rear 63⅞		
Ground clearance.........................(in.)		11¼
Life preservers............Jacket type.................		5
Life ring...		1
Loaded waterline length............................(in.)		344
Loaded freeboard: at coaming (in.).....Front 29.....Rear 29		
at deck (in.)........Front 24.....Rear 16		
Loaded draft (in.) at front wheels 42........at rear wheels 51		
Cargo space (cu ft):		
to top of coaming 198..............under tarp. bows 385		
Electrical system............................(volts)		6
Capacities..............Fuel, 70 octane gasoline....(gal)		40
Cooling system.............(qt)		20
Crankcase (refill)..........(qt)		10
Pintle height.........................(in.)		48
Brakes............................Hydraulic (Hydrovac)		

PERFORMANCE

Maximum gradability............................(percent)	60
Turning radius (ft)........Land—Left 36.........Right 35	
Water—Left 17½....Right 12½	
Angle of approach....................................(deg)	38
Angle of departure...................................(deg)	25
Cruising range.....Land..............................(miles)	240
Water......Top speed, 2nd gear (miles)	30
Water...Cruising speed, 3rd gear (miles)	50

Maximum allowable speed (mph)	1st	2nd	3rd	4th	5th
Land........	7	11	22	40	50
Water.......	—	6.4	5.4	—	—

ENGINE

Manufacturer......GMC....................Model 270	
Type............In-line, 4 cycle.....Number of cylinders	6
Displacement................................(cu in.)	269.5
Governed speed..............................(rpm)	2,750
Brake horsepower.................................	104
Ignition type...............................Battery	

ADDITIONAL DATA

Winch capacity.......................................(lb)	10,000

. . . .

. . . .

. . . .

LANDING VEHICLE, TRACKED, MK I—LVT (1)

Technical Manuals: TM 9-784,
TM 9-1784.

Parts List: SNL G-156

Manufacturers: See additional data.

RA PD 45420

Classification:

Purpose: For use in rough terrain, swamp land, and self-propulsion in exposed waters. Also used for landing on beach through surf.

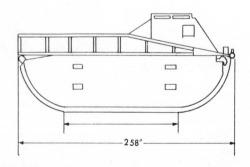

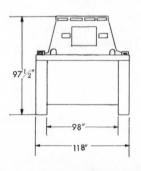

LANDING VEHICLE, TRACKED, MK I—LVT (1)

GENERAL DATA

Crew, operating.....3......Passenger capacity, including crew		24
Weight..................Unloaded................(lb)		27,500
Payload, including crew and		
passengers..............(lb)		4,500
Hoisting weight...........(lb)		32,000
Shipping dimensions........(cu ft) ....(sq ft)		
Track width.......................................(in.)		14¼
Ground clearance...................................(in.)		18¼
Ground pressure...........................(lb per sq in.)		10.25
Electrical system.................................(volts)		6
Capacities...............Fuel, 70 octane gasoline....(gal)		80
Cooling system............(qt)		44
Crankcase................(qt)		9
Brakes.......................................Mechanical		

PERFORMANCE

Maximum gradability.............................(percent)		38
Turning radius (ft)........Right ....Left		
Angle of approach.................................(deg)		46
Angle of departure................................(deg)		58
Fuel consumption, average conditions (land)...(miles per gal)		3
Cruising range, average conditions (miles) Land 225.Water 210		
Maximum allowable speed (mph) Land 10–12.......Water 5–6		
Number of speeds forward................................		3

ENGINE

Manufacturer......Hercules..............Model WXLC3		
Type.............In-line, 4 cycle.....Number of cylinders		6
Displacement.......................................(cu in.)		404
Governed speed....................................(rpm)		2,900
Brake horsepower..		146
Ignition type.......................................Battery		

ADDITIONAL DATA

This vehicle was produced first by Donald Roebling, and later in mass
production by Food Machinery Corporation, Borg-Warr.er Corporation, Graham-Paige, and St. Louis Car Company. This vehicle is now
out of production.

LANDING VEHICLE, TRACKED (UNARMORED), MK II—LVT (2)

Technical Manuals: Parts List: SNL G-167

Manufacturers: Borg-Warner Corp.; Food Machinery Corp.; Graham-Paige, and St. Louis Car Co.

Armament: One Gun, machine, cal. .50, HB M2; one to three Guns, machine, cal. .30, M1919A4 (flexible).

Ammunition: 2,000 rounds, cal. .30; 1,000 rounds, cal. .50.

RA PD 309076

Classification:

Purpose: For use in rough terrain, swamp land, and self-propulsion in exposed waters. Also used for landing on beach through surf.

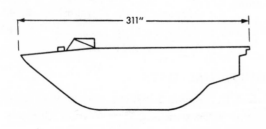

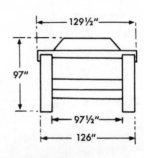

LANDING VEHICLE, TRACKED (UNARMORED)
MK II—LVT (2)

GENERAL DATA

Crew. 3–6
Weight. . . . . .Unloaded. . . . .(lb) 24,400
Payload, cargo, exclusive of
crew. . . . .(lb) 6,500
Hoisting weight. . . . .(lb) 30,900
Shipping dimensions. . . . .(cu ft) . . . .(sq ft)
Tread, center to center. . . . .(in.)
Track width. . . . .(in.) 14¼
Ground clearance. . . . .(in.) 18
Ground pressure, empty. . . . .(lb per sq in.) 9
Electrical system. . . . .(volts) 12
Capacities. . . . . .Fuel, 80 octane gasoline. . . .(gal) 106
Cooling system. . . . . . .Air-cooled
Oil tank. . . . .(qt) 23
Transmission and differential.(qt) 24
Brakes. . . . . .Mechanical
Communication. . . . . .Radio

PERFORMANCE

Maximum gradability, loaded. . . . .(percent) 63
Turning radius (ft). . . . . .Right . . . . .Left
Angle of approach. . . . .(deg) 35
Angle of departure. . . . .(deg) 30
Fuel consumption, average conditions. . . . .(miles per gal)
Cruising range, average conditions (miles) Land .Water
Maximum allowable speed (mph) Land 20. . . . . . . .Water 7.5
Number of speeds forward. . .Land 5. . . . . .Water

ENGINE

Manufacturer. . . . . . .Continental. . . . . .Model W670-9A
Type. . .Single row static radial, 4-cycle. . .Number of cylinders 7
Displacement. . . . .(cu in.) 667
Governed speed. . . . .(rpm) 2,400
Brake horsepower. . . . .(emergency use) 250
Ignition type. . . . . .Battery

ADDITIONAL DATA

This vehicle is an improved design of the Landing vehicle, tracked, Mark I
and incorporates a light tank M3 power train.

LANDING VEHICLE, TRACKED (ARMORED), ARMY TYPE, MK II—LVT (A) (2)

Technical Manuals:

Parts List: SNL G-168

Manufacturer: Food Machinery Corp.

Armament: One Gun, machine, cal. .50, HB M2 (flexible); one to three Guns, machine, cal. .30, M1919A4 (flexible).

Ammunition: 1,000 rounds, cal. .50; 2,000 rounds, cal. .30.

RA PD 309075

Classification:

Purpose: For use in rough terrain, swamp land, and self-propulsion in exposed waters. Also used for landing on beach through surf.

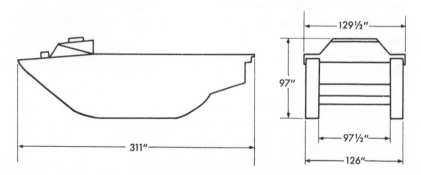

LANDING VEHICLE, TRACKED (ARMORED), ARMY TYPE, MK II—LVT (A) (2)

GENERAL DATA

Crew			4
Weight	Unloaded	(lb)	27,600
	Payload, cargo, exclusive of crew	(lb)	5,200
	Hoisting weight	(lb)	32,800
Shipping dimensions	(cu ft)	(sq ft)	
Track width		(in.)	14¼
Ground clearance		(in.)	18
Ground pressure, empty		(lb per sq in.)	10.2
Electrical system		(volts)	12
Capacities	Fuel, 80 octane gasoline	(gal)	104
	Cooling system	Air-cooled	
	Oil tank	(qt)	23
	Transmission and differential	(qt)	24
Brakes		Mechanical	
Communication		Radio	

PERFORMANCE

Maximum gradability, loaded	(percent)	60
Turning radius (ft) Right	Left	
Angle of approach	(deg)	35
Angle of departure	(deg)	30
Fuel consumption, average conditions	(miles per gal)	
Cruising range, average conditions (miles): Land 200 Water 60		
Maximum allowable speed (mph) Land 20 Water 7.5		
Number of speeds forward...Land 5 Water		

ENGINE

Manufacturer......Continental Model W670-9A		
Type...Single row static radial, 4 cycle...Number of cylinders		7
Displacement	(cu in.)	667
Governed speed	(rpm)	2,400
Brake horsepower	(emergency use)	250
Ignition type	Battery	

ADDITIONAL DATA

This vehicle is essentially the same as Landing vehicle, tracked, Mark II (unarmored) except for the addition of armor plate on certain parts of the vehicle.

CAR, ARMORED, LIGHT, M8, (6 x 6)

Technical Manual: TM 9-743   Parts List: SNL G-136

Manufacturer: Ford Motor Co.

Armament: One Gun, 37-mm, M6; one Gun, machine, cal. .30, M1919A4 (flexible).

Ammunition: 80 rounds, 37-mm; 400 rounds, cal. .30 (carbine) M1; 1500 rounds, cal. .30 (machine gun); 16 hand grenades; 4 Pots, smoke, M1 or M2; 6 Mines, antitank, HE, M1, with fuze, M1.

RA PD 308906

Classification: Standard

Purpose: To provide high speed mobility, defensive firepower, and crew protection for reconnaissance.

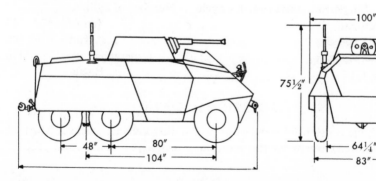

CAR, ARMORED, LIGHT, M8, (6 x 6)

GENERAL DATA

Crew... 4
Weight...............Gross.......................(lb) 16,500
Shipping dimensions........(cu ft) 695..........(sq ft) 194
Tires—Combat...........Ply...12......Size...9.00 x 20
Tread, center to center...............................(in.) 76
Ground clearance.....................................(in.) 11½
Ground pressure—tires, at 4-inch penetration....(lbs per sq in.) 11.7
Electrical system.....................................(volts) 12
Capacities..............Fuel, 70 octane gasoline.....(gal) 59
                        Cooling system..............(qt) 23
                        Crankcase (refill)...........(qt) 7
Brakes.............................Hydraulic (Hydrovac)
Communication..........Radio..............Interphone

PERFORMANCE

Maximum gradability..............................(percent) 60
Turning radius.......................................(ft) 27½
Fording depth..(in.) 32
Angle of approach....................................(deg) 60
Angle of departure...................................(deg) 60
Fuel consumption, average conditions.........(miles per gal) 7½
Cruising range, average conditions.................(miles) 400
Maximum allowable speed.........................(mph) 56

                              1st 2nd 3rd 4th
                Cruising speed.. 8   15   32   56

ENGINE

Manufacturer......Hercules..................Model JXD
Type.............In-line, 4 cycle.....Number of cylinders 6
Displacement...................................(cu in.) 320
Governed speed...........................Not governed
Brake horsepower................................. 110
Ignition type....................................Battery

ADDITIONAL DATA

....
....

CAR, ARMORED, T17E1, (4 x 4)

Technical Manuals: TM 9-741, TM 9-1741A,   Parts List: SNL G-122
TM 9-1741B, TM 9-1741C

Manufacturer: Chevrolet Motor Division (General Motors Corp.)

Armament: One Gun, 37-mm, M6; two Guns, machine, cal. .30, M1919A4 (flexible); one Gun, machine, cal. .30, M1919A4 (fixed); one Gun, sub-machine, cal. .45, M1928A1; one British smoke mortar.

Ammunition: 103 rounds, 37-mm; 450 rounds, cal. .45; 5,250 rounds, cal. .30; 12 hand grenades; 14 smoke projectiles.

RA PD 45963

Classification: None (British only)

Purpose: Special—To provide high speed mobility, defensive firepower, and crew protection for reconnaissance.

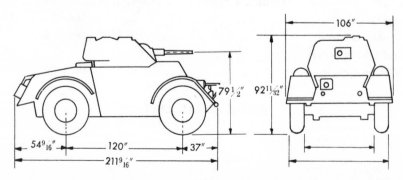

CAR, ARMORED, T17E1, (4 x 4)

GENERAL DATA

Crew... 5
Weight...................Gross...................(lb) 29,100
Shipping dimensions........(cu ft) 1,205..........(sq ft) 156
Tires—Combat............Ply......Size... 14.00 x 20
Tread, center to center.............................(in.) 89
Ground clearance....................................(in.) 13¼
Ground pressure—at 4-inch penetration........(lbs per sq in.) 17.95
Electrical system...................................(volts) 24
Capacities...............Fuel, 70 octane gasoline.....(gal) 137
                        Cooling system, each engine...(qt) 25
                        Crankcase (refill), each engine.(qt) 8
Brakes.....................Hydraulic (Twin Hydrovac)
Communication...........Radio...............Interphone

PERFORMANCE

Maximum gradability............................(percent) 57
Turning radius....................................(ft) 27½
Fording depth.....................................(in.) 32
Angle of approach................................(deg) 57
Angle of departure...............................(deg) 40
Fuel consumption, average conditions.........(miles per gal) 3.3
Cruising range, average conditions................(miles) 450
Maximum allowable speed (mph)...........low transfer case 24
                                       high transfer case 55

ENGINES (Two)

Manufacturer......GMC.....................Model 270
Type.............In-line, 4 cycle......Number of cylinders 6
Displacement......................................(cu in.) 269.5
Governed speed............................Not governed
Brake horsepower.................................... 104
Ignition type...................................Battery

ADDITIONAL DATA

....
....
....

19

CAR, ARMORED, T17E2, (4 x 4)

Technical Manuals: TM 9-741, TM 9-1741A,   Parts List: SNL G-122
TM 9-1741B, TM 9-1741C.

Manufacturer: Chevrolet Motor Division (General Motors Corp.)

Armament: Two Guns, machine, cal. .50, HB, M2; one Gun, submachine, cal. .45, M1928A1.

Ammunition: 2,610 rounds, cal. .50; 450 rounds, cal. .45; 12 hand grenades.

RA PD 308900

Classification: None (British only)

Purpose: To provide high speed mobility, defensive firepower, and crew protection for reconnaissance.

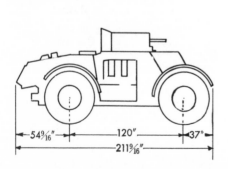
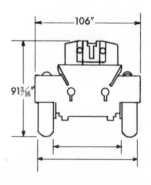

20

CAR, ARMORED, T17E2, (4 x 4)

GENERAL DATA

Crew. 3
Weight. . . . . .Gross. . . . .(lb)   26,000
Shipping dimensions. . . . . . .(cu ft)   . . . .(sq ft) 156
Tires—Combat. . . . . .Ply. . .   . . .Size . . . 14.00 x 20
Tread, center to center . . . .(in.)   89
Ground clearance. . . . .(in.) $13\frac{1}{4}$
Ground pressure—at 4-inch penetration. . . . . (lbs per sq in.)   15.4
Electrical system. . . . .(volts)   24
Capacities. . . . . .Fuel, 70 octane gasoline . . . . .(gal)   137
Cooling system, each. . . . .(qt)   25
Crankcase (refill) each. . . . .(qt)   8
Brakes. . . . . .Hydraulic (Twin Hydrovac)
Communication. . . . . .Radio. . . . . .Interphone

PERFORMANCE

Maximum gradability. . . . .(percent)   57
Turning radius. . . . .(ft) $27\frac{1}{2}$
Fording depth. . . . .(in.)   32
Angle of approach. . . . .(deg)   57
Angle of departure. . . . .(deg)   40
Fuel consumption, average conditions. . . . .(miles per gal)   3.3
Cruising range, average conditions. . . . .(miles)   450
Maximum allowable speed (mph). . . . . .low transfer case   24
high transfer case   55

ENGINES (Two)

Manufacturer. . . . . . .GMC. .Model 270
Type. . . . . .In-line, 4 cycle. . . . . . .Number of cylinders   6
Displacement. . . . .(in.)   269.5
Governed speed. . . . . .Not governed
Brake horsepower.   104
Ignition type. . . . . .Battery

ADDITIONAL DATA

. . . .
. . . .
. . . .
. . . .

CAR, ARMORED, UTILITY, M20, (6 x 6)

Technical Manual: TM 9-743   Parts List: SNL G-176

Manufacturer: Ford Motor Co.

Armament: One Gun, machine, cal. .50, HB, M2; five Carbines, cal. .30; one Launcher, rocket, AT, M1.

Ammunition: 1,000 rounds, cal. .50; 500 rounds, cal. .30; 12 hand grenades; 10 rockets, AT, M6.

RA PD 308907

Classification: Standard

Purpose: To provide a highly mobile armored personnel and cargo carrier and field commanders car.

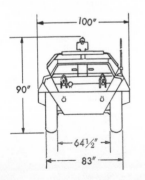

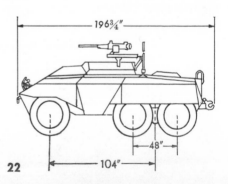

CAR, ARMORED, UTILITY, M20, (6 x 6)

GENERAL DATA

Crew...	6
Weight....................Gross....................(lb)	14,500
Shipping dimensions........(cu ft) 695...........(sq ft) 194	
Tires—Combat...........Ply...12......Size...9.00 x 20	
Tread, center to center..............................(in.)	76
Ground clearance....................................(in.)	11½
Ground pressure—at 3-inch penetration........(lbs per sq in.)	10.5
Electrical system...................................(volts)	12
Capacities...............Fuel, 70 octane gasoline.....(gal)	56
Cooling system..............(qt)	23
Crankcase (refill)...........(qt)	7
Brakes.........................Hydraulic (Hydrovac)	
Communication...........Radio.............Interphone	

PERFORMANCE

Maximum gradability...........................(percent)	60
Turning radius......................................(ft)	28
Fording depth......................................(in.)	32
Angle of approach.................................(deg)	60
Angle of departure................................(deg)	60
Fuel consumption, average conditions..........(miles per gal)	7
Cruising range, average conditions..................(miles)	400
Maximum allowable speed..........................(mph)	56

	1st	2nd	3rd	4th
Cruising speed.	8	15	32	56

ENGINE

Manufacturer.....Hercules..................Model JXD	
Type..............In-line, 4 cycle......Number of cylinders	6
Displacement.......................................(cu in.)	320
Governed speed...........................Not governed	
Brake horsepower.......................................	110

ADDITIONAL DATA

....

....

....

....

CAR, SCOUT, M3A1, (4 x 4)

Technical Manuals: TM 9-705, TM 9-1705, TM 9-1706, TM 9-1709.   Parts List: SNL G-67

Manufacturer: White Motor Co.

Armament: One Gun, machine, cal. .30, M1919A4, flexible; one Gun, machine, cal. .50, HB, M2, flexible; one Gun, submachine, cal. .45, M1928A1.

Ammunition: 8,000 rounds, cal. .30; 750 rounds, cal. .50; 540 rounds, cal. .45.

RA PD 66367

Classification: Standard

Purpose: To provide mobility and crew protection for reconnaissance in combat.

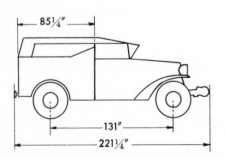
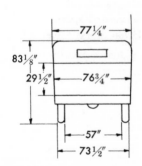

CAR, SCOUT, M3A1, (4 x 4)

GENERAL DATA

Crew, operating . . . . 2 . . . . Passenger capacity including crew   8
Weight . . . . Net . . . . (lb)   8,900
                          Payload . . . . (lb)   2,850
                          Gross . . . . (lb)   11,750
                          Boxed for export . . . . (lb)   12,951
Shipping dimensions . . . . (cu ft) 723 . . . . (sq ft) 118
Tires—Combat . . . . Size . . . 8.25 x 20
Tread, center to center (in.) . Front 63¼ . . . . Rear 65¼
Ground clearance . . . . (in.)   15¾
Ground pressure . . . . (lbs per sq in.)   60
Electrical system . . . . (volts)   12
Capacities . . . . Fuel, 70 octane gasoline . . . . . (gal)   30
                        Cooling system . . . . (qt)   19
                        Crankcase (refill) . . . . (qt)   6
Brakes . . . . Hydraulic (Hydrovac)
Communication . . . . Radio

PERFORMANCE

Maximum gradability . . . . (percent)   60
Turning radius . . . . (ft)   28½
Fording depth . . . . (in.)   28
Angle of approach . . . . (deg)   37
Angle of departure . . . . (deg)   35
Fuel consumption, average conditions . . . . (miles per gal)   8½
Cruising range, average conditions . . . . (miles)   250
Maximum allowable speed . . . . (mph)   55½

	1st	2nd	3rd	4th
Cruising speed . .	11.1	17.6	32.3	55.5

ENGINE

Manufacturer . . . . . . Hercules . . . . Model JXD
Type . . . . In-line, 4 cycle . . . . . . Number of cylinders   6
Displacement . . . . (cu in.)   320
Governed speed . . . . Not governed
Brake horsepower   110
Ignition type . . . . Battery

ADDITIONAL DATA

. . . .
. . . .
. . . .

CAR, HALF-TRACK, M2

Technical Manuals: TM 9-710A, TM 9-1710, Parts List: SNL G-102
TM 9-1710C, TM 9-1711.

Manufacturers: The Autocar Co.; White Motor Co.

Armament: One Gun, machine, cal. .50, HB, M2; one Gun, machine, cal. .30, M1919A4; one Gun, submachine, cal. .45, M1928A1.

Ammunition: 700 rounds, cal. .50; 7,750 rounds, cal. .30; 14 Mines, AT HE, M1, w/fuze; 10 hand grenades.

RA PD 309054

Classification: Standard

Purpose: To transport cargo and personnel in combat zone.

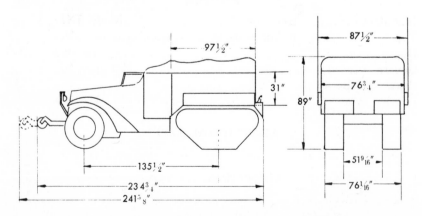

CAR, HALF-TRACK, M2

GENERAL DATA

Crew...		10
Weight.............Payload—w/winch...........(lb)		3140
Payload—w/o winch.........(lb)		3640
Gross.....................(lb)		17,800
Shipping dimensions........w/winch (cu ft) 896....(sq ft) 147		
w/o winch (cu ft) 868..(sq ft) 147		
Tires—Combat............Ply...12......Size...8.25 x 20		
Tread, center to center.....Front......................(in.)		$64\frac{1}{2}$
Track width...(in.)		$12\frac{1}{4}$
Ground clearance...(in.)		$11\frac{3}{16}$
Ground pressure, tires......................(lbs per sq in.)		29.4
Electrical system.................................(volts)		12
Capacities.............Fuel, 80 octane gasoline.....(gal)		60
Cooling system.............(qt)		26
Crankcase (refill)...........(qt)		12
Brakes.............................Hydraulic (Hydrovac)		
Communication.....................................Radio		

PERFORMANCE

Maximum gradability...........................(percent)		60
Turning radius (ft)........Right 30.............Left $29\frac{1}{2}$		
Fording depth....................................(in.)		32
Maximum vertical obstacle vehicle will climb............(in.)		12
Angle of approach (deg)....With winch 33..Without winch 37		
Angle of departure.................................(deg)		45
Fuel consumption, average conditions.........(miles per gal)		$2\frac{1}{2}$
Cruising range, average conditions...................(miles)		120
Maximum allowable speed..........................(mph)		45

	1st	2nd	3rd	4th
Cruising speed..	9	17	26	45

Manufacturer......White...................Model 160 AX		
Type.............In-line, 4 cycle.....Number of cylinders		6
Displacement....................................(cu in.)		386
Governed speed........................Not governed		
Brake horsepower..		148
Ignition type.....................................Battery		

ADDITIONAL DATA

Winch capacity.....................................(lb)		10,000

CAR, HALF-TRACK, M2A1

Technical Manuals: TM 9-710A, TM 9-1710,   Parts List: SNL G-102
TM 9-1710C, TM 9-1711.

Manufacturers: The Autocar Co.; White Motor Co.

Armament: One Gun, machine, cal. .50, HB M2, (flexible); one Gun, machine, cal. .30, M1919A4 (flexible); one Gun, submachine, cal. .45, M1928A1.

Ammunition: 700 rounds, cal. .50; 7,750 rounds, cal. .30; 540 rounds, cal. .45; 14 mines, AT HE, w fuze; 10 hand grenades.

RA PD 308917

Classification: Standard

Purpose: To transport cargo and personnel in combat zone.

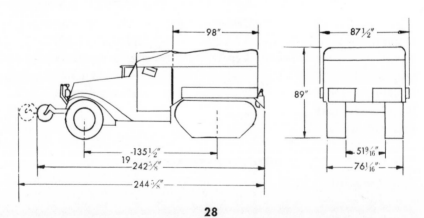

CAR, HALF-TRACK, M2A1

GENERAL DATA

Crew........			10
Weight........	Payload—w/winch.........(lb)		3,100
	Payload—w/o winch........(lb)		3,600
	Gross........(lb)		18,080
Shipping dimensions.......	w/winch (cu ft) 896....(sq ft) 147		
	w/o winch (cu ft) 868..(sq ft) 147		
Tires—Combat..........	Ply ... 12.....Size ... 8.25 x 20		
Tread, center to center.....Front..................(in.)			64½
Track width........(in.)			12¼
Ground clearance........(in.)			11¾₆
Ground pressure, tires........(lbs per sq in.)			29.4
Electrical system........(volts)			12
Capacities........	Fuel, 80 octane gasoline.....(gal)		60
	Cooling system........(qt)		26
	Crankcase (refill)........(qt)		12
Brakes........Hydraulic (Hydrovac)			
Communication........Radio			

PERFORMANCE

Maximum gradability........(percent)	60
Turning radius (ft)........Right 30.............Left 29½	
Fording depth........(in.)	32
Maximum vertical obstacle vehicle will climb........(in.)	12
Angle of approach (deg)....With winch 33..Without winch 37	
Angle of departure........(deg)	45
Fuel consumption, average conditions........(miles per gal)	3.6
Cruising range, average conditions........(miles)	220
Maximum allowable speed........(mph)	45

	1st	2nd	3rd	4th
Cruising speed..	9	17	26	45

ENGINE

Manufacturer......White........Model 160AX	
Type.............In-line, 4 cycle......Number of cylinders	6
Displacement........(cu in.)	386
Governed speed........Not governed	
Brake horsepower........	148
Ignition type........Battery	

ADDITIONAL DATA

Winch capacity........(lb)	10,000

CARRIER, PERSONNEL, HALF-TRACK, M3

Technical Manuals: TM 9-710A, TM 9-1710,   Parts List: SNL G-102
TM 9-1710C, TM 9-1711.

Manufacturers: The Autocar Co.; Diamond T Motor Car Co.; White Motor Co.

Armament: One Gun, machine, cal. .30, M1919A4; one Gun, submachine, cal. 45, M1928A1; provision for 12 rifles, U. S., cal. .30, M1, M1903, or M1903A1.

Ammunition: 4,000 rounds, cal. .30; 540 rounds, cal. .45; 24 Mines, AT, w/fuze, M1; 22 hand grenades.

RA PD 309053

Classification: Standard

Purpose: To transport cargo and personnel in combat zone.

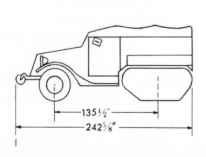

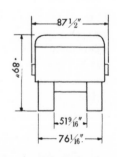

CARRIER, PERSONNEL, HALF-TRACK, M3

GENERAL DATA

Crew.   13

Weight. . . . . .Payload—w/winch. . . . .(lb)   3,000

Payload—w/o winch. . . . .(lb)   3,500

Gross. . . . .(lb) 17,650

Shipping dimensions. . . . . . .w/winch (cu ft) 924. . . .(sq ft) 148

w/o winch (cu ft) 903. .(sq ft) 148

Tires—Combat. . . . . .Ply . . . 12 . . . . .Size . . . 8.25 x 20

Tread, center to center . . . .Front. . . . .(in.)   64½

Track width. . . . .(in.)   12¼

Ground clearance. . . . .(in.)   11³⁄₁₆

Ground pressure, tires. . . . .(lbs per sq in.)   29.4

Electrical system. . . . .(volts)   12

Capacities. . . . . .Fuel, 80 octane gasoline . . . . .(gal)   60

Cooling system. . . . .(qt)   26

Crankcase (refill). . . . .(qt)   12

Brakes. . . . . .Hydraulic (Hydrovac)

Communication. . . . . .Radio

PERFORMANCE

Maximum gradability . . . .(percent)   60

Turning radius (ft). . . . . . .Right 30. . . . . .Left 29½

Fording depth. . . . .(in.)   32

Maximum vertical obstacle vehicle will climb . . . .(in.)   12

Angle of approach (deg) . . . .With winch 33. .Without winch 37

Angle of departure. . . . .(deg)   45

Fuel consumption, average conditions . . . .(miles per gal)   3.6

Cruising range, average conditions. . . . .(miles)   220

Maximum allowable speed. . . . .(mph)   45

	1st	2nd	3rd	4th
Cruising speed. .	9	17	26	45

ENGINE

Manufacturer. . . . . . White. . . . . .Model 160AX

Type. . . . . .In-line, 4 cycle. . . . . . .Number of cylinders   6

Displacement. . . . .(cu in.)   386

Governed speed. . . . . .Not governed

Brake horsepower   148

ADDITIONAL DATA

Winch capacity. . . . .(lb) 10,000

. . . .

. . . .

CARRIER, PERSONNEL, HALF-TRACK, M3A1

Technical Manuals: TM 9-710A, TM 9-1710, Parts List: SNL G-102
TM 9-1710C, TM 9-1711.

Manufacturers: The Autocar Co.; Diamond T Motor Co.; White Motor Co.

Armament: One Gun, machine, cal. .50, HB, M2 (flexible); one Gun, machine, cal. .30, M1919A4 (flexible); one Gun, submachine, cal. .45, M1928A1; provision for 12 rifles, cal. .30, M1, M1903, or M1903A1.

Ammunition: 700 rounds, cal. .50; 7,750 rounds, cal. .30; 540 rounds, cal. .45; 24 Mines, AT, w/fuze, M1; 22 hand grenades.

RA PD 308918

Classification: Standard

Purpose: To transport cargo and personnel in combat zone.

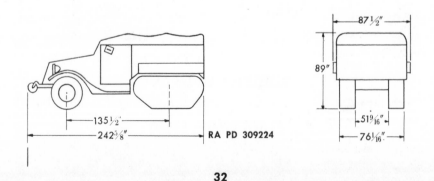

RA PD 309224

CARRIER, PERSONNEL, HALF-TRACK, M3A1

GENERAL DATA

Crew			13
Weight	Payload—w/winch	(lb)	3,000
	Payload—w/o winch	(lb)	3,500
	Gross	(lb)	18,425
Shipping dimensions	w/winch (cu ft) 980	(sq ft) 128	
	w/o winch (cu ft) 959	(sq ft) 128	
Tires—Combat	Ply ... 12 ..... Size ... 8.25 x 20		
Tread, center to center	Front	(in.)	64½
Track width		(in.)	12¼
Ground clearance		(in.)	11³⁄₁₆
Ground pressure, tires		(lbs per sq in.)	29.4
Electrical system		(volts)	12
Capacities	Fuel, 80 octane gasoline	(gal)	60
	Cooling system	(qt)	26
	Crankcase (refill)	(qt)	12
Brakes	Hydraulic (Hydrovac)		
Communication	Radio		

PERFORMANCE

Maximum gradability	(percent)	60
Turning radius (ft)	Right 30	Left 29½
Fording depth	(in.)	32
Maximum vertical obstacle vehicle will climb	(in.)	12
Angle of approach (deg)	With winch 33	Without winch 37
Angle of departure	(deg)	45
Fuel consumption, average conditions	(miles per gal)	3.6
Cruising range, average conditions	(miles)	220
Maximum allowable speed	(mph)	45

	1st	2nd	3rd	4th
Cruising speed	9	17	26	45

ENGINE

Manufacturer	White	Model 160AX
Type	In-line, 4 cycle	Number of cylinders ... 6
Displacement	(cu in.)	386
Governed speed	Not governed	
Brake horsepower		• 148
Ignition type	Battery	

ADDITIONAL DATA

Winch capacity	(lb)	10,000

CARRIER, PERSONNEL, HALF-TRACK, M5

Technical Manuals: TM 9-707,   Parts List: SNL G-147
      TM 9-1707A, TM 9-1707B.

Manufacturer: International Harvester Co.

Armament: One Gun, machine, cal. .30; one Gun, submachine, cal. .45, M1928A1; provision for 12 rifles, cal. .30, M1 or M1903.

Ammunition: 4,000 rounds, cal. .30; 540 rounds, cal. .45; 22 hand grenades; 24 Mines, AT w/fuze, M1.

RA PD 66329

Classification: Standard

Purpose: To transport cargo and personnel in combat zone.

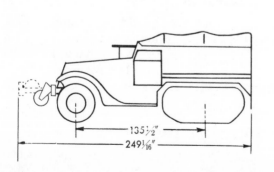

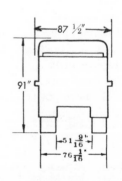

34

CARRIER, PERSONNEL, HALF-TRACK, M5

GENERAL DATA

Crew..			13
Weight.................	Payload w/winch............	(lb)	3,000
	Payload w/o winch.........	(lb)	3,500
	Gross.....................	(lb)	18,900
Shipping dimensions.......	w/winch (cu ft) 927......	(sq ft)	146
	w/o winch (cu ft) 901.....	(sq ft)	146
Tires—Combat...........	Ply...12.....Size...9.00 x 20		
Tread, center to center.....	Front.....................	(in.)	66½
Track width.................		(in.)	12¼
Ground clearance...........		(in.)	11³⁄₁₆
Ground pressure, tires.....................		(lbs per sq in.)	
Electrical system.............		(volts)	12
Capacities...............	Fuel, 80 octane gasoline.....	(gal)	60
	Cooling system.............	(qt)	31
	Crankcase (refill)...........	(qt)	8
Brakes.............................	Hydraulic (Hydrovac)		
Communication......................................	Radio		

PERFORMANCE

Maximum gradability............................	(percent)	60
Turning radius (ft)....... Right 28...............	Left 30	
Fording depth...	(in.)	32
Maximum vertical obstacle vehicle will climb.............	(in.)	11
Angle of approach (deg)....With winch 36..Without winch 40		
Angle of departure................................	(deg)	32
Fuel consumption, average conditions..........	(miles per gal)	3.6
Cruising range, average conditions..................	(miles)	220
Maximum allowable speed..........................	(mph)	42
Number of speeds forward................................		4

ENGINE

Manufacturer......IHC....................	Model Red-450B	
Type............In-line, 4 cycle.....	Number of cylinders	6
Displacement..	(cu in.)	451
Governed speed.......................................	(rpm)	2,600
Brake horsepower.......................................		141
Ignition type.......................................	Battery	

ADDITIONAL DATA

Winch capacity.......................................	(lb)	10,000

....

....

CARRIER, PERSONNEL, HALF-TRACK, M5A1

Technical Manuals: TM 9-707, TM 9-1707A.   Parts List: SNL G-147

Manufacturer: International Harvester Co.

Armament: One Gun, machine, cal. .30, M1919A4 (flexible); one Gun, machine, cal. .50, HB, M2 (flexible); one Gun, submachine, cal. .45, M1928A1; twelve Rifles, cal. .30, M1, M1903, or M1903A1.

Ammunition: 7,750 rounds, cal. .30; 700 rounds, cal. .50; 540 rounds, cal. .45; 22 hand grenades.

RA PD 308922

Classification: Standard

Purpose: Used to transport cargo and personnel in combat zone.

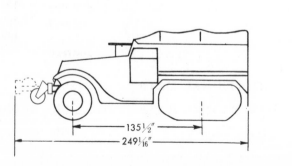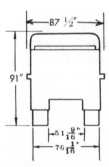

CARRIER, PERSONNEL, HALF-TRACK, M5A1

GENERAL DATA

Crew			13
Weight	Payload, w/winch	(lb)	3,000
	Payload, w/o winch	(lb)	3,500
	Gross	(lb)	19,675
Shipping dimensions	w/winch (cu ft) 927	(sq ft)	146
	w/o winch (cu ft) 901	(sq ft)	146
Tires—Combat	Ply . . . 12 . . . . . Size . . . 9.00 x 20		
Tread, center to center	Front	(in.)	66½
Track width		(in.)	12¼
Ground clearance		(in.)	11³⁄₁₆
Ground pressure, tires		(lbs per sq in.)	
Electrical system		(volts)	12
Capacities	Fuel, 80 octane gasoline	(gal)	60
	Cooling system	(qt)	31
	Crankcase (refill)	(qt)	8
Brakes	Hydraulic (Hydrovac)		
Communication	Radio		

PERFORMANCE

Maximum gradability	(percent)	60
Turning radius (ft) . . . . Right 28 . . . . Left 30		
Fording depth	(in.)	32
Maximum vertical obstacle vehicle will climb	(in.)	11
Angle of approach (deg) . . . . w/winch 36 . . . . w/o winch 40		
Angle of departure	(deg)	32
Fuel consumption, average conditions	(miles per gal)	4.15
Cruising range, average conditions	(miles)	225
Maximum allowable speed	(mph)	42
Number of speeds forward		4

ENGINE

Manufacturer . . . . . . IHC . . . . Model Red-450B		
Type . . . . In-line, 4 cycle . . . . . . Number of cylinders		6
Displacement	(cu in.)	451
Governed speed	(rpm)	2,600
Brake horsepower		141
Ignition type	Battery	

ADDITIONAL DATA

Winch capacity	(lb)	10,000

CAR, HALF-TRACK, M9A1

Technical Manuals: TM 9-707, TM 9-1707A.   Parts List: SNL G-147

Manufacturer: International Harvester Co.

Armament: One Gun, machine, cal. .50, M2; one Gun, machine, cal. .30, 1919A4; one Gun, submachine, cal. .45.

Ammunition: 7,750 rounds, cal. .30; 700 rounds, cal. .50; 540 rounds, cal. .45; 10 hand grenades; 14 Mines AT, HE, M1 w/fuze.

RA PD 308922

Classification: Substitute standard

Purpose: Used to transport cargo and personnel in combat zone.

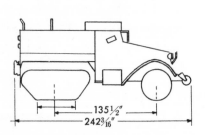

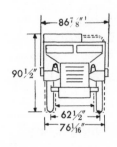

CAR, HALF-TRACK, M9A1

GENERAL DATA

Crew. 10
Weight. . . . . .Payload, w/winch. . . . .(lb) 3,000
Payload, w/o winch. . . . .(lb) 3,500
Gross. . . . .(lb) 19,050
Shipping dimensions. . . . . . .w/ winch (cu ft) . . . .(sq ft)
w/o winch (cu ft) . . .(sq ft)
Tires—Combat. . . . . .Ply . . . 12 . . . . .Size . . . 9.00 x 20
Tread, center to center . . . . .Front. . . . .(in.) 66½
Track width. . . . .(in.) 12¼
Ground clearance. . . . .(in.) 11¾₆
Ground pressure, tires. . . . .(lbs per sq in.)
Electrical system. . . . .(volts) 12ˈ
Capacities. . . . . .Fuel, 80 octane gasoline. . . . .(gal) 60
Cooling system. . . . .(qt) 31
Crankcase (refill). . . . .(qt) 10½
Brakes. . . . . .Hydraulic (Hydrovac)
Communication. . . . . .Radio

PERFORMANCE

Maximum gradability. . . . .(percent) 60
Turning radius (ft) . . . . .Right 28. . . . . .Left 30
Fording depth. . . . .(in.) 32
Maximum vertical obstacle vehicle will climb. . . . .(in.) 12
Angle of approach (deg) . . . .With winch 36. .Without winch 40
Angle of departure. . . . .(deg) 32
Fuel consumption, average conditions. . . . .(miles per gal) 3.6
Cruising range, average conditions. . . . .(miles) 220
Maximum allowable speed. . . . .(mph) 42
Number of speeds forward. 4

ENGINE

Manufacturer. . . . . .IHC. . . . . .Model Red-450B
Type. . . . . .In-line, 4 cycle. . . . . . .Number of cylinders 6
Displacement. . . . .(cu in.) 451
Governed speed. . . . .(rpm) 2,600
Brake horsepower. 141
Ignition type. . . . . .Battery

ADDITIONAL DATA

Winch capacity. . . . .(lb) 10,000
. . . .

CARRIER, CARGO, T14

Technical Manual: TM 9-751. Parts List: SNL G-158

Manufacturer: Pressed Steel Car Co.

Armament: One Gun, machine, cal. .50, HB, M2 (flexible); one Launcher, grenade (carbine); five Carbines, cal. .30, M1.

Ammunition: 1,000 rounds, cal. .50; 12 Grenades, hand; 10 Grenades, rifle, M9A1.

RA PD 308914

Classification:

Purpose: Used in conjunction with 155-mm gun motor carriage, M12. Carries ammunition for 155-mm gun.

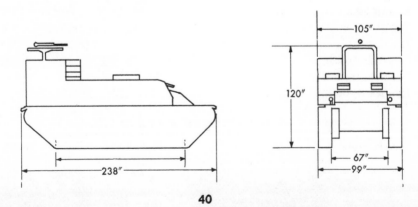

CARRIER, CARGO, T14

GENERAL DATA

Crew... 6
Weight...................Gross......................(lb) 47,000
Shipping dimensions.......(cu ft) ....(sq ft)
Tread, center to center............................(in.) 83
Track width...(in.) 16
Ground clearance....................................(in.) 22
Ground pressure........................(lbs per sq in.) 10
Electrical system..................................(volts) 12
Capacities..............Fuel, 80 octane gasoline.....(gal) 200
Cooling system........Air cooled
Oil tank...................(qt) 36
Transmission and differential..(qt) 128
Brakes....................................Mechanical
Communication..........Radio..............Interphone

PERFORMANCE

Maximum gradability............................(percent) 60
Turning radius......................................(ft) 31
Fording depth......................................(in.) 36
Maximum width of ditch vehicle will cross...............(in.) 72
Maximum vertical obstacle vehicle will climb..............(in.) 24
Fuel consumption, average conditions..........(miles per gal) .75
Cruising range, average conditions..................(miles) 140
Maximum allowable speed..........................(mph) 24

	1st	2nd	3rd	4th	5th
Cruising speed.....	2	5	9	14	21

ENGINE

Manufacturer......Continental............Model R975-C1
Type.............Radial, 4 cycle......Number of cylinders 9
Displacement.....................................(cu in.) 973
Governed speed...................................(rpm) 2,400
Brake horsepower................................... 400
Ignition type...................................Magneto

ADDITIONAL DATA

Carries the following ammunition for 155-mm gun motor carriage M12:
40 rounds, Charge, propelling, NH powder, 155-mm gun, M1917,
M1917A1; 50 rounds, Fuze, PD, M51 w/booster M21; 10 shells, HE,
155-mm gun, MK 111A1 or M101; 50 Primers, percussion, 21 grain,
MK 11A1.

....

CARRIER, LIGHT CARGO, T15

Technical Manuals: TM 9-893, TM 9-1893A,   Parts List: SNL G-154
TM 9-1893B.

Manufacturer: The Studebaker Corp.

Armament: One Rifle, automatic, cal. .30, Browning, M1918; one Gun, submachine, cal. .45, M1928A1; two Carbines, cal. .30, M1; one Launcher, rocket, AT, M1 (not used if equipped with Browning automatic rifle).

Ammunition: 375 rounds, cal. .45; 300 rounds, cal. .30 (for carbines); 300 rounds, cal. .30 (automatic rifle).

RA PD 54022

Classification:

Purpose: To transport personnel and materiel over snow, and for limited operation on the ground.

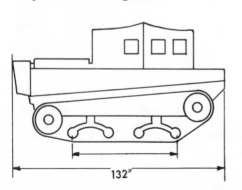

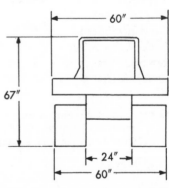

CARRIER, LIGHT CARGO, T15

GENERAL DATA

Crew			2
Weight	Net	(lb)	3,390
	Payload	(lb)	1,260
	Gross	(lb)	4,650
Shipping dimensions	(cu ft)	(sq ft) 55	
Track width		(in.)	18
Ground clearance		(in.)	12
Ground pressure		(lbs per sq in.)	2
Electrical system		(volts)	12
Capacities	Fuel, 75 octane gasoline	(gal)	25
	Cooling system	(qt)	10½
	Crankcase (refill)	(qt)	5
Brakes		Mechanical	
Communication		Radio	

PERFORMANCE

Maximum gradability	(percent)	100
Turning radius	(ft)	13½
Fording depth (Floats at 44 inches)	(in.)	41
Maximum vertical obstacle vehicle will climb	(in.)	19
Angle of approach	(deg)	32
Angle of departure	(deg)	11
Fuel consumption, average conditions	(miles per gal)	5
Cruising range, average conditions	(miles)	125
Maximum allowable speed	(mph)	23.5

	1st	2nd	3rd	4th	5th
Cruising speed	6.6	11.8	17.6	13.1	23.5

ENGINE

Manufacturer	Studebaker	Model 6-170
Type	In-line, 4 cycle	Number of cylinders 6
Displacement	(cu in.)	169.6
Governed speed	Not governed	
Brake horsepower		75
Ignition type	Battery	

ADDITIONAL DATA

....

....

43

CARRIER, UNIVERSAL, T16

Technical Manual: TM 9-746.

Parts List: SNL G-166

Manufacturer: Ford Motor Co.

Armament: Supplied by British.

Ammunition: Supplied by British.

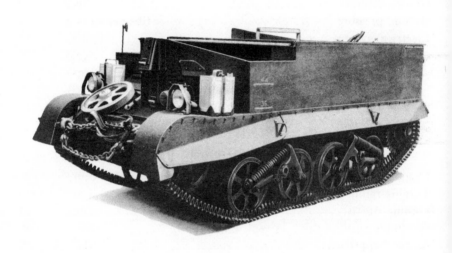

RA PD 308901

Classification: None (British only—Universal Bren Carrier)

Purpose: For light reconnaissance and cargo and personnel carrying.

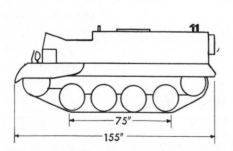

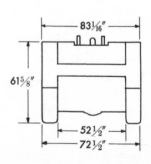

CARRIER, UNIVERSAL, T16

GENERAL DATA

Crew..			4
Weight.................Net........................(lb)			7,700
	Payload.................(lb)		1,800
	Gross...................(lb)		9,500
Shipping dimensions.......(cu ft) ....(sq ft)			
Track width..............................(in.)			10
Ground clearance...................................(in.)			10½
Ground pressure.........................(lbs per sq in.)			6.4
Electrical system....................................(volts)			12
Capacities..............Fuel, 72 octane gasoline.....(gal)			23.8
	Cooling system............(qt)		26
	Crankcase (refill)...........(qt)		6
Brakes.....................................Mechanical			
Communication.......................Supplied by British			

PERFORMANCE

Maximum gradability............................(percent)	60
Turning radius......................................(ft)	16
Fording depth.......................................(in.)	44
Maximum width of ditch vehicle will cross..............(in.)	36
Maximum vertical obstacle vehicle will climb............(in.)	18
Fuel consumption, average conditions.........(miles per gal)	4
Cruising range, average conditions................ .(miles)	95
Maximum allowable speed.........................(mph)	30

	1st	2nd	3rd	4th
Cruising range.	4.7	9.8	17.8	30

ENGINE

Manufacturer......Ford....................Model GAU370	
Type..............V-8, 4 cycle........Number of cylinders	8
Displacement.......................................(cu in.)	239
Governed speed...................................(rpm)	3,600
Brake horsepower.......................................	100
Ignition type.......................................Battery	

ADDITIONAL DATA

....
....
....

CARRIAGE, MOTOR, MULTIPLE GUN, M13

Technical Manuals: TM 9-710A, TM 9-1710,   Parts List: SNL G-102
TM 9-1710C, TM 9-1711.

Manufacturer: White Motor Co.

Armament: Two Guns, machine, cal. .50, HB, M2, turret type; one
Gun, submachine, cal. .45, M1928A1; one Rifle, cal. .30, M1903, with
Launcher, grenade; three Carbines, cal. .30, M1.

Ammunition: 5,000 rounds, cal. .50; 480 rounds, cal. .45; 34 grenades.

RA PD 66385

Classification: Substitute standard

Purpose: To provide mobility for antiaircraft machine guns.

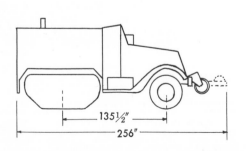

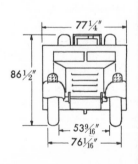

CARRIAGE, MOTOR, MULTIPLE GUN, M13

GENERAL DATA

Crew			5
Weight	Gross	(lb)	19,800
	Boxed for export	(lb)	21,532
Shipping dimensions	(cu ft) boxed 1,188	(sq ft)	145
Tires—Combat	Ply . . . 12	Size . . . 8.25 x 20	
Tread, center to center (in.)	Front—64½	Rear—63¹³⁄₁₆	
Track width		(in.)	12¼
Ground clearance		(in.)	17⅛
Ground pressure, tires		(lbs per sq in.)	33.4
Electrical system		(volts)	12
Capacities	Fuel, 80 octane gasoline	(gal)	60
	Cooling system	(qt)	26
	Crankcase (refill)	(qt)	12
Brakes		Hydraulic (Hydrovac)	
Communication		Radio	

PERFORMANCE

Maximum gradability	(percent)	60
Turning radius	(ft)	30
Maximum vertical obstacle vehicle will climb	(in.)	12
Fording depth	(in.)	32
Angle of approach	(deg)	33
Angle of departure	(deg)	45
Fuel consumption, average conditions	(miles per gal)	3.3
Cruising range, average conditions	(miles)	200
Maximum allowable speed	(mph)	45

	1st	2nd	3rd	4th
Cruising speed	9	17	26	45

ENGINE

Manufacturer	White	Model 160 AX	
Type	In-line, 4 cycle	Number of cylinders	6
Displacement		(cu in.)	386
Maximum engine speed, not governed		(rpm)	3,200
Brake horsepower			148
Ignition type		Battery	

ADDITIONAL DATA

Winch capacity	(lb)	10,000
Basic chassis	Carriage, motor, 75-mm gun, M3	

CARRIAGE, MOTOR, MULTIPLE GUN, M14

Technical Manual: TM 9-707, TM 9-1707A.   Parts List: SNL G-147

Manufacturer: International Harvester Co.

Armament: Two Guns, machine, cal. .50, HB, M2, turret type; one Gun, submachine, cal. .45, M1928A1; one Rifle, cal. .30, M1903, with Launcher, grenade; three Carbines, cal. .30, M1.

Ammunition: 5,000 rounds, cal. .50; 480 rounds, cal. .45; 36 grenades.

RA PD 66387

Classification: Substitute standard

Purpose: To provide mobility for antiaircraft guns.

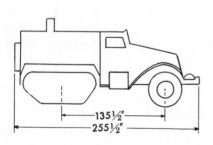

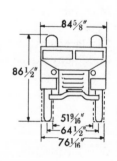

CARRIAGE, MOTOR, MULTIPLE GUN, M14

GENERAL DATA

Crew				5
Weight	Net		(lb)	16,800
	Payload		(lb)	3,000
	Gross		(lb)	19,800
Shipping dimensions	(cu ft) 1,069	(sq ft) 145		
Tires—Combat	Ply . . . 10	Size . . . 9.00 x 20		
Tread, center to center (in.)	Front—64½	Rear—63¹³⁄₁₆		
Track width			(in.)	12¼
Ground clearance			(in.)	18¼
Ground pressure, tires			(lbs per sq in.)	33.5
Electrical system			(volts)	12
Capacities	Fuel, 80 octane gasoline		(gal)	60
	Cooling system		(qt)	31
	Crankcase (refill)		(qt)	8
Brakes		Hydraulic (Hydrovac)		
Communication		Radio		

PERFORMANCE

Maximum gradability	(percent)	60
Turning radius (ft)	Right 28	Left 30
Maximum vertical obstacle vehicle will climb	(in.)	12
Fording depth	(in.)	32
Angle of approach	(deg)	36
Angle of departure	(deg)	32
Fuel consumption, average conditions	(miles per gal)	3.3
Cruising range, average conditions	(miles)	200
Maximum allowable speed	(mph)	42

	1st	2nd	3rd	4th
Cruising speed	8.5	16	24	42

ENGINE

Manufacturer	IHC	Model Red-450-B	
Type	In-line, 4 cycle	Number of cylinders	6
Displacement		(cu in.)	451
Governed speed		(rpm)	2,600
Brake horsepower			141
Ignition type		Battery	

ADDITIONAL DATA

Winch capacity	(lb)	10,000
Basic chassis	Carrier, personnel, half-track, M5	

CARRIAGE, MOTOR, MULTIPLE GUN, M15

Technical Manuals: TM 9-708, TM 9-1710, Parts List: SNL G-102
TM 9-1710C, TM 9-1711.

Manufacturer: The Autocar Co.

Armament: One Gun, automatic, 37-mm, M1A2; two Guns, machine, cal. .50, HB, M2.

Ammunition: 240 rounds, 37-mm shell, HE M54 or AP M59; 3,400 rounds, cal. .50.

RA PD 308959

Classification: Limited standard

Purpose: To provide mobility for antiaircraft guns.

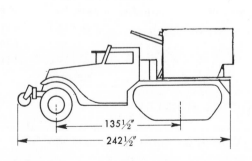

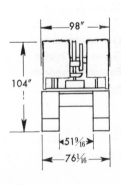

CARRIAGE, MOTOR, MULTIPLE GUN, M15

GENERAL DATA

Crew		7
Weight	Gross (lb)	20,000
Shipping dimensions	(cu ft) 1116, boxed 1338 (sq ft) 131	
Tires—Combat	Ply . . . 12 . . . . . Size . . . 8.25 x 20	
Tread, center to center (in.)	Front—64½ . . . . Rear—63¹³⁄₁₆	
Track width	(in.)	12¼
Ground clearance	(in.)	17⅛
Ground pressure, tires	(lbs per sq in.)	33.5
Electrical system	(volts)	12
Capacities	Fuel, 80 octane gasoline (gal)	60
	Cooling system (qt)	26
	Crankcase (refill) (qt)	12
Brakes	Hydraulic (Hydrovac)	
Communication	Radio	

PERFORMANCE

Maximum gradability	(percent)	60
Turning radius	(ft)	30
Fording depth	(in.)	32
Maximum vertical obstacle vehicle will climb	(in.)	12
Angle of approach	(deg)	37
Angle of departure	(deg)	45
Fuel consumption, average conditions	(miles per gal)	3.3
Cruising range, average conditions	(miles)	200
Maximum allowable speed	(mph)	45

	1st	2nd	3rd	4th
Cruising speed	9	17	26	45

ENGINE

Manufacturer	White Model 160AX	
Type	In-line, 4 cycle Number of cylinders	6
Displacement	(cu in.)	386
Governed speed	Not governed	
Brake horsepower		148
Ignition type	Battery	

ADDITIONAL DATA

Basic chassis . . . . Carrier, personnel, half-track, M3

. . . .

. . . .

CARRIAGE, MOTOR, MULTIPLE GUN, M15A1

Technical Manuals: TM 9-710A, TM 9-1710,   Parts List: SNL G-102
TM 9-1710C, TM 9-1711.

Manufacturer: The Autocar Co.

Armament: One Gun, 37-mm, M1A2; two Guns, machine, cal. .50, HB, M2; one Rifle, cal. .30, M1903 with Launcher, grenade; one Gun, submachine, cal. .45; five Carbines, cal. .30, M1.

Ammunition: 1,200 rounds, cal. .50; 200 rounds, 37-mm; 540 rounds, cal. .45; 10 rifle grenades M9A1; 12 hand grenades.

RA PD 309117

Classification: Standard

Purpose: To provide a highly mobile antiaircraft weapon.

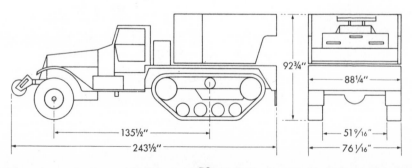

CARRIAGE, MOTOR, MULTIPLE GUN, M15A1

GENERAL DATA

Crew...			7
Weight...................Net....................(lb)			17,600
	Payload..................(lb)		2,500
	Gross.....................(lb)		20,100
Shipping dimensions........(cu ft) 1116..........(sq ft) 131			
Tires—Combat............Ply...12.....Size...8.25 x 20			
Tread, center to center (in.).Front 64½..........Rear 63¹³⁄₁₆			
Ground clearance.................................(in.)			17⅛
Track width.......................................			12¼
Ground pressure, tires.....................(lbs per sq in.)			33.5
Electrical system.................................(volts)			12
Capacities...............Fuel, 80 octane gasoline.....(gal)			60
	Cooling system............(qt)		26
	Crankcase (refill)...........(qt)		12
Brakes..........................Hydraulic (Hydrovac)			
Communication...................................Radio			

PERFORMANCE

Maximum gradability...............................(percent)	60
Turning radius..(ft)	30
Fording depth..(in.)	32
Maximum vertical obstacle vehicle will climb............(in.)	12
Angle of approach.................................(deg)	
Angle of departure................................(deg)	
Fuel consumption, average conditions.........(miles per gal)	
Cruising range, average conditions....................(miles)	
Maximum allowable speed..........................(mph)	45

	1st	2nd	3rd	4th
Cruising speed.....	9	17	26	45

ENGINE

Manufacturer......White.................Model 160 AX	
Type.............In line, 4 cycle.....Number of cylinders	6
Displacement......................................(cu in.)	386
Governed speed.............................Not governed	
Brake horsepower...................................	148
Ignition type......................................Battery	

ADDITIONAL DATA

Basic chassis..............Carrier, personnel, half-track, M3

....

....

CARRIAGE, MOTOR, MULTIPLE GUN, M16

Technical Manuals: TM 9-710A, TM 9-1710,   Parts List: SNL G-102
TM 9-1710C, TM 9-1711.

Manufacturer: White Motor Co.

Armament: Four Guns, machine, cal. .50, HB, M2, turret type; one Gun, submachine, cal. .45, M1928A1; one Rifle, cal. .30, M1903, w/Launcher, grenade; three Carbines, cal. .30, M1.

Ammunition: 5,000 rounds, cal. .50, in belts; 480 rounds, cal. .45, in clips; 26 grenades.

RA PD 308921

Classification: Standard

Purpose: To provide mobility for machine guns.

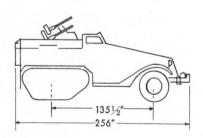

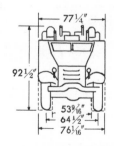

CARRIAGE, MOTOR, MULTIPLE GUN, M16

GENERAL DATA

Crew.. 5
Weight................Gross...................(lb) 19,800
                  Boxed for export...........(lb) 21,532
Shipping dimensions.......(cu ft) boxed 1188.....(sq ft)
Tires—Combat...........Ply...12.....Size...8.25 x 20
Tread, center to center (in.)..Front 64½..........Rear 63¹³⁄₁₆
Track width.................................(in.) 12¼
Ground clearance............................(in.) 17⅛
Ground pressure, tires..............(lbs per sq in.) 30
Electrical system..................................(volts) 12
Capacities...............Fuel, 80 octane gasoline.....(gal) 60
               Cooling system.............(qt) 26
               Crankcase (refill)..........(qt) 8
Brakes...........................Hydraulic (Hydrovac)
Communication....................................Radio

PERFORMANCE

Maximum gradability........................(percent) 60
Turning radius.......................................(ft) 30
Maximum vertical obstacle vehicle will climb............(in.) 12
Fording depth..(in.) 32
Angle of approach.................................(deg) 33
Angle of departure................................(deg) 45
Fuel consumption, average conditions.........(miles per gal) 3.3
Cruising range, average conditions...................(miles) 200
Maximum allowable speed........................(mph) 45

	1st	2nd	3rd	4th
Cruising speed.....	9	17	26	45

ENGINE

Manufacturer......White...................Model 160AX
Type.............In-line, 4 cycle.....Number of cylinders 6
Displacement.......................................(cu in.) 386
Maximum engine speed (not governed)...............(rpm) 3200
Brake horsepower... 148
Ignition type.....................................Battery

ADDITIONAL DATA

Winch capacity..(lb) 10,000
Basic chassis..............Carrier, personnel, half-track, M3

CARRIAGE, MOTOR, MULTIPLE GUN, M17

Technical Manual: TM 9-707, TM 9-1707A.   Parts List: SNL G-147

Manufacturer: International Harvester Co.

Armament: Four Guns, machine, cal. .50, HB, M2, turret type; one Gun, submachine, cal. .45, M1928A1; one Rifle, cal. .30, M1903, w/Launcher, grenade; three Carbines, cal. .30, M1.

Ammunition: 5,000 rounds, cal. .50 in belts; 480 rounds, cal. .45 in clips; 36 grenades.

RA PD 308921

Vehicle illustrated above: M16. M17 is similar in appearance. No photo available at date of publication.

Classification: Substitute standard

Purpose: To provide mobility for antiaircraft machine guns.

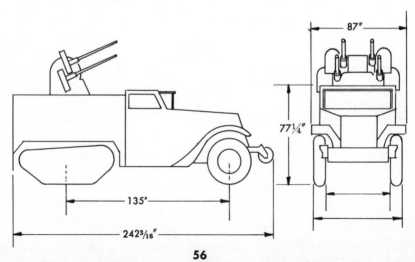

56

CARRIAGE, MULTIPLE GUN, M17

GENERAL DATA

Crew.	5
Weight. . . . . Gross (approx). . . . . (lb)	19,700
Shipping dimensions. . . . . . . (cu ft) . . . . (sq ft)	
Tires—Combat. . . . . Ply . . . 12 . . . . . . Size . . . 9.00 x 20	
Tread, center to center (in.). Front 64½. . . . . Rear 63¹³⁄₁₆	
Track width. . . . .(in.)	12¼
Ground clearance. . . . .(in.)	17⅛
Ground pressure, tires. . . . .(lbs per sq in.)	33.5
Electrical system. . . . .(volts)	12
Capacities. . . . . .Fuel, 80 octane gasoline. . . . .(gal)	60
	Cooling system. . . . .(qt)	31
	Crankcase (refill). . . . .(qt)	8
Brakes. . . . . .Hydraulic (Hydrovac)	
Communication. . . . . .Radio	

PERFORMANCE

Maximum gradability. . . . .(percent)	60
Turning radius. . . . .(ft)	30
Maximum vertical obstacle vehicle will climb. . . . .(in.)	12
Fording depth. . . . .(in.)	32
Angle of approach. . . . .(deg)	36
Angle of departure. . . . .(deg)	45
Fuel consumption, average conditions. . . . .(miles per gal)	3.3
Cruising range, average conditions. . . . .(miles)	200
Maximum allowable speed. . . . .(mph)	42

	1st	2nd	3rd	4th
Cruising speed.	8.5	16	24	42

ENGINE

Manufacturer. . . . . . .IHC. . . . . .Model Red-450-B	
Type. . . . . .In-line, 4 cycle. . . . . .Number of cylinders	6
Displacement. . . . .(cu in.)	450
Governed speed. . . . .(rpm)	2,650
Brake horsepower.	141
Ignition type. . . . . .Battery	

ADDITIONAL DATA

Winch capacity. . . . .(lb)	10,000
Basic chassis. . . . . .Carrier, personnel, half-track, M5	

CARRIAGE, MOTOR, 37-MM GUN, M6
(¾-TON, 4 x 4)

Technical Manual: TM 9-750A, TM 9-1808A.   Parts List: SNL G-121

Manufacturer: Dodge Bros. Corp. (Div. of Chrysler Corp.)
Model WC-55.

Armament: One Gun, 37-mm, M3; four Rifles, cal. .30, M1903, with
Launcher, grenade.

Ammunition: 80 rounds 37-mm; 18 grenades.

RA PD 66373

Classification: Standard

Purpose: To provide mobility for 37-mm antitank gun.

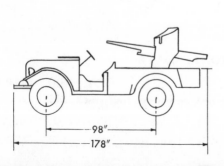

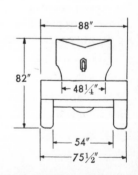

CARRIAGE, MOTOR, 37-MM GUN, M6
(¾-TON, 4 x 4)

GENERAL DATA

Crew		4
Weight	Net (lb)	5,850
	Payload (lb)	1,200
	Gross (lb)	7,050
	Boxed for export (lb)	8,900
Shipping dimensions (cu ft) 708, boxed 605 (sq ft) 102		
Tires—Combat Ply 8 Size 9.00 x 16		
Tread, center to center (in.)		64½
Ground clearance (in.)		10⅝
Ground pressure, tires (lbs per sq in.)		40
Electrical system (volts)		6
Capacities Fuel, 70 octane gasoline (gal)		30
	Cooling system (qt)	17
	Crankcase (refill) (qt)	5
Brakes Hydraulic		
Communication Radio		

PERFORMANCE

Maximum gradability (percent)	60
Turning radius (ft)	22
Fording depth (in.)	35
Maximum vertical obstacle vehicle will climb (in.)	12
Angle of approach (deg)	36½
Angle of departure (deg)	31
Fuel consumption, average conditions (miles per gal)	8.0
Cruising range, average conditions (miles)	240
Maximum allowable speed (mph)	54

ENGINE

Manufacturer Dodge Model T-214	
Type In-line, 4 cycle Number of cylinders	6
Displacement (cu in.)	230.2
Governed speed (rpm)	3,200
Brake horsepower	94
Ignition type Battery	

ADDITIONAL DATA

Winch capacity (lb)	5,000
Basic chassis Weapons carrier, ¾-ton, 4 x 4	

CARRIAGE, MOTOR, 57-MM GUN, T48

Technical Manuals: TM 9-710A, TM 9-1710,   Parts List: SNL G-102
           TM 9-1710C, TM 9-1711.

Manufacturer: Diamond T Motor Car Co.

Armament: One Gun, 57-mm, M1; five Rifles, cal. .30, w/Launcher, grenade.

Ammunition: 99 rounds, 57-mm; 22 grenades.

RA PD 308919

Classification: None (British only)

Purpose: To provide mobility for antitank weapon and protection for crew.

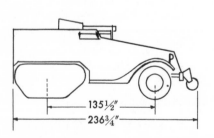

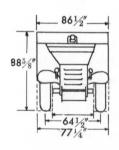

CARRIAGE, MOTOR, 57-MM GUN, T48

GENERAL DATA

Crew			5
Weight	Gross	(lb)	19,800
	Boxed for export	(lb)	22,300
Shipping dimensions	(cu ft) 1051, boxed 1226	(sq ft)	
Tires—Combat	Ply . . . 12 . . . . . Size . . . 8.25 x 20		
Tread, center to center (in.)	Front 64½ . . . . Rear 63^{13}⁄₁₆		
Track width		(in.)	12¼
Ground clearance		(in.)	17⅛
Ground pressure, tires		(lbs per sq in.)	33
Electrical system		(volts)	12
Capacities	Fuel, 80 octane gasoline	(gal)	60
	Cooling system	(qt)	26
	Crankcase (refill)	(qt)	8
Brakes	Hydraulic (Hydrovac)		
Communication	Radio		

PERFORMANCE

Maximum gradability	(percent)	60
Turning radius	(ft)	30
Fording depth	(in.)	32
Maximum vertical obstacle vehicle will climb	(in.)	12
Angle of approach	(deg)	33
Angle of departure	(deg)	45
Fuel consumption, average conditions	(miles per gal)	3.3
Cruising range, average conditions	(miles)	200
Maximum allowable speed	(mph)	45

	1st	2nd	3rd	4th
Cruising speed	9	17	26	45

ENGINE

Manufacturer	White . . . . Model 160 AX	
Type	In-line, 4 cycle . . . . . . Number of cylinders	6
Displacement	(cu in.)	386
Maximum engine speed (not governed)	(rpm)	3,200
Brake horsepower		148
Ignition type	Battery	

ADDITIONAL DATA

Winch capacity	(lb)	10,000
Basic chassis	Carrier, personnel, half-track, M3	

CARRIAGE, MOTOR, 75-MM GUN, M3

Technical Manuals: TM 9-710A, TM 9-1710,   Parts List: SNL G-102
                   TM 9-1710C, TM 9-1711.

Manufacturer: The Autocar Co.

Armament: One Gun, 75-mm, M1897A4; one Rifle, cal. .30, M1903, w/Launcher, grenade; four Carbines, cal. .30, M1.

Ammunition: 59 rounds, 75-mm, HE and AP; 22 grenades.

RA PD 66369

Classification: Standard

Purpose: To provide highly mobile 75-mm gun.

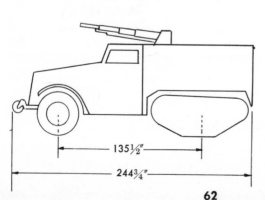

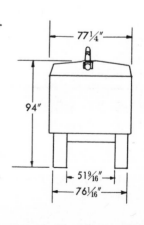

CARRIAGE, MOTOR, 75-MM GUN, M3

GENERAL DATA

Crew. 5
Weight. . . . . .Net. . . . .(lb) 17,450
. . . . .Payload. . . . .(lb) 2,550
. . . . .Gross. . . . .(lb) 20,000
. . . . .Boxed for export. . . . .(in.) 18,237
Shipping dimensions. . . . .(cu ft) 1076, boxed 1200. (sq ft) 127
Tires—Combat. . . . . .Ply . . . 12. . . . . .Size . . . 8.25 x 20
Tread, center to center, front. . . . .(in.) 64½
Track width. . . . .(in.) 12¼
Ground clearance. . . . .(in.) 17⅛
Ground pressure, tires. . . . .(lbs per sq in.) 33.5
Electrical system. . . . .(volts) 12
Capacities. . . . . .Fuel, 80 octane gasoline . . . . .(gal) 60
. . . . .Cooling system. . . . .(qt) 26
. . . . .Crankcase (refill). . . . .(qt) 12
Brakes. . . . . .Hydraulic (Hydrovac)
Communication. . . . . .Radio

PERFORMANCE

Maximum gradability. . . . .(percent) 60
Turning radius. . . . .(ft) 30
Fording depth. . . . .(in.) 32
Maximum vertical obstacle vehicle will climb. . . . .(in.) 12
Angle of approach. . . . .(deg) 37
Angle of departure. . . . .(deg) 45
Fuel consumption, average conditions. . . . .(miles per gal) 3.3
Cruising range, average conditions. . . . .(miles) 200
Maximum allowable speed. . . . .(mph) 45

	1st	2nd	3rd	4th
Cruising speed..	9	17	26	45

ENGINE

Manufacturer. . . . . . .White. . . . . .Model 160 AX
Type. . . . . .In-line, 4 cycle. . . . . .Number of cylinders 6
Displacement. . . . .(cu in.) 386
Governed speed. . . . . .Not governed
Brake horsepower. 148
Ignition type. . . . . .Battery

ADDITIONAL DATA

. . . .
. . . .

CARRIAGE, MOTOR, 75-MM GUN, M3A1

Technical Manuals: TM 9-710A, TM 9-1710, Parts List: SNL G-102
TM 9-1710C, TM 9-1711.

Manufacturer: The Autocar Co.

Armament: One Gun, 75-mm, M1897A4; one Rifle, cal. .30, M1903,
w/Launcher, grenade; four Carbines, cal. .30, M1.

Ammunition: 59 rounds, 75-mm, HE and AP; 22 grenades.

RA PD 66369

Classification: Standard

Purpose: To provide highly mobile 75-mm gun.

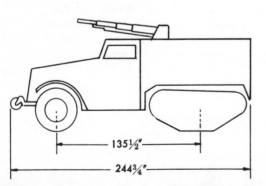

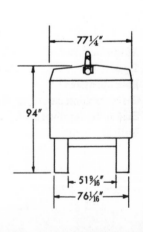

64

CARRIAGE, MOTOR, 75-MM GUN, M3A1

GENERAL DATA

Crew.. 5
Weight................Net.......................(lb) 17,450
                  Payload...................(lb) 2,550
                  Gross.....................(lb) 20,000
Shipping dimensions........(cu ft) 959...........(sq ft) 127
Tires—Combat...........Ply...12......Size...8.25 x 20
Tread, center to center, front.........................(in.) 64½
Track width...(in.) 12¼
Ground clearance.......................................(in.) 17⅛
Ground pressure, tires......................(lbs per sq in.) 33.5
Electrical system.....................................(volts) 21
Capacities..............Fuel, 80 octane gasoline.....(gal) 60
                  Cooling system.............(qt) 26
                  Crankcase (refill)...........(qt) 12
Brakes.........................Hydraulic (Hydrovac)
Communication.................................Radio

PERFORMANCE

Maximum gradability............................(percent) 60
Turning radius.......................................(ft) 30
Fording depth.......................................(in.) 32
Maximum vertical obstacle vehicle will climb.........(in.) 12
Angle of approach..................................(deg) 37
Angle of departure.................................(deg) 45
Fuel consumption, average conditions.........(miles per gal) 3.3
Cruising range, average conditions................(miles) 200
Maximum allowable speed...........................(mph) 45

                    1st 2nd 3rd 4th
Cruising speed.. 9   17   26   45

ENGINE

Manufacturer......White.................Model 160 AX
Type.............In-line, 4 cycle......Number of cylinders 6
Displacement......................................(cu in.) 386
Governed speed...........................Not governed
Brake horsepower.. 148
Ignition type..................................Battery

ADDITIONAL DATA

....

....

CARRIAGE, MOTOR, 75-MM HOWITZER, M8

Technical Manuals: TM 9-732B, TM 9-1727B, Parts List: SNL G-127
 TM 9-1727C, TM 9-1727D, TM 9-1727E,
 TM 9-1727F, TM 9-1727G, TM 9-1732A.

Manufacturer: Cadillac Motor Car Div. (General Motors Corp.)

Armament: One Howitzer, 75-mm, M2 or M3; one Gun, machine, cal. .50, HB, M2 (flexible), one Gun, submachine, cal. .45, M1928A1; three Carbines, cal. .30.

Ammunition: 46 rounds, 75-mm; 400 rounds, cal. .50; 600 rounds, cal. .45; 735 rounds, cal. .30; 6 grenades, 2 fragmentation, 2 smoke, 2 thermite-incendiary.

RA PD 308911

Classification: Standard

Purpose: To provide mobility for 75-mm howitzer and protection for crew.

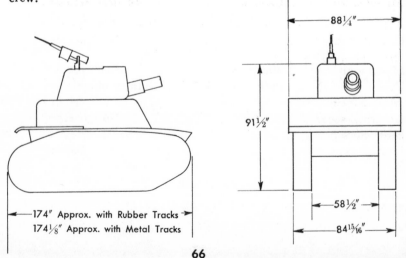

174″ Approx. with Rubber Tracks
174⅛″ Approx. with Metal Tracks

88¼″

91½″

58½″

84¹⁵⁄₁₆″

CARRIAGE, MOTOR, 75-MM HOWITZER, M8

GENERAL DATA

Crew..		4
Weight..................Gross......................(lb)		34,580
Shipping dimensions........(cu ft) 954............(sq ft) 109		
Track width...(in.)		11⅝
Ground clearance...(in.)		15⅛
Ground pressure.............................(lbs per sq in.)		11.35
Electrical system....................................(volts)		12
Capacities...............Fuel, 80 octane gasoline.....(gal)		89
	Cooling system, each.........(qt)	35
	Crankcase (refill) each.......(qt)	8
Brakes.....................................Mechanical		
Communication.....................................Radio		

PERFORMANCE

Maximum gradability..............................(percent)	60
Turning radius...(ft)	21
Fording depth...(in.)	36
Maximum width of ditch vehicle will cross...............(in.)	65
Maximum vertical obstacle vehicle will climb............(in.)	24
Fuel consumption, average conditions..........(miles per gal)	1.5
Cruising range, average conditions...................(miles)	130
Maximum allowable speed..........................(mph)	35

ENGINES (TWO)

Manufacturer......Cadillac.............Model—Series 42	
Type..............V-8, 4 cycle.........Number of cylinders	8
Governed speed.............................Not governed	
Brake horsepower, each...................................	125
Ignition type.......................................Battery	

ADDITIONAL DATA

Basic chassis.............................Tank, light, M5

....

....

....

....

CARRIAGE, MOTOR, 75-MM HOWITZER, T30

Technical Manuals: TM 9-710A, TM 9-1710,   Parts List: SNL G-102
TM 9-1710C, TM 9-1711.

Manufacturer: White Motor Co.

Armament: One Howitzer, 75-mm, M1A1; one Gun, machine, cal. .50, HB, M2 (flexible); one Gun, submachine, cal. .45, M1928A1; four Carbines, cal. .30, M1.

Ammunition: 60 rounds, 75-mm howitzer; 300 rounds, cal. .50; 540 rounds, cal. .45.

RA PD 308920

Classification: None

Purpose: To provide mobility for 75-mm howitzer.

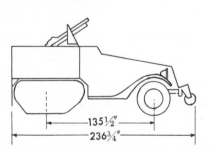

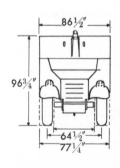

CARRIAGE, MOTOR, 75-MM HOWITZER, T30

GENERAL DATA

Crew			5
Weight	Gross	(lb)	19,500
	Boxed for export	(lb)	21,836
Shipping dimensions	(cu ft) 1049, boxed 1197. (sq ft)		
Tires—Combat	Ply . . . 12 . . . . . Size . . . 8.25 x 20		
Tread, center to center (in.)	Front 64½ . . . . Rear 63¹³⁄₁₆		
Track width		(in.)	12¼
Ground clearance		(in.)	17⅛
Ground pressure, tires		(lbs per sq in.)	33
Electrical system		(volts)	12
Capacities	Fuel, 80 octane gasoline	(gal)	60
	Cooling system	(qt)	26
	Crankcase (refill)	(qt)	8
Brakes	Hydraulic (Hydrovac)		
Communication	Radio		

PERFORMANCE

Maximum gradability	(percent)	60
Turning radius	(ft)	30
Fording depth	(in.)	32
Maximum vertical obstacle vehicle will climb	(in.)	12
Angle of approach	(deg)	37
Angle of departure	(deg)	45
Fuel consumption, average conditions	(miles per gal)	3.3
Cruising range, average conditions	(miles)	200
Maximum allowable speed	(mph)	45

	1st	2nd	3rd	4th
Cruising speed	9	17	26	45

ENGINE

Manufacturer	White	Model 160 AX	
Type	In-line, 4 cycle	Number of cylinders	6
Displacement		(cu in.)	386
Maximum engine speed (not governed)		(rpm)	3200
Brake horsepower			148
Ignition type		Battery	

ADDITIONAL DATA

Basic chassis . . . . Carrier, personnel, half-track, M3

. . . .

. . . .

CARRIAGE, MOTOR, 76-MM GUN, T70

Technical Manuals: TM 9-755.   Parts List: SNL G-163

Manufacturer: Buick Motor Div. (General Motors Corp.)

Armament: One Gun, 76-mm, M1A1; one Gun, machine, cal. .50, HB, M2, five Carbines, cal. .30, M1.

Ammunition: 45 rounds, 76-mm; 800 rounds, cal. .50; 450 rounds, cal. .30; 6 smoke grenades, WP M50; 2 fragmentation grenades; 4 smoke pots.

RA PD 308908

Classification:

Purpose: To provide mobility and crew protection for 76-mm gun.

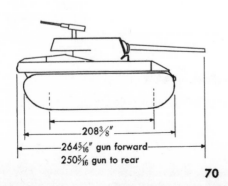

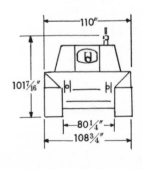

CARRIAGE, MOTOR, 76-MM GUN, T70

GENERAL DATA

Crew..			5
Weight...................	Gross....................	(lb)	37,500
Shipping dimensions.......	(cu ft)	..........(sq ft)	
Track width..		(in.)	14¾
Ground clearance....................................		(in.)	14
Ground pressure............................		(lbs per sq in.)	11.9
Electrical system....................................		(volts)	24
Capacities..............	Fuel, 80 octane, gasoline.....	(gal)	160
	Oil tank....................	(qt)	48
	Cooling system.......	Air-cooled	
	Transmission...............	(qt)	44
	Differential................	(qt)	20
Brakes.......................................		Mechanical	
Communication...........	Radio..............	Interphone	

PERFORMANCE

Maximum gradability..............................	(percent)	60
Turning radius.......................................	(ft)	28
Fording depth.......................................	(in.)	48
Maximum width of ditch vehicle will cross..............	(in.)	
Maximum vertical obstacle vehicle will climb............	(in.)	36
Fuel consumption, average conditions..........	(miles per gal)	1.0
Cruising range, average conditions...................	(miles)	150
Maximum allowable speed...........................	(mph)	55

	1st	2nd	3rd
Cruising speed......	16	34	55

ENGINE

Manufacturer......	Continental............	Model R975-C1	
Type.............	Radial, 4 cycle......	Number of cylinders	9
Displacement.......................................		(cu in.)	973
Governed speed.....................................		(rpm)	2,400
Brake horsepower....................................			400
Ignition type......................................		Magneto	

ADDITIONAL DATA

....
....
....

CARRIAGE, MOTOR, 3-IN. GUN, M10

Technical Manuals: TM 9-752A, TM 9-1750, Parts List: SNL G-130
TM 9-1750B, TM 9-1750G.

Manufacturer: Fisher Tank Division (General Motors Corp.)

Armament: One Gun, 3-in., M7; one Gun, machine, cal. .50, HB, M2 (flexible); five Carbines, cal. .30, M1.

Ammunition: 54 rounds, 3-in.; 450 rounds, cal. .30; 1,000 rounds, cal. .50; 6 smoke grenades; 6 fragmentation grenades.

RA PD 66379

Classification: Standard

Purpose: To provide mobility and crew protection for antitank gun.

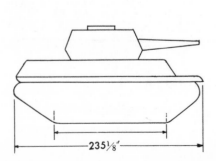

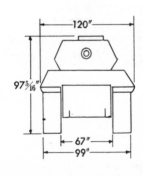

CARRIAGE, MOTOR, 3-IN. GUN, M10

GENERAL DATA

Crew		5
Weight........Gross	(lb)	66,000
Shipping dimensions.......(cu ft) 1,638	(sq ft) 202	
Track width	(in.)	16⁹⁄₁₆
Ground clearance	(in.)	18
Ground pressure	(lbs per sq in.)	13.5
Electrical system	(volts)	24
Capacities........Fuel, 50 cetane Diesel fuel oil	(gal)	165
Oil tank, each	(qt)	28
Crankcase (refill)	(qt)	16
Transmission and differential	(qt)	152
Cooling system	(qt)	120
Brakes	Mechanical	
Communication.......Radio	Interphone	

PERFORMANCE

Maximum gradability	(percent)	50
Turning radius	(ft)	31
Fording depth	(in.)	36
Maximum width of ditch vehicle will cross	(in.)	72
Maximum vertical obstacle vehicle will climb	(in.)	24
Fuel consumption, average conditions	(miles per gal)	1.4
Cruising range, average conditions	(miles)	200
Maximum allowable speed	(mph)	29

	1st	2nd	3rd	4th	5th
Cruising speed..	2	6	10	16	25

ENGINE

Manufacturer......GMC	Model 6046 Series 71	
Type..Twin Six, 2 cycle Diesel	Number of cylinders	12
Displacement	(cu in.)	850
Governed speed	(rpm)	2,100
Brake horsepower		420
Ignition type	Compression	

ADDITIONAL DATA

Basic chassis	Tank, medium, M4A2

....

....

CARRIAGE, MOTOR, 3-IN. GUN, M10A1

Technical Manual: TM 9-731G, TM 9-1731B, Parts List: SNL G-170
　　TM 9-1731C, TM 9-1750, TM 9-1750B.

Manufacturer: Ford Motor Co.

Armament: One Gun, 3-in., M7; one Gun, machine, cal. .50, HB M2,
　(flexible); five Carbines, cal. .30, M1.

Ammunition: 54 rounds, 3-in.; 1,000 rounds, cal. .50; 450 rounds, cal.
　.30; 6 smoke grenades; 6 fragmentation grenades.

RA PD 66381

Classification: Standard

Purpose: To provide mobility and crew protection for 3-in. antitank gun.

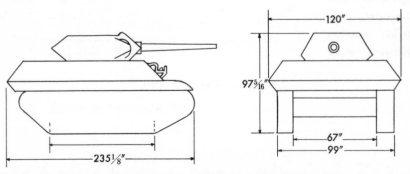

CARRIAGE, MOTOR, 3-IN. GUN, M10A1

GENERAL DATA

Crew.. 5
Weight..................Gross....................(lb) 63,000
Shipping dimensions........(cu ft) 1,638..........(sq ft) 202
Track width..(in.) 16⁹⁄₁₆
Ground clearance....................................(in.) 18
Ground pressure..........................(lbs per sq in.) 13.1
Electrical system..................................(volts) 24
Capacities.............Fuel, 80 octane gasoline.....(gal) 192
                       Crankcase (refill)...........(qt) 32
                       Transmission and differential..(qt) 152
                       Cooling system..............(qt) 56
Brakes..Mechanical
Communication...........Radio...............Interphone

PERFORMANCE

Maximum gradability..........................(percent) 50
Turning radius.......................................(ft) 31
Fording depth.......................................(in.) 36
Maximum width of ditch vehicle will cross..............(in.) 72
Maximum vertical obstacle vehicle will climb............(in.) 24
Fuel consumption, average conditions.........(miles per gal) .9
Cruising range, average conditions..................(miles) 160
Maximum allowable speed..........................(mph) 28

	1st	2nd	3rd	4th	5th
Cruising speed..	2	6	10	16	24

ENGINE

Manufacturer......Ford...................Model GAA-V8
Type..............V-8, 4 cycle........Number of cylinders 8
Displacement....................................(cu in.) 1,100
Governed speed....................................(rpm) 2,800
Brake horsepower..................................... 500
Ignition type..Magneto

ADDITIONAL DATA

Basic chassis........................Tank, medium, M4A3

....

....

CARRIER, 81-MM MORTAR, HALF-TRACK, M4

Technical Manuals: TM 9-710A, TM 9-1710C, Parts List: SNL G-102
TM 9-1711.

Manufacturer: White Motor Co.

Armament: One Mortar, 81-mm, M1; one Gun, machine, cal. .50, BH M2, (flexible); one Gun, machine, cal. .30, M1919A4 (flexible).

Ammunition: 108 rounds, 81-mm; 540 rounds, cal. .45; 1,600 rounds, cal. .30; 20 grenades.

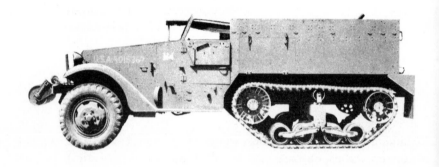

RA PD 66371

Classification: Substitute standard

Purpose: To provide mobility for 81-mm mortar and protection for crew.

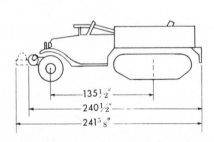

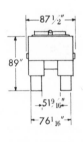

CARRIER, 81-MM MORTAR, HALF-TRACK, M4

GENERAL DATA

Crew. 6
Weight. . . . . .Net. . . . .(lb) 14,700
Payload. . . . .(lb) 2,700
Gross. . . . .(lb) 17,400
Shipping dimensions. . . . . . .(cu ft) 1,060. . . . .(sq ft) 143
Tires—Combat. . . . . .Ply. . .12. . . . . . .Size. . .8.25 x 20
Tread, center to center (in.).Front 64½. . . . . .Rear 63¹³⁄₁₆
Track width. . . . .(in.) 12¼
Ground clearance. . . . .(in.) 17⅛
Ground pressure, tires. . . . .(lbs per sq in.) 29.8
Electrical system. . . . .(volts) 12
Capacities. . . . . .Fuel, 80 octane gasoline. . . . .(gal) 60
Cooling system. . . . .(qt) 26
Crankcase (refill). . . . .(qt) 12
Brakes. . . . . .Hydraulic (Hydrovac)
Communication. . . . . .Radio

PERFORMANCE

Maximum gradability. . . . .(percent) 60
Turning radius. . . . .(ft) 30
Fording depth. . . . .(in.) 32
Maximum vertical obstacle vehicle will climb. . . . .(in.) 12
Angle of approach. . . . .(deg) 37
Angle of departure. . . . .(deg) 45
Fuel consumption, average conditions. . . . .(miles per gal) 3.3
Cruising range, average conditions. . . . .(miles) 200
Maximum allowable speed. . . . .(mph) 45

	1st	2nd	3rd	4th
Cruising speed. .	9	17	26	45

ENGINE

Manufacturer. . . . . . .White. . . . . .Model 160 AX
Type. . . . . .In-line, 4 cycle. . . . . .Number of cylinders 6
Displacement. . . . .(cu in.) 386
Governed speed. . . . . .Not governed
Brake horsepower. 148
Ignition type. . . . . .Battery

ADDITIONAL DATA

Winch capacity. . . . .(lb) 10,000
Basic chassis. . . . . Car, half-track, M2

CARRIER, 81-MM MORTAR, HALF-TRACK, M4A1

Technical Manuals: TM 9-710A, TM 9-1710,   Parts List: SNL G-102
             TM 9-1710C, TM 9-1711.

Manufacturer: White Motor Co.

Armament: One Mortar, 81-mm., M1; one Gun, submachine, cal. .45, M1928A1; one Gun, machine, cal. .30, M1919A4; one Launcher, rocket, M1.

Ammunition: 96 rounds, 81-mm; 540 rounds, cal. .45 in clips; 2,000 rounds, cal. .30; 12 grenades; 10 rockets, HE, AT.

RA PD 309120

Classification: Standard

Purpose: To provide armored carrier for 81-mm mortar.

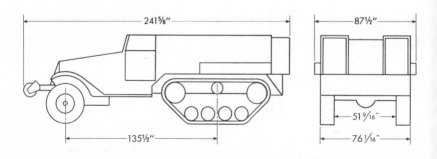

CARRIER, 81-MM MORTAR, HALF-TRACK, M4A1

GENERAL DATA

Crew. 6
Weight. . . . . Gross. . . . . (lb) 18,000
                       Boxed for export. . . . . (lb) 20,550
Shipping dimensions. . . . . . . (cu ft) 1126, boxed 1074. (sq ft)
Tires—Combat. . . . . Ply. . .12. . . . . Size. . .8.25 x 20
Tread, center to center (in.). . Front 64$\frac{1}{2}$ . . . . Rear 63$\frac{13}{16}$
Track width. . . . . (in.) 12$\frac{1}{4}$
Ground clearance. . . . . (in.) 17$\frac{1}{8}$
Ground pressure, tires. (lbs per sq in.) 33
Electrical system. . . . . (volts) 12
Capacities. . . . . Fuel, 80 octane gasoline. . . . . (gal) 60
                       Cooling system. . . . . (qt) 26
                       Crankcase (refill). . . . . (qt) 8
Brakes. . . . . Hydraulic (Hydrovac)
Communication. . . . . .Radio

PERFORMANCE

Maximum gradability. . . . . (percent) 60
Turning radius. . . . . (ft) 30
Maximum vertical obstacle vehicle will climb. . . . . (in.) 12
Fording depth. . . . . (in.) 32
Angle of approach. . . . . (deg) 33
Angle of departure. . . . . (deg) 45
Fuel consumption, average conditions. . . . . (miles per gal) 3.3
Cruising range, average conditions. . . . . (miles) 200
Maximum allowable speed. . . . . (mph) 45

                                     1st 2nd 3rd 4th
                Cruising speed. . 9   17   26   45

ENGINE

Manufacturer. . . . . .White. . . . . Model 160 **AX**
Type. . . . . In-line, 4 cycle. . . . . . .Number of cylinders 6
Displacement. . . . . (cu in.) 386
Maximum engine speed (not governed). . . . .(rpm) 3,200
Brake horsepower. 148
Ignition type. . . . . .Battery

ADDITIONAL DATA

Winch capacity. . . . .(lb) 10,000
Basic chassis. . . . . Car, half-track, M2

CARRIER, MORTAR, 81-MM, HALF-TRACK, M21

Technical Manuals: TM 9-710A, TM 9-1710,   Parts List: SNL G-102
TM 9-1710C, TM 9-1711.

Manufacturer: White Motor Co.

Armament: One Mortar, 81-mm, M1; one Gun, machine, cal. .50.

Ammunition: 96 rounds, 81-mm; 400 rounds, cal. .50; 12 hand grenades;
12 mines.

RA PD 309115

Classification: Standard

Purpose: To provide a self-propelled mount for 81-mm mortar.

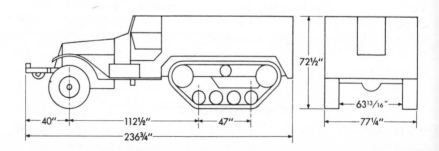

CARRIER, MORTAR, 81-MM, HALF-TRACK, M21

GENERAL DATA

Crew		6
Weight	Gross (lb)	18,500
Shipping dimensions (cu ft) 1,116 (sq ft) 131		
Tires—Combat Ply Size 8.25 x 20		
Tread, center to center (in.) Front 64½ Rear 63¹³⁄₁₆		
Ground clearance (in.)		17⅛
Ground pressure, tires (lbs per sq in.)		29.4
Electrical system (volts)		12
Capacities Fuel, 80 octane gasoline (gal)		60
Cooling system (qt)		26
Crankcase (refill) (qt)		10
Brakes Hydraulic (Hydrovac)		
Communication Radio		

PERFORMANCE

Maximum gradability (percent)	60
Turning radius (ft)	30
Fording depth (in.)	32
Maximum vertical obstacle vehicle will climb (in.)	12
Angle of approach (deg)	
Angle of departure (deg)	
Fuel consumption, average conditions (miles per gal)	
Cruising range, average conditions (miles)	220
Maximum allowable speed (mph)	45

	1st	2nd	3rd	4th
Cruising speed	9	17	26	45

ENGINE

Manufacturer White Model 160 AX	
Type In-line, 4 cycle Number of cylinders	6
Displacement (cu in.)	386
Governed speed Not governed	
Brake horsepower	148
Ignition type Battery	

ADDITIONAL DATA

Winch capacity (lb)	10,000
Basic chassis Carrier, personnel, half-track, M3	

CARRIAGE, MOTOR, 105-MM HOWITZER, M7

Technical Manuals: TM 9-731E, TM 9-1750,   Parts List: SNL G-128
    TM 9-1750B, TM 9-1750D, TM 9-1751.

Manufacturer: American Locomotive Co.

Armament: One Howitzer, 105-mm, M2A1; one Gun, machine, cal. .50,
   HB M2 (flexible); three Guns, submachine, cal. .45, M1928A1.

Ammunition: 69 rounds, 105-mm; 300 rounds, cal. .50; 1,620 rounds, cal.
   .45; 6 smoke grenades; 2 fragmentation grenades.

RA PD 308933

Classification: Standard

Purpose: To provide mobility for 105-mm howitzer.

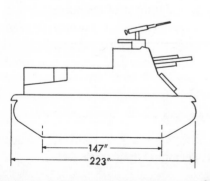

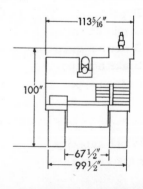

CARRIAGE, MOTOR, 105-MM HOWITZER, M7

GENERAL DATA

Crew...			7
Weight..................Gross....................(lb)			52,000
Shipping dimensions........(cu ft) 1462..........(sq ft) 175			
Track width..(in.)			16⁹⁄₁₆

Crew... 7
Weight..................Gross....................(lb) 52,000
Shipping dimensions........(cu ft) 1462..........(sq ft) 175
Track width..(in.) 16%6
Ground clearance....................................(in.) 17
Ground pressure............................(lbs per sq in.) 10
Electrical system...................................(volts) 24
Capacities...............Fuel, 80 octane gasoline.....(gal) 175
Oil tank...................(qt) 36
Transmission..............(qt) 26
Differential................(qt) 120
Cooling system........Air-cooled
Brakes..Mechanical

PERFORMANCE

Maximum gradability............................(percent) 60
Turning radius.......................................(ft) 31
Fording depth.......................................(in.) 42
Maximum width of ditch vehicle will cross.............(in.) 72
Maximum vertical obstacle vehicle will climb........:...(in.) 24
Fuel consumption, average conditions..........(miles per gal) 1.0
Cruising range, average conditions...................(miles) 165
Maximum allowable speed..........................(mph) 25

	1st	2nd	3rd	4th	5th
Cruising speed..	2	4.8	8.3	13.2	20.3

ENGINE

Manufacturer......Continental.............Model R975C1
Type.............Radial, 4 cycle.......Number of cylinders 9
Displacement.......................................(cu in.) 973
Governed speed....................................(rpm) 2400
Brake horsepower..................................... 400
Ignition type....................................Magneto

ADDITIONAL DATA

Basic chassis originally—Tank, medium, M3; later Tank, medium, M4.

....

....

CARRIAGE, MOTOR, 105-MM HOWITZER, T19

Technical Manuals: TM 9-710A, TM 9-1710,   Parts List: SNL G-102
TM 9-1710C, TM 9-1711.

Manufacturer: Diamond T Motor Car Co.

Armament: One Howitzer, 105-mm, M2A1; one Gun, machine, cal. .50, HB, M2 (flexible); one Gun, submachine, cal. .45, M1928A1.

Ammunition: 8 rounds, 105-mm; 200 rounds, cal. .50; 540 rounds, cal. .45, in clips.

RA PD 12556

Classification: None

Purpose: To provide mobility for 105-mm howitzer and protection for crew.

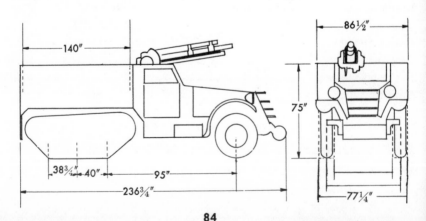

CARRIAGE, MOTOR, 105-MM HOWITZER, T19

GENERAL DATA

Crew		6
Weight	Net (lb)	17,400
	Payload (lb)	2,600
	Gross (lb)	20,000
Shipping dimensions (cu ft)	(sq ft)	
Tires—Combat Ply . . .12	Size. . .8.25 x 20	
Tread, center to center (in.) . .Front 64½	Rear 63¹³⁄₁₆	
Track width	(in.)	12¼
Ground clearance	(in.)	17⅛
Ground pressure, tires	(lbs per sq in.)	33.5
Electrical system	(volts)	12
Capacities	Fuel, 80 octane gasoline (gal)	60
	Cooling system (qt)	26
	Crankcase (refill) (qt)	8
Brakes	Hydraulic (Hydrovac)	
Communication	Radio	

PERFORMANCE

Maximum gradability	(percent)	60
Turning radius	(ft)	30
Fording depth	(in.)	32
Angle of approach	(deg)	37
Angle of departure	(deg)	45
Fuel consumption, average conditions	(miles per gal)	3.3
Cruising range, average conditions	(miles)	200
Maximum allowable speed	(mph)	45

	1st	2nd	3rd	4th
Cruising speed	9	17	26	45

ENGINE

Manufacturer	White	Model 160-AX
Type	In-line, 4 cycle	Number of cylinders
Displacement		(cu in.)	386
Maximum engine speed (not governed)	(rpm)	3,200
Brake horsepower		148

Number of cylinders: 6

ADDITIONAL DATA

Basic chassis . . . . Carrier, personnel, half-track, M3

. . . .

. . . .

CARRIAGE, MOTOR, 155-MM GUN, M12

Technical Manuals: TM 9-751, TM 9-1750,   Parts List: SNL G-158
    TM 1750B, TM 9-1750D, TM 9-1751.

Manufacturer: Pressed Steel Car Co.

Armament: One Gun, 155-mm, M1918M1; five Carbines, cal. .30; one
   Launcher, grenade.

Ammunition: 10 rounds, 155-mm; 12 hand grenades; 10 rifle grenades.

RA PD 66383

Classification: Standard

Purpose: To provide mobility for 155-mm gun and protection for crew.

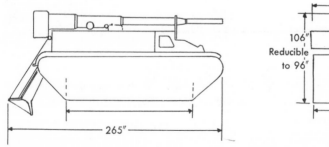

CARRIAGE, MOTOR, 155-MM GUN, M12

GENERAL DATA

Crew..		6
Weight.....................Gross....................(lb)		58,000
Shipping dimensions.......(cu ft) 1,550..........(sq ft) 193		
Track width..(in.)		16⁹⁄₁₆
Ground clearance.....................................(in.)		20
Ground pressure..........................(lbs per sq in.)		12
Electrical system....................................(volts)		24
Capacities..............Fuel, 80 octane gasoline.....(gal)		200
	Oil tank....................(qt)	40
	Transmission and differential..(qt)	152
	Cooling system........Air-cooled	
Brakes...................................Mechanical		
Communication...........Radio..............Interphone		

PERFORMANCE

Maximum gradability............................(percent)	60
Turning radius..(ft)	31
Fording depth...(in.)	36
Maximum width of ditch vehicle will cross.............(in.)	72
Maximum vertical obstacle vehicle will climb............(in.)	24
Fuel consumption, average conditions.........(miles per gal)	.75
Cruising range, average conditions...................(miles)	140
Maximum allowable speed.........................(mph)	24

	1st	2nd	3rd	4th	5th
Cruising speed..	2	5	9	14	21

ENGINE

Manufacturer......Continental.............Model R975C-1		
Type.............Radial, 4 cycle.....Number of cylinders		9
Displacement.....................................(cu in.)		973
Governed speed....................................(rpm)		2,400
Brake horsepower......................................		400
Ignition type....................................Magneto		

ADDITIONAL DATA

Basic chassis originally—Tank, medium, M3; later Tank, medium, M4.

....

....

....

TANK, LIGHT, M3

Technical Manuals: TM 9-726, TM 9-1726A,
TM 9-1726B, TM 1726C, TM 9-1726F,
TM 9-1728.

Parts List:
SNL G-103,
Vol. I

Manufacturer: American Car & Foundry Co.

Armament: One Gun, 37-mm, M5 or M6; five Guns, machine, cal. .30,
M1919A4, flexible; one Gun, submachine, cal. .45, M1928A1.

Ammunition: 103 rounds, 37-mm; 5,500 rounds, cal. .30; 350 rounds,
cal. .45.

RA PD 4747

Classification: Limited standard

Purpose: To provide firepower, mobility and crew protection for offensive
combat.

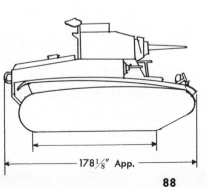

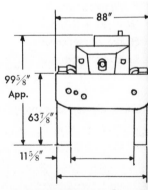

TANK, LIGHT, M3

GENERAL DATA

Crew 4

Weight . . . . (Fighting, approx.) . . . . (lb)   28,000

Shipping dimensions . . . . (cu ft) 924 . . . . (sq ft) 106

Track width . . . . (in.) $11\frac{5}{8}$

Ground clearance . . . . (in.) $16\frac{1}{2}$

Ground pressure . . . . (lb per sq in.)   10.5

Electrical system . . . . (volts)   12

Capacities . . . . Fuel, 80 octane gasoline . . . . (gal)   56

                      Oil tank . . . . (qt)   24

                      Transmission and differential . (qt)   24

                      Cooling system . . . . . . Air-cooled

Brakes . . . . Mechanical

Communication . . . . Radio . . . . Intra-tank phone

PERFORMANCE

Maximum gradability . . . . (percent)   57

Turning radius . . . . (ft)   21

Fording depth . . . . (in.)   40

Maximum width of ditch vehicle will cross . . . . (in.)   72

Maximum vertical obstacle vehicle will climb . . . . (in.)   24

Fuel consumption, average conditions . . . . (miles per gal)   1.10

Cruising range, average conditions . . . . (miles)   60

Maximum allowable speed . . . . (mph)   36

ENGINE

Manufacturer . . . . . . Continental* . . . . Model W670-9A

Type . . . . Radial, 4 cycle . . . . . Number of cylinders   7

Displacement . . . . (cu in.)   668

Governed speed . . . . (rpm)   2,400

Brake horsepower   242

Ignition type . . . . Magneto

ADDITIONAL DATA

*Some models are powered with Guiberson engines, Model T-1020 series
4, 1021 cubic inch displacement, using 50 cetane Diesel fuel oil. Miles
per gallon (under average operating conditions) 1.5. Cruising range
(under average operating conditions) 84.

TANK, LIGHT, M3A1

Technical Manuals: TM 9-927, TM 9-1726A, Parts List: SNL G-103,
  TM 9-1726B, TM 9-1726C, TM 9-1726F.   Vol. V

Manufacturer: American Car & Foundry Co.

Armament: One Gun, 37-mm, M6; one Gun, submachine, cal. .45,
  M1928A1; one Gun, machine, cal. .30, M1919A5 (fixed); two Guns,
  machine, cal. .30, M1919A4 (flexible).

Ammunition: 111 rounds, 37-mm; 350 rounds, cal. .45; 7,000 rounds, cal.
  .30; 12 hand grenades, two smoke, two thermite, eight fragmentation.

RA PD 45946

Vehicle illustrated above has riveted hull. It is commonly known as "The
  Honey" by British, and "General Stuart" in U. S. Army.

Classification: Limited standard

Purpose: To provide firepower, mobility, and crew protection.

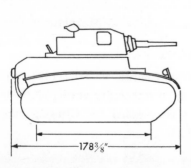

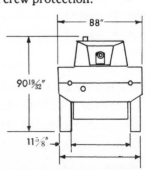

TANK, LIGHT, M3A1

GENERAL DATA

Crew		4
Weight	(Fighting) (lb)	28,515
Shipping dimensions	(cu ft) 940 (sq ft) 108	
Track width	(in.)	11⅝
Ground clearance	(in.)	16½
Ground pressure	(lb per sq in.)	10.5
Electrical system	(volts)	12
Capacities	Fuel, 80 octane gasoline (gal)	56
	Oil tank (qt)	24
	Transmission (qt)	24
	Cooling system Air-cooled	
Brakes	Mechanical	
Communication	Radio Intra-tank phone	

PERFORMANCE

Maximum gradability	(percent)	57
Turning radius	(ft)	21
Fording depth	(in.)	40
Maximum width of ditch vehicle will cross	(in.)	72
Maximum vertical obstacle vehicle will climb	(in.)	24
Fuel consumption, average conditions	(miles per gal)	1.10
Cruising range, average condition	(miles)	60
Maximum allowable speed	(mph)	36

ENGINE

Manufacturer	Continental* Model W670-9A	
Type	Radial, 4 cycle Number of cylinders	7
Displacement	(cu in.)	668
Governed speed	(rpm)	2,400
Brake horsepower		242
Ignition type	Magneto	

ADDITIONAL DATA

*Some models are powered with Guiberson engine, Model T-1020 Series 4, 1021 cubic inch displacement using 50 cetane Diesel fuel oil. Miles per gallon (under average operating conditions) 1.5. Cruising range (under average operating conditions) 84.

TANK, LIGHT, M3A3

Technical Manuals: TM 9-727, TM 9-1726A,   Parts List: SNL G-103,
     TM 9-1726C, TM 9-1727B, TM 9-1727F.   Vol. VII

Manufacturer: American Car & Foundry Co.

Armament: One Gun, 37-mm, M6; one Gun, machine, cal. .30, M1919A5
(fixed); two Guns, machine, cal. .30, M1919A4 (flexible); one Gun,
submachine, cal. .45, M1928A1.

Ammunition: 174 rounds, 37-mm; 7,500 rounds, cal. .30; 540 rounds, cal.
.45; 12 hand grenades.

RA PD 66427

Classification: Limited standard

Purpose: To provide firepower, mobility and crew protection for offensive
combat.

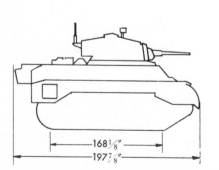
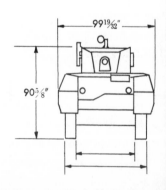

TANK, LIGHT, M3A3

GENERAL DATA

Crew.. 4
Weight................(Fighting)..................(lb) 31,280
Shipping dimensions......(cu ft) 940............(sq ft) 108
Track width..(in.) $11\frac{5}{8}$
Ground clearance......................................(in.) $16\frac{1}{2}$
Ground pressure........................... (lb per sq in.) 11.2
Electrical system....................................(volts) 12
Capacities.............Fuel, 80 octane gasoline......(gal) 100
                       Oil tank...................(qt) 24
                       Transmission and differential...(qt) 24
                       Cooling system.........Air-cooled
Brakes...Mechanical
Communication.........Radio.............Interphone

PERFORMANCE

Maximum gradability..........................(percent) 58
Turning radius.......................................(ft) 21
Fording depth.......................................(in.) 40
Maximum width of ditch vehicle will cross.............(in.) 72
Maximum vertical obstacle vehicle will climb...........(in.) 24
Fuel consumption, average conditions.........(miles per gal) 1.10
Cruising range, average conditions..................(miles) 110
Maximum allowable speed..........................(mph) 36

ENGINES

Manufacturer.....Continental............Model W670-9A
Type............Radial, 4 cycle......Number of cylinders 7
Displacement......................................(cu in.) 668
Governed speed....................................(rpm) 2400
Brake horsepower................................... 242
Ignition type.......................................Magneto

ADDITIONAL DATA

Has welded hull.

....
....

TANK, LIGHT, M5
TANK, LIGHT, M5A1

Technical Manuals: TM 9-732, TM 9-1727B, TM 9-1727C, TM 9-1727D, TM 9-1727E, TM 9-1727F, TM 9-1727G, TM 9-1727K.

Parts Lists: SNL G-103, Vols. II and VIII

Manufacturer: Cadillac Motor Car Division (General Motors Corp.).

Armament: One Gun, 37-mm, M6; one Gun, machine, cal. .30, M1919A4 (fixed); two Guns, machine, cal. .30, M1919A4 (flexible); one Gun, submachine, cal. .45, M1928A1.

Ammunition: 123 rounds, 37-mm; 720 rounds, cal. .45; 6,500 rounds, cal. .30; 12 hand grenades.

RA PD 45979

Vehicle illustrated above: Light tank, M5A1

Classification: Standard

Purpose: To provide firepower, mobility, and crew protection for offensive combat.

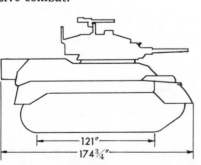

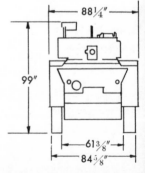

TANK, LIGHT, M5
TANK, LIGHT, M5A1

GENERAL DATA

Crew		4
Weight (Fighting)	(lb)	32,340
Shipping dimensions (cu ft) 861	(sq ft)	109
Track width	(in.)	11⅝
Ground clearance	(in.)	16½
Ground pressure	(lb per sq in.)	11.6
Electrical system	(volts)	12
Capacities Fuel, 80 octane gasoline	(gal)	89
Crankcase (refill) each	(qt)	8
Differential and transmission	(qt)	32
Transfer case (each)	(qt)	15
Cooling system (each)	(qt)	35
Brakes Mechanical		
Communications Radio Intra-tank phone		

PERFORMANCE

Maximum gradability	(percent)	60
Turning radius	(ft)	21
Fording depth	(in.)	36
Maximum width of ditch vehicle will cross	(in.)	72
Maximum vertical obstacle vehicle will climb	(in.)	24
Fuel consumption, average conditions	(miles per gal)	1.10
Cruising range, average conditions	(miles)	98
Maximum allowable speed	(mph)	40

ENGINES (TWO)

Manufacturer Cadillac Model—series 42		
Type V8, 4 cycle Number of cylinders		8
Displacement	(cu in.)	346
Governed speed Not governed		
Brake horsepower	(each)	125
Ignition type Battery		

ADDITIONAL DATA

Light tanks M5 and M5A1 are alike except for a slight bulge in the turret of the M5A1 to accommodate the radio.

. . . .

. . . .

TANK, LIGHT, T9E1

Technical Manuals: TM 9-724, TM 9-1724A.   Parts List: SNL G-148

Manufacturer: Marmon-Herrington Co. Inc.

Armament: One Gun, 37-mm, M6; one Gun, machine, cal. .30, 1919A4 (flexible); one Gun, submachine, cal. .45, M1928A1.

Ammunition: 50 rounds, 37-mm; 2,500 rounds, cal. .30; 450 rounds, cal. .45; 12 hand grenades (4 MKII), (2 MKIII), (4 smoke M8), (2 thermite).

RA PD 308903

Classification: None

Purpose: Airborne.

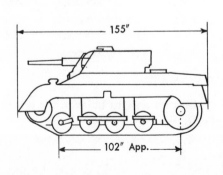

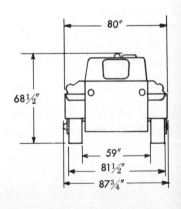

TANK, LIGHT, T9E1

GENERAL DATA

Crew.	3
Weight. . . . . .Net (airborne). . . . .(lb)	15,800
Shipping dimensions. . . . . .(cu ft) 534. . . . .(sq ft) 114	
Track width. . . . .(in.)	11¼
Ground clearance. . . . .(in.)	10
Ground pressure . . . .(lb per sq in.)	6.16
Electrical system. . . . .(volts)	12
Capacities. . . . . .Fuel, 73 octane gasoline. . . . . .(gal)	55
Crankcase (refill). . . . .(qt)	12
Transmission and differential. . .(qt)	18
Cooling system . . . . .Air-cooled	
Brakes. . . . . .Mechanical	
Communication. . . . . .Radio. . . . . .Intra-tank phone	

PERFORMANCE

Maximum gradability. . . . .(percent)	63
Turning radius. . . . .(ft)	38
Fording depth. . . . .(in.)	42
Maximum width of ditch vehicle will cross. . . . .(in.)	65
Maximum vertical obstacle vehicle will climb. . . . .(in.)	12⅜
Fuel consumption, average conditions. . . . .(miles per gal)	2.5
Cruising range, average conditions. . . . .(miles)	135
Maximum allowable speed. . . . .(mph)	40

	1st	2nd	3rd	4th
Cruising speed.	7	13	28	42

ENGINE

Manufacturer. . . . .Lycoming. . . . . .Model O-435-T	
Type. . . . . .Horizontally opposed, 4 cycle. .Number of cylinders	6
Displacement. . . . .(cu in.)	434
Governed speed. . . . .(rpm)	2800
Brake horsepower.	162
Ignition type. . . . . .Battery	

ADDITIONAL DATA

. . . .

. . . .

. . . .

. . . .

TANK, MEDIUM, M3

Technical Manuals: TM 9-750, TM 9-1750,
TM 9-1750D, TM 9-1750E, TM 9-1750H,
TM 9-1751, TM 9-1752.

Parts List:
SNL G-104,
Vol. I

Manufacturers: American Locomotive Co., Baldwin Locomotive Works, Detroit Tank Arsenal (Chrysler), Pressed Steel Car Co., Pullman Standard Car Mfg. Co.

Armament: One Gun, 75-mm, M2 (Tank); one Gun, 37-mm, M5 or M6; three Guns, machine, M1919A4; one Gun, submachine, cal. .45, M1928A1.

Ammunition: 50 rounds, 75-mm; 179 rounds, 37-mm; 1,200 rounds, cal. .45; 9,200 rounds, cal. .30; 14 hand grenades.

See page 101.

RA PD 66433

Vehicle illustrated above has riveted hull. M3 series medium tanks are commonly known as "General Lee". Classification: Limited standard

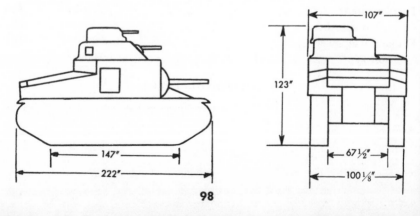

TANK, MEDIUM, M3A1

Technical Manuals: TM 9-750, TM 9-1750,
TM 9-1750D, TM 9-1750E, TM 9-1750H,
TM 9-1751, TM 9-1752.

Parts List:
SNL G-104,
Vol. XII

Manufacturer: American Locomotive Co.

Armament: One Gun, 75-mm, M2 (Tank); one Gun, 37-mm, M5 or M6; three Guns, machine, M1919A4; one Gun, submachine, cal. .45, M1928A1.

Ammunition: 50 rounds, 75-mm; 179 rounds, 37-mm; 1,200 rounds, cal. .45; 9,200 rounds, cal. .30; 14 hand grenades.

See page 101.

RA PD 66435

Vehicle illustrated above has cast hull.

Classification: Limited standard

Purpose: To provide firepower, mobility, and crew protection for offensive combat.

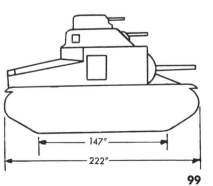

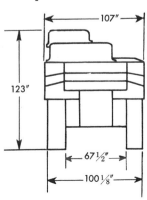

TANK, MEDIUM, M3A2

Technical Manuals: TM 9-750, TM 9-1750,
TM 9-1750D, TM 9-1750E, TM 9-1750H,
TM 9-1751, TM 9-1752.

Parts List:
SNL G-104,
Vol. XII

Manufacturer: Baldwin Locomotive Works.

Armament: One Gun, 75-mm, M2 (Tank); one Gun, 37-mm, M5 or M6;
three Guns, machine, M1919A4; one Gun, submachine, cal. .45,
M1928A1.

Ammunition: 50 rounds, 75-mm; 179 rounds, 37-mm; 1,200 rounds, cal.
.45; 9,200 rounds, cal. .30; 14 hand grenades.

See page 101

RA PD 66437

Vehicle illustrated above has welded hull.

Classification: Limited standard

Purpose: To provide firepower, mobility, and crew protection for offensive combat.

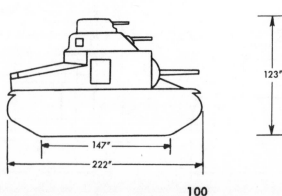
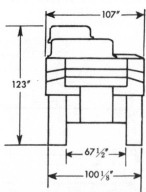

TANK, MEDIUM, M3
TANK, MEDIUM, M3A1
TANK, MEDIUM, M3A2

GENERAL DATA

Crew...	7
Weight...............(Fighting, approx.)...........(lb)	60,000
Shipping dimensions......(cu ft) 1,736..........(sq ft) 169	
Track width...................................(in.)	16⁹⁄₁₆
Ground clearance..............................(in.)	$17\frac{1}{8}$
Ground pressure......................... (lb per sq in.)	12.75
Electrical system................................(volts)	24
Capacities.............Fuel, 80 octane gasoline......(gal)	175
Oil tank.....................(qt)	36
Transmission................(qt)	26
Differential..................(qt)	120
Cooling system.........Air-cooled	
Brakes (hydraulic booster on old models).......Mechanical	
Communication.........Radio.......Intra-tank phone	

PERFORMANCE

Maximum gradability............................(percent)	60
Turning radius.......................................(ft)	31
Fording depth.......................................(in.)	40
Maximum width of ditch vehicle will cross.............(in.)	72
Maximum vertical obstacle vehicle will climb............(in.)	24
Fuel consumption, average conditions........(miles per gal)	.75
Cruising range, average conditions..................(miles)	125
Maximum allowable-speed.........................(mph)	24

	1st	2nd	3rd	4th	5th
Cruising speed.	2	5	9	14	21

ENGINE

Manufacturer.....Continental*..........Model R975-EC2	
Type.............Radial, 4 cycle......Number of cylinders	9
Displacement....................................(cu in.)	973
Governed speed.................................(rpm)	2,100
Brake horsepower...............................	400
Ignition type....................................Magneto	

ADDITIONAL DATA

*Some M3 and M3A2 tanks are powered with Guiberson Diesel engines, Model T-1400, 1402 cubic inch displacement, using 50 cetane Diesel oil fuel. Weights are based on steel chevron track, T54E1.

TANK, MEDIUM, M3A3, AND
TANK, MEDIUM, M3A5

Technical Manuals: TM 9-753, TM 9-1750,
TM 9-1750G, TM 9-1750H.

Parts List:
SNL G-104,
Vols. V and X

Manufacturer: Baldwin Locomotive Works.

Armament: One Gun, 75-mm, M2; one Gun, 37-mm, M5 and M6; three Guns, machine, cal. .30, M1919A4; one Gun, submachine, cal. .45.

Ammunition: 50 rounds, 75-mm; 179 rounds, 37-mm; 1,200 rounds, cal. .45; 9,200 rounds, cal. .30; 14 hand grenades.

RA PD 66439

Vehicle illustrated above: Tank, medium, M3A3, welded hull.

Classification: Limited standard

Purpose: To provide firepower, mobility, and crew protection for offensive combat.

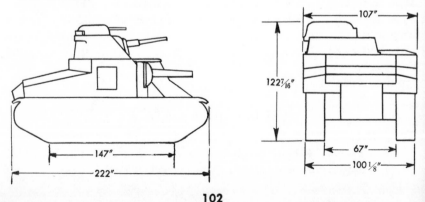

TANK, MEDIUM, M3A3, AND
TANK, MEDIUM, M3A5

GENERAL DATA

Crew..	6
Weight—See add'l data...(Fighting).....................	
Shipping dimensions......(cu ft) 1,620..........(sq ft) 162	
Track width...(in.)	16⁹⁄₁₆
Ground clearance.......................................(in.)	17⅛
Ground pressure—See additional data........ (lb per sq in.)	
Electrical system......................................(volts)	24
Capacities.............Fuel, 50 cetane, Diesel fuel oil..(gal)	148
Oil tank....................(qt)	32
Transmission and differential...(qt)	136
Cooling system...............(qt)	128
Brakes...Mechanical	
Communication.........Radio..........Intra-tank phone	

PERFORMANCE

Maximum gradability............................(percent)	60
Turning radius.......................................(ft)	31
Fording depth—See additional data....................(in.)	
Maximum width of ditch vehicle will cross.............(in.)	72
Maximum vertical obstacle vehicle will climb...........(in.)	24
Fuel consumption, average conditions........(miles per gal)	1.1
Cruising range, average conditions..................(miles)	150
Maximum allowable speed...........................(mph)	29

	1st	2nd	3rd	4th	5th
Cruising speed.	2	6	10	16	25

ENGINE

Manufacturer.....GMC..............Model 6046 series 71	
Type......Twin-Six, 2 cycle, Diesel........No. of cylinders	12
Displacement.......................................(cu in.)	850
Governed speed....................................(rpm)	2,100
Brake horsepower....................................	420
Ignition type.............................Compression	

ADDITIONAL DATA

Weights and ground pressure based on steel chevron track T54E1.

	M3A3	M3A5
Weight........................	62,240	64,000
Ground pressure...............	13.2	13.5
Fording depth.................	36	40
Hull......................welded		riveted

TANK, MEDIUM, M3A4

Technical Manuals: TM 9-730C, TM 9-1750,
TM 9-1750F, TM 9-1750H, TM 9-1750J.

Parts List:
SNL G-104, Vol. III

Manufacturer: Detroit Tank Arsenal (Chrysler).

Armament: One Gun, 75-mm, M2; one Gun, 37-mm, M5 and M6; three
Guns, machine, cal. .30, M1919A4; one Gun, submachine, cal. .45.

Ammunition: 50 rounds, 75-mm; 179 rounds, 37-mm; 1,200 rounds, cal.
.45; 9,200 rounds, cal. .30; 14 hand grenades.

RA PD 66441

Vehicle illustrated above has riveted hull.

Classification: Limited standard

Purpose: To provide firepower, mobility and crew protection for offensive combat.

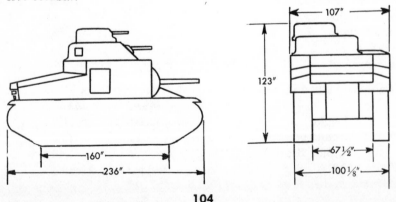

TANK, MEDIUM, M3A4

GENERAL DATA

Crew.. 6
Weight...............(Fighting, approx.)...........(lb) 64,000
Shipping dimensions......(cu ft) 1,828..........(sq ft) 178
Track width..(in.) 16⁹⁄₁₆
Ground clearance..................................(in.) 17⅛
Ground pressure..........................(lbs per sq in.) 12.1
Electrical system..................................(volts) 24
Capacities.............Fuel, 70 octane gasoline......(gal) 160
                      Oil tank....................(qt) 32
                      Transmission and differential...(qt) 72
                      Cooling system..............(qt) 128
Brakes..Mechanical
Communication.........Radio..........Intra-tank phone

PERFORMANCE

Maximum gradability..........................(percent) 60
Turning radius....................................(ft) 31
Fording depth....................................(in.) 40
Maximum width of ditch vehicle will cross..........(in.) 78
Maximum vertical obstacle vehicle will climb..........(in.) 24
Fuel consumption, average conditions........(miles per gal) .6
Cruising range, average conditions.................(miles) 90
Maximum allowable speed.........................(mph) 23

	1st	2nd	3rd	4th	5th
Cruising speeds	2	5	9	14	20

ENGINE

Manufacturer.....Chrysler....................Model A-57
Type............Multi-bank, 4 cycle..Number of cylinders 30
Displacement.....................................(cu in.) 1253
Governed speed (no load)........................(rpm) 2600
Brake horsepower.................................... 460
Ignition type....................................Battery

ADDITIONAL DATA

Weight based on steel chevron track, T54E1.

....
....
....
....

TANK, MEDIUM, M4, AND
TANK, MEDIUM, M4 (105-MM HOW.)

Technical Manuals: TM 9-731A, TM 9-1730C, TM 9-1750D, TM 9-1731E, TM 9-1731G, TM 9-1731K, TM 9-1750.

Parts List: SNL G-104, Vols. VI and XIV

Manufacturers: Baldwin Locomotive Works, American Locomotive Co.; Detroit Tank Arsenal (Chrysler); Pressed Steel Car Co.; Pullman Standard Car Mfg. Co.

For Armament and Ammunition see page 554.

RA PD 308904

Vehicle illustrated above: Tank, medium, M4, (105-mm How.) M4 series medium tanks are commonly known as "General Sherman."

Classification: Standard

Purpose: To provide firepower, mobility, and crew protection for offensive combat.

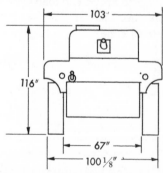

147"
232"
add 15" length and 1⅛" width when sand shields are used.

103'
116"
67"
100⅛"

TANK, MEDIUM, M4, AND
TANK, MEDIUM, M4 (105-MM HOW.)

GENERAL DATA

Crew		5
Weight	(Fighting), M4 (lb)	67,300
	M4 (105-mm How.) (lb)	68,500
Shipping dimensions (cu ft) 1,452	(sq ft) 166	
Track width	(in.)	16⁹⁄₁₆
Ground clearance	(in.)	17³⁄₈
Ground pressure	M4 (lbs per sq in.)	13.4
	M4 (105-mm How.) (lbs per sq in.)	13.6
Electrical system	(volts)	24
Capacities	Fuel, 80 octane, gasoline (gal)	175
	Oil tank (qt)	36
	Transmission and differential (qt)	128
	Cooling system Air cooled	
Brakes	Mechanical	
Communication	Radio Interphone	

PERFORMANCE

Maximum gradability	(percent)	60
Turning radius	(ft)	31
Fording depth	(in.)	36
Maximum width of ditch vehicle will cross	(in.)	72
Maximum vertical obstacle vehicle will climb	(in.)	24
Fuel consumption, average conditions	(miles per gal)	.75
Cruising range, average conditions	(miles)	125
Maximum allowable speed	(mph)	24

	1st	2nd	3rd	4th	5th
Cruising speed	2	5	9	14	21

ENGINE

Manufacturer Continental	Model R975-C1	
Type Radial, 4 cycle	Number of cylinders	9
Displacement	(cu in.)	973
Governed speed	(rpm)	2,400
Brake horsepower		400
Ignition type	Magneto	

ADDITIONAL DATA

Tank, medium, M4 (105-mm How.), is identical with Tank, medium, M4, except carries 105-mm howitzer, T8 instead of 75-mm gun, M3. Weights based on chevron steel track T54E1.

TANK, MEDIUM, M4A1

Technical Manuals: TM 9-731A, TM 9-1730C,
TM 9-1731E, TM 9-1731G, TM 9-1731K,
TM 9-1750, TM 9-1750B, TM 9-1750D,
TM 9-1750K.

Parts List:
SNL G-104,
Vol. XI

Manufacturers: Lima Locomotive Works, Inc., Pacific Car & Foundry
Co., Pressed Steel Car Co.

Armament: One Gun, 75-mm, M3; one Gun, machine, cal. .50, HB, M2;
two Guns, machine, cal. .30, M1919A4 (flexible); one Gun, submachine,
cal. .45, M1928A1.

Ammunition: 90 rounds, 75-mm; 6,250 rounds, cal. .30; 600 rounds, cal.
.45; 300 rounds, cal. .50; 12 hand grenades.

RA PD 308926

Classification: Standard

Purpose: To provide firepower, mobility and crew protection for offensive combat.

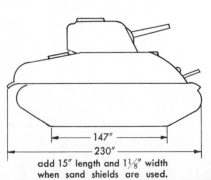

147"
230"
add 15" length and 1⅛" width
when sand shields are used.

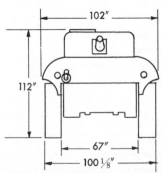

102"
112"
67"
100⅛"

108

TANK, MEDIUM, M4A1

GENERAL DATA

Crew... 5
Weight................(Fighting)................(lb) 67,300
Shipping dimensions......(cu ft) 1,540..........(sq ft) 165
Track width..(in.) 16⁹⁄₁₆
Ground clearance..................................(in.) 17³⁄₈
Ground pressure.........................(lbs per sq in.) 13.4
Electrical system...................................(volts) 24
Capacities.............Fuel, 80 octane gasoline......(gal) 175
                      Oil tank....................(qt) 36
                      Transmission and differential...(qt) 128
                      Cooling system........Air-cooled
Brakes.....................................Mechanical
Communication.........Radio...............Interphone

PERFORMANCE

Maximum gradability...........................(percent) 60
Turning radius.......................................(ft) 31
Fording depth.......................................(in.) 36
Maximum width of ditch vehicle will cross.............(in.) 72
Maximum vertical obstacle vehicle will climb............(in.) 24
Fuel consumption, average conditions........(miles per gal) .75
Cruising range, average conditions.................(miles) 125
Maximum allowable speed........................(mph) 24

	1st	2nd	3rd	4th	5th
Cruising speed.	2	5	9	14	21

ENGINE

Manufacturer.....Continental............Model R975-C1
Type.............Radial, 4 cycle.....Number of cylinders 9
Displacement......................................(cu in.) 973
Governed speed....................................(rpm) 2,400
Brake horsepower................................... 400
Ignition type......................................Magneto

ADDITIONAL DATA

Weight based on chevron steel track T54E1.

....
....
....

TANK, MEDIUM, M4A2

Technical Manuals: TM 9-731B, TM 9-1731F, TM 9-1731G, TM 9-1731K, TM 9-1750, TM 9-1750B, TM 9-1750G.

Parts List: SNL G-104, Vol. VII

Manufacturers: Federal Machine and Welding Co.; Fisher Tank Div., (General Motors Corp.); Pullman Standard Car Mfg. Co.

Armament: One Gun, 75-mm, M3; one Gun, machine, cal. .30, M1919A4 (flexible); one Gun, submachine, cal. .45, M1928A1; one Gun, machine, cal. .50, HB, M2.

Ammunition: 97 rounds, 75-mm; 6,250 rounds, cal. .30; 600 rounds, cal. .45; 300 rounds, cal. .50; 12 hand grenades.

RA PD 308927

Classification: Standard

Purpose: To provide firepower, mobility, and crew protection for offensive combat.

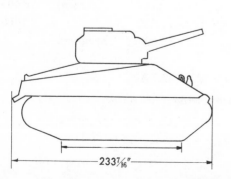

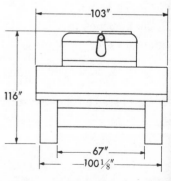

TANK, MEDIUM, M4A2

GENERAL DATA

Crew		5
Weight	(Fighting)	70,100
Shipping dimensions	(cu ft) 1,526 .... (sq ft) 167	
Track width	(in.)	16⁹⁄₁₆

Crew.. 5
Weight..............(Fighting).................... 70,100
Shipping dimensions......(cu ft) 1,526..........(sq ft) 167
Track width...................................(in.) 16$\frac{9}{16}$
Ground clearance...............................(in.) 18
Ground pressure..................... (lb per sq in.) 13.9
Electrical system..............................(volts) 24
Capacities ....Fuel, 50 cetane, Diesel fuel oil..(gal) 148
Oil tank....................(qt) 32
Crankcase (refill) each.........(qt) 16
Transmission and differential....(qt) 152
Cooling system..............(qt) 106
Brakes....................................Mechanical
Communication.........Radio...............Interphone

PERFORMANCE

Maximum gradability........................(percent) 60
Turning radius...............................(ft) 31
Fording depth.................................(in.) 40
Maximum width of ditch vehicle will cross.........(in.) 72
Maximum vertical obstacle vehicle will climb..........(in.) 24
Fuel consumption, average conditions........(miles per gal) 1.1
Cruising range, average conditions................(miles) 150
Maximum allowable speed.......................(mph) 29

	1st	2nd	3rd	4th	5th
Cruising speed	2	6	10	16	25

ENGINE

Manufacturer . GMC..................Model 6046, Series 71
Type.........Twin six, 2 cycle Diesel...Number of cylinders 6
Displacement.....................................(cu in.) 850
Governed speed..................................(rpm) 2,100
Brake horsepower..................................... 420
Ignition type................................Compression

ADDITIONAL DATA

Weight based on chevron steel track T54E1.

. . . .
. . . .
. . . .

TANK, MEDIUM, M4A3 AND
TANK, MEDIUM, M4A3 (105-MM HOW.)

Technical Manuals: TM 9-759, TM 9-1731B, TM 9-1731C, TM 9-1731G, TM 9-1731K, TM 9-1750, TM 9-1750B.

Parts List: SNL G-104, Vols. XIII and XV

Manufacturer: Ford Motor Co.

Armament: One Gun, 75-mm, M3 or one Howitzer, 105-mm, T8; one Gun, machine, cal. .50, HB, M2; one Gun, machine, cal. .30, M1919A4 (flexible); one Gun, submachine, cal. .45, M1928A1.

Ammunition: 97 rounds, 75-mm; or 68 rounds, 105-mm; 300 rounds, cal. .50; 6,250 rounds, cal. .30; 600 rounds, cal. .45; 12 hand grenades.

RA PD 308928

Vehicle illustrated above: Tank, medium, M4A3.

Classification: Standard

Purpose: To provide firepower, mobility and crew protection for offensive combat.

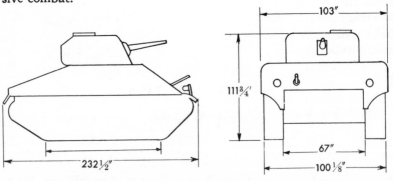

Add 15" length and 1⅛" width when sand shields are used.

TANK, MEDIUM, M4A3 AND
TANK, MEDIUM, M4A3 (105-MM HOW.)

GENERAL DATA

Crew.. 5
Weight.................(Fighting) M4A3.............(lb) 68,400
                    M4A3 (105-mm How.) (lb) 69,600
Shipping dimensions......(cu ft) 1,530..........(sq ft) 166
Track width.......................................(in.) 16
Ground clearance..................................(in.) $17\frac{3}{8}$
Ground pressure........M4A3............. (lb per sq in.) 13.6
              M4A3 (105-mm How.)
                      (lb per sq in.) 13.8
Electrical system..................................(volts) 24
Capacities............Fuel, 80 octane gasoline......(gal) 175
            Oil tank...................(qt) 32
            Transmission and differential...(qt) 128
            Cooling system..............(qt) 56
Brakes.......................................Mechanical
Communication.........Radio.............. Interphone

PERFORMANCE

Maximum gradability...........................(percent) 60
Turning radius.......................................(ft) 31
Fording depth......................................(in.) 36
Maximum width of ditch vehicle will cross...........(in.) 72
Maximum vertical obstacle vehicle will climb..........(in.) 24
Fuel consumption, average conditions........(miles per gal) .8
Cruising range, average conditions..................(miles) 130
Maximum allowable speed........................(mph) 28

	1st	2nd	3rd	4th	5th
Cruising speed.	2	6	10	16	24

ENGINE

Manufacturer.....Ford..................Model GAA-V8
Type............V8, 4 cycle.........Number of cylinders 8
Displacement......................................(cu in.) 1,100
Governed speed..................................(rpm) 2,600
Brake horsepower.................................... 500
Ignition type...................................Magneto

ADDITIONAL DATA

Weights and ground pressure based on steel chevron track T54E1. Tank, medium, M4A3 (105-mm How.) is identical with Tank, medium, M4A3, except carries 105-mm howitzer, T48, instead of 75-mm gun, M3.

TANK, MEDIUM, M4A4

Technical Manuals: TM 9-754, TM 9-1731E, TM 9-1731G, TM 9-1731K, TM 9-1750, TM 9-1750F, TM 9-1750J.

Parts List: SNL G-104, Vol. IX

Manufacturer: Detroit Tank Arsenal (Chrysler).

Armament: One Gun, 75-mm, M3; one Gun, machine, cal. .50, HB, M2; one Gun, machine, cal. .30, M1919A4 (flexible); one Gun, submachine, cal. .45, M1928A1.

Ammunition: 97 rounds, 75-mm; 6,250 rounds, cal. .30; 600 rounds, cal. .45; 300 rounds, cal. .50; 12 hand grenades.

RA PD 308909

Classification: Standard

Purpose: To provide firepower, mobility and crew protection for offensive combat.

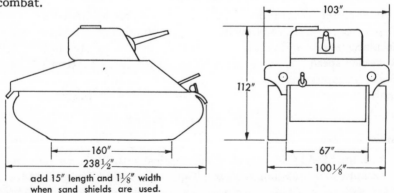

add 15″ length and 1⅛″ width when sand shields are used.

TANK, MEDIUM, M4A4

GENERAL DATA

Crew... 5

Weight................(Fighting)................(lb) 71,900

Shipping dimensions......(cu ft) 1,529..........(sq ft) 170

Track width...(in.) 16$\frac{9}{16}$

Ground clearance.................................(in.) 17$\frac{1}{8}$

Ground pressure............................ (lb per sq in.) 13.3

Electrical system....................................(volts) 24

Capacities.............Fuel, 70 octane gasoline......(gal) 140

Oil tank....................(qt) 32

Transmission and differential...(qt) 152

Cooling system...............(qt) 128

Brakes...Mechanical

Communication.........Radio..............Interphone

PERFORMANCE

Maximum gradability............................(percent) 60

Turning radius.......................................(ft) 35

Fording depth..(in.) 42

Maximum width of ditch vehicle will cross.............(in.) 78

Maximum vertical obstacle vehicle will climb..........(in.) 24

Fuel consumption, average conditions........ (miles per gal) .6

Cruising range, average conditions.................(miles) 80

Maximum allowable speed........................(mph) 23

	1st	2nd	3rd	4th	5th
Cruising speed	2	5	9	14	20

ENGINE

Manufacturer.....Chrysler...................Model A-57

Type............Multi-bank, 4 cycle..Number of cylinders 30

Displacement......................................(cu in.) 1,253

Governed speed (no load)..........................(rpm) 2,600

Brake horsepower................................... 460

Ignition type....................................Battery

ADDITIONAL DATA

Weight based on steel chevron track T54E1.

....

....

....

TANK, MEDIUM, M4A6

Technical Manuals: TM 9-1731G, TM 9-1731K,   Parts List:
     TM 9-1750, TM 9-1750B, TM 9-1750K.   SNL G-104,
                                                  Vol. XIII

Manufacturer: Detroit Tank Arsenal (Chrysler).

Armament: One Gun, 75-mm, M3; one Gun, machine, cal. .50, HB, M2; one Gun, machine, cal. .30, M1919A4 (flexible); one Gun, submachine, cal. .45, M1928A1.

Ammunition: 97 rounds, 75-mm; 300 rounds, cal. .50; 600 rounds, cal. .45; 6,250 rounds, cal. .30; 12 hand grenades.

RA PD 308925

Classification:

Purpose: To provide firepower, mobility, and crew protection for offensive combat.

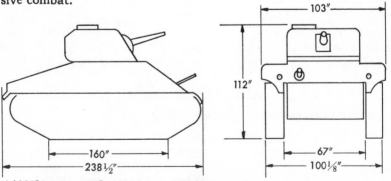

Add 15″ length and 18″ width when sand shields are used.

TANK, MEDIUM, M4A6

GENERAL DATA

Crew		5
Weight	(Fighting)	(lb) 68,900
Shipping dimensions	(cu ft) 1,529	(sq ft) 170
Track width		(in.) 16⁹⁄₁₆
Ground clearance		(in.) 17⅛
Ground pressure		(lbs per sq in.) 12.7
Electrical system		(volts) 24
Capacities	Fuel, 50 cetane, Diesel fuel oil	(gal) 140
	Oil tank	(qt) 60
	Transmission and differential	(qt) 152
	Cooling system	Air-cooled
Brakes		Mechanical
Communication	Radio	Interphone

PERFORMANCE

Maximum gradability	(percent)	60
Turning radius	(ft)	35
Fording depth	(in.)	42
Maximum width of ditch vehicle will cross	(in.)	78
Maximum vertical obstacle vehicle will climb	(in.)	24
Fuel consumption, average conditions	(miles per gal)	.8
Cruising range, average conditions	(miles)	
Maximum allowable speed	(mph)	30

	1st	2nd	3rd	4th	5th
Cruising speed	3	6	11	18	27

ENGINE

Manufacturer	Caterpillar	Model RD1820
Type	Radial, 4 cycle, Diesel	No. of cylinders 9
Displacement		(cu in.) 1,820
Governed speed		(rpm) 2,000
Brake horsepower		450
Ignition type		Compression

ADDITIONAL DATA

Weight based on chevron steel track T54E1.

. . . .

. . . .

. . . .

TANK, MEDIUM, M4E6

Technical Manuals: Parts List:

Manufacturer: Pullman Standard Car Mfg. Co.

Armament: One Gun, 76-mm, M3; one Gun, machine, cal. .50, HB, M2;
two Guns, machine, cal. .30, M1919A4; one Gun, submachine, cal. .45,
M1928A1.

Ammunition: 56 rounds, 76-mm; 5,000 rounds, cal. .30; 300 rounds, cal.
.50; 600 rounds, cal. .45; 12 grenades.

RA PD 308987

Classification: None

Purpose: To provide firepower, mobility and crew protection for offensive
combat.

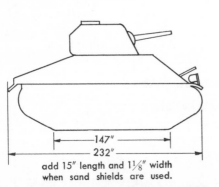

add 15″ length and 1⅛″ width
when sand shields are used.

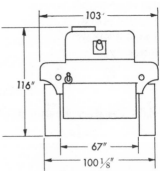

TANK, MEDIUM, M4E6

GENERAL DATA

Crew..		5
Weight...............(Fighting)...............(lb)		
Shipping dimensions......(cu ft) ....(sq ft)		
Track width......................................(in.)		16⁹⁄₁₆
Ground clearance.................................(in.)		17³⁄₈
Ground pressure.............................(lbs per sq in.)		
Electrical system.................................(volts)		24
Capacities............Fuel, 80 octane, gasoline......(gal)		175
	Oil tank...................(qt)	36
	Transmission and differential...(qt)	128
	Cooling system.........Air-cooled	
Brakes....................................Mechanical		
Communication.........Radio..........Intra-tank phone		

PERFORMANCE

Maximum gradability...........................(percent)	27
Turning radius.....................................(ft)	35
Fording depth.....................................(in.)	36
Maximum width of ditch vehicle will cross.............(in.)	72
Maximum vertical obstacle vehicle will climb..........(in.)	24
Fuel consumption, average conditions........(miles per gal)	
Cruising range, average conditions.................(miles)	
Maximum allowable speed........................(mph)	24

	1st	2nd	3rd	4th	5th
Cruising speed.	2	5	9	14	21

ENGINE

Manufacturer......Continental.............Model R-975-C1	
Type.............Radial, 4 cycle......Number of cylinders	9
Displacement.....................................(cu in.)	973
Governed speed....................................(rpm)	2,400
Brake horsepower..	400
Ignition type....................................Magneto	

ADDITIONAL DATA

Weight based on chevron steel track, T54E1.

....

....

....

TANK, HEAVY, M6

Technical Manual: TM 9-721   Parts List: SNL G-118, Vol. I

Manufacturer: Baldwin Locomotive Works

Armament: One Gun, 3-in., M7; one Gun, 37-mm, M6; two Guns, machine, cal. .50 HB, M2; two Guns, machine, cal. .30, M1919A4 (flexible); two Guns, submachine, cal. .45, M1928A1.

Ammunition: 75 rounds, 3-in.; 202 rounds, 37-mm; 5,200 rounds, cal. .50; 1,260 rounds, cal. .45; 7,500 rounds, cal. .30; 12 hand grenades.

RA PD 66457

Classification: Standard

Purpose: To provide firepower, mobility, and crew protection for offensive combat.

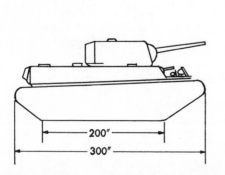

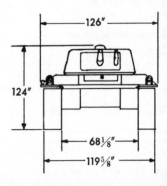

TANK, HEAVY, M6

GENERAL DATA

Crew... 6
Weight...............(Fighting).................(lb) 120,000
Shipping dimensions......(cu ft) 2,442...........(sq ft) 244
Track width......................................(in.) 25¾
Ground clearance.................................(in.) 20½
Ground pressure..........................(lbs per sq in.) 12.5
Electrical system.................................(volts) 24
Capacities.............Fuel, 80 octane gasoline......(gal) 322
                      Oil tank....................(qt) 98
                      Torque converter............(gal) 26
                      Converter reduction..........(qt) 8-10
                      Transmission and differential...(qt) 168
                      Cooling system........Air-cooled
Brakes................Hydraulic—mechanical (Budd disk)
Communication.........Radio..........Intra-tank phone

PERFORMANCE

Maximum gradability...........................(percent) 60
Turning radius....................................(ft) 28
Fording depth.....................................(in.) 36
Maximum width of ditch vehicle will cross.............(in.) 132
Maximum vertical obstacle vehicle will climb..........(in.) 42
Fuel consumption, average conditions.........(miles per gal) .3
Cruising range, average conditions.................(miles) 100
Maximum allowable speed..........................(mph) 23

ENGINE

Manufacturer.....Wright....................Model G-200
Type............Radial, 4 cycle......Number of cylinders 9
Displacement....................................(cu in.) 1,823
Governed speed...................................(rpm) 2,300
Brake horsepower................................... 775
Ignition type......................................Magneto

ADDITIONAL DATA

....
....
....
....

TANK, HEAVY, M6A1

Technical Manual: TM 9-721.   Parts List: SNL G-118, Vol. II

Manufacturer: Baldwin Locomotive Works

Armament: One Gun, 3-in., M7; one Gun, 37-mm, M6; two Guns, machine, cal. .50 HB, M2; two Guns, machine, cal. .30, M1919A4 (flexible); two Guns, submachine, cal. .45, M1928A1.

Ammunition: 75 rounds, 3-in.; 202 rounds, 37-mm; 5,200 rounds, cal. .50; 1,260 rounds, cal. .45; 7,500 rounds, cal. .30; 12 hand grenades.

RA PD 308905

Classification: Standard

Purpose: To provide firepower, mobility and crew protection for offensive combat.

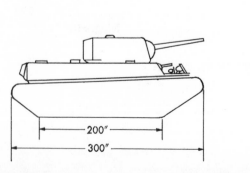

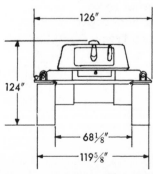

TANK, HEAVY, M6A1

GENERAL DATA

Crew..		6
Weight................(Fighting)..................(lb)		120,000
Shipping dimensions......(cu ft) 2,442 ....(sq ft) 244		
Track width.....................................(in.)		25¾
Ground clearance................................(in.)		20½
Ground pressure.........................(lbs per sq in.)		12.5
Electrical system..............................(volts)		24
Capacities..............Fuel, 80 octane gasoline......(gal)		334
	Oil tank....................(qt)	98
	Transmission and differential...(qt)	168
	Torque converter...........(gal)	26
	Converter reduction.........(qt)	8-10
	Cooling system........Air-cooled	
Brakes.................Hydraulic—mechanical (Budd Disk)		
Communication..........Radio..........Intra-tank phone		

PERFORMANCE

Maximum gradability............................(percent)	60
Turning radius.......................................(ft)	28
Fording depth.......................................(in.)	36
Maximum width of ditch vehicle will cross..............(in.)	132
Maximum vertical obstacle vehicle will climb...........(in.)	42
Fuel consumption, average conditions.........(miles per gal)	.3
Cruising range, average conditions.................(miles)	100
Maximum allowable speed.........................(mph)	23

ENGINE

Manufacturer.....Wright....................Model G-200	
Type.............Radial, 4 cycle.....Number of cylinders	9
Displacement.......................................(cu in.)	1,823
Governed speed....................................(rpm)	2,300
Brake horsepower...................................	775
Ignition type.................................Magneto	

ADDITIONAL DATA

....

....

....

....

TANK, HEAVY, T1E1

Technical Manuals: Parts List: SNL G-118, Vol. III

Manufacturer: Baldwin Locomotive Works

Armament: One Gun, 3-in., M7; one Gun, 37-mm, M6; two Guns, machine, cal. .50 HB, M2; two Guns, machine, cal. .30, M1919A4 (flexible); two Guns, submachine, cal. .45, M1928A1.

Ammunition: 75 rounds, 3-in.; 202 rounds, 37-mm; 5,200 rounds, cal. .50; 1,260 rounds, cal. .45; 7,500 rounds, cal. .30; 12 hand grenades.

RA PD 309125

Classification:

Purpose: To provide firepower, mobility, and crew protection for offensive combat.

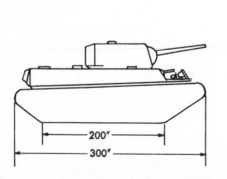

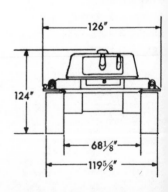

TANK, HEAVY, T1E1

GENERAL DATA

Crew..			6
Weight.................	Gross..............	(approx.) (lb)	120,000
Shipping dimensions.....	(cu ft) 2,442..........	(sq ft) 244	
Track width...................................		(in.)	25¾
Ground clearance................................		(in.)	20½
Ground pressure............................		(lbs per sq in.)	12.5
Electrical system................................		(volts)	24
Capacities..............	Fuel, 80 octane gasoline......	(gal)	322
	Oil tank...................	(qt)	98
	Cooling system........	Air cooled	
Brakes	Electric control, mechanical parking		
Communication.........	Radio................	Interphone	

PERFORMANCE

Maximum gradability............................	(percent)	60
Turning radius....................................	On axis	
Fording depth...........................	(in.)	36
Maximum width of ditch vehicle will cross............	(in.)	132
Maximum vertical obstacle vehicle will climb...........	(in.)	42
Fuel consumption, average conditions.........	(miles per gal)	.3
Cruising range, average conditions.................	(miles)	100
Maximum allowable speed........................	(mph)	22

ENGINE

Manufacturer.....	Wright...................	Model G-200	
Type............	Radial, 4 cycle......	Number of cylinders	9
Displacement.......................................		(cu in.)	1;823
Governed speed....................................		(rpm)	1,950
Brake horsepower...................................			775
Ignition type......................................		Magneto	

ADDITIONAL DATA

. . . .

. . . .

. . . .

. . . .

VEHICLE, TANK RECOVERY, T-2

Technical Manuals: TM 9-739, TM 9-1739.   Parts List: SNL G-169

Manufacturer: Baldwin Locomotive Works.

Armament: Two Guns, machine, cal. .30, M1919A4.

Ammunition: 2,000 rounds, cal. .30; 14 hand grenades; 3 smoke pots.

RA PD 66694

Classification: None

Purpose: To recover tanks disabled on battlefield.

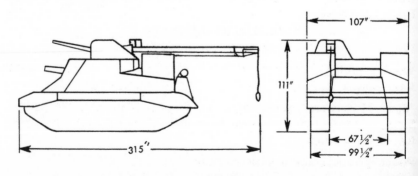

VEHICLE, TANK RECOVERY, T-2

GENERAL DATA

Crew.   6
Weight. . . . . Net (w/o armament fuel and
                        crew). . . . .(lb)   65,620
Shipping dimensions, w/o crane mounted (cu ft) 1736 (sq ft) 169
Track width. . . . .(in.)   16⁹⁄₁₆
Ground clearance. . . . .(in.)   15
Ground pressure: (fully equipped). . . . .(lbs per sq in.)   12.5
Electrical system. . . . .(volts)   12
Capacities. . . . . Fuel, 80 octane gsoline. . . . . .(gal)   175
                   Cooling system. . . . . . . .Air cooled
                   Oil tank. . . . .(qt)   36
                   Transmission and differential. .(qt)   144
Brakes. . . . . .Mechanical

PERFORMANCE

Maximum gradability. . . . .(percent)   35
Turning radius. . . . .(ft)   35
Fording depth. . . . .(in.)   42
Maximum width of ditch vehicle will cross. . . . .(in.)   72
Maximum vertical obstacle vehicle will climb. . . . .(in.)   24
Fuel consumption, average conditions. . . . .(miles per gal)   .75
Cruising range, average conditions. . . . .(miles)   100
Maximum allowable speed. . . . .(mph)   25

	1st	2nd	3rd	4th	5th
Cruising speed	2	5	9	14	21

ENGINE

Manufacturer   Continental. . . . . .Model R-975-C1
Type. . . . . .Radial, 4 cycle. . . . . . .Number of cylinders   9
Displacement. . . . .(cu in.)   973
Governed speed. . . . . : . . . .(rpm)   2,100
Brake horsepower.   400

ADDITIONAL DATA

Winch capacity. . . . .(lb)   60,000
Basic chassis. . . . . .Medium Tank M3

*Some Models are powered with two General Motors, Diesel engines, Series 71, Model 6046. 375 Brake horsepower (both engines) using Diesel fuel oil of 50 cetane.

Power operated crane mounted on turret.

TRUCK-TRAILER, 45-TON, TANK TRANSPORTER, M19
TRUCK, 12-TON, 6 x 4, M20

Technical Manuals: TM 10-1225. Parts List: SNL G-159

Manufacturer: Diamond T Motor Car Co., Model 980-981

RA PD 66686

Classification: Limited standard

Purpose: To recover and transport damaged tanks and materiel weighing up to 90,000 pounds in connection with Trailer, 45-ton, 12-wheel, M9, component of 45-ton tank transporter truck-trailer, M19.

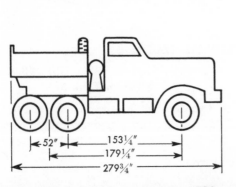

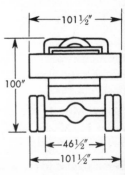

TRUCK-TRAILER, 45-TON, TANK TRANSPORTER, M19
TRUCK, 12-TON, 6 x 4, M20

GENERAL DATA

Crew			2
Weight	Net	(lb)	26,600
	Payload	(lb)	18,400
	Gross	(lb)	45,000
Shipping dimensions	(cu ft) 1,620	(sq ft) 194	
Tires	Ply ... 14	Size ... 12.00 x 20	
Tread, center to center (in.) Front 75⅞		Rear 74	
Ground clearance		(in.)	11⅛
Electrical system		(volts)	6
Capacities	Fuel, 50 cetane Diesel fuel oil	(gal)	150
	Cooling system	(qt)	61
	Crankcase (refill)	(qt)	26
Brakes		Air	

PERFORMANCE

Maximum gradability	(percent)	25
Turning radius (ft) ... Right 32½	Left 36	
Fording depth	(in.)	32
Angle of approach	(deg)	40½
Angle of departure	(deg)	51
Fuel consumption, average conditions, with towed load	(miles per gal)	2
Cruising range, average conditions	(miles)	300
Maximum allowable speed	(mph)	22
Number of speeds forward		5

ENGINE

Manufacturer ... Hercules	Model DFXE	
Type ... Diesel, 4 cycle	Number of cylinders	6
Displacement	(cu in.)	893
Governed speed	(rpm)	1,600
Brake horsepower		
Ignition type	Compression	

ADDITIONAL DATA

Winch capacity	(lb)	40,000

Was equipped with open cab and provision for truck mount
M36 for antiaircraft machine gun after August 1943.

Winch mounted in center.

TRUCK-TRAILER, 45-TON, TANK TRANSPORTER, M19
TRAILER, 45-TON, 12-WHEEL, M9

Technical Manuals: TM 10-1242.   Parts List: SNL G-159

Manufacturers: Fruehauf Trailer Co.; Pointer Willamette Co.; Rogers Brothers; Winter-Weiss Co.

RA PD 308935

Vehicle illustrated above: Fruehauf Trailer Co.

Classification: Limited standard

Purpose: To recover and transport damaged tanks and materiel weighing up to 90,000 pounds in connection with truck M20, component of 45-ton tank transporter truck-trailer, M19.

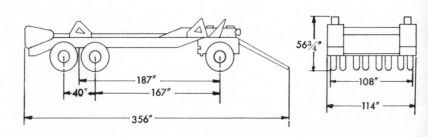

TRUCK-TRAILER, 45-TON, TANK TRANSPORTER, M19
TRAILER, 45-TON, 12-WHEEL, M9

GENERAL DATA

Body type.............................Tank recovery
Weight...............Net.........................(lb)   22,000
                     Payload....................(lb)   90,000
                     Gross......................(lb)   112,000
Loading height, loaded............................(in.)   39
Ground clearance..................................(in.)   12
Tires.................Operating.....................   24
                     Spares........................   2
                     Ply...........................   14
                     Size.......................... 8.25 x 15
Brakes...Air
Towing tractor..................Truck, 12-ton, 6 x 4, M20
Shipping dimensions......(cu ft)   ....(sq ft)

ADDITIONAL DATA

....
....
....
....

TRUCK-TRAILER, 40-TON, TANK RECOVERY, M25
TRUCK-TRACTOR, M26

Technical Manuals: TM 9-767, TM 9-1767,   Parts List: SNL G-160
TM 9-1767A, TM 9-1767B, TM 9-1767C.

Manufacturer: Pacific Car and Foundry Co.

RA PD 308932

Classification: Standard

Purpose: To recover and transport damaged tanks and materiel weighing
up to 80,000 pounds in connection with semitrailer M15, component
of 40-ton tank recovery truck-trailer M25.

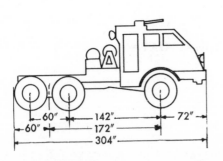
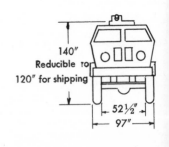

TRUCK-TRAILER, 40-TON, TANK RECOVERY, M25
TRUCK-TRACTOR, M26

GENERAL DATA

Crew...			7
Weight...............	Net...................(lb)		48,000
	Fifth wheel load...........(lb)		55,000
	Gross.....................(lb)		103,000
	Semitrailer maximum gross....(lb)		116,300
Shipping dimensions......(cu ft)	..........(sq ft)		
Tires...Ply (combat) 20...(desert) 14.....Size...14.00 x 24			
Tread, center to center (in.)Front 82 ....Rear 98			
Ground clearance....................................(in.)			14¼
Electrical system...............................(volts)			12
Capacities............Fuel, 70 octane gasoline......(gal)			120
	Cooling system..............(qt)		58
	Crankcase..................(qt)		
Brakes...Air			

PERFORMANCE

Maximum gradability............................(percent)	30
Turning radius......................................(ft)	46
Fording depth.......................................(in.)	42
Angle of approach................................(deg)	32½
Fuel consumption, average conditions.........(miles per gal)	2.2
Cruising range, average conditions.................(miles)	265
Maximum allowable speed.........................(mph)	28
Number of speeds forward................................	12

ENGINE

Manufacturer.....Hall-Scott...................Model 440	
Type.............In-line, 4 cycle.....Number of cylinders	6
Displacement...................................(cu in.)	1,090
Governed speed.................................(rpm)	2,100
Brake horsepower.......................................	270
Ignition type..Battery	

ADDITIONAL DATA

Winch capacity (lb)....Front 35,000....Rear (2) each 60,000

....

....

....

TRUCK-TRAILER, 40-TON, TANK RECOVERY, M25
SEMITRAILER, M15

Technical Manuals: TM 9-767, TM 9-1767D.   Parts List: SNL G-160
Manufacturer: Fruehauf Trailer Co.

RA PD 308912

Classification: Standard

Purpose: To recover and transport damaged tanks and materiel weighing
up to 80,000 pounds in connection with truck-tractor M26. Component of 40-ton tank recovery truck-trailer M25

TRUCK-TRAILER, 40-TON, TANK RECOVERY, M25
SEMITRAILER, M15

GENERAL DATA

Body type............................Low-bed platform

Trailer weight..........Net........................(lb)   36,300

                    Payload....................(lb)   80,000

                    Gross......................(lb) 116,300

Loading height.....................................(in.) $40\frac{1}{2}$

Tires.................Operating......................   8

                Ply...(combat) 20...(desert)...14

                Size...........................14.00 x 24

Tread................(reducible to 124 inches)......(in.)   131

Brakes...Air

Towing tractor......................Truck-tractor M26

Ground clearance, under bed........................(in.)   28

ADDITIONAL DATA

....

....

....

....

TRUCK, ¼-TON, 4 x 4

Technical Manuals: Willys-Overland, TM 10-1103, TM 10-1513.
Ford, TM 10-1101 (C1), TM 10-1349.

Parts List: SNL G-503

Manufacturers: Willys-Overland Motors, Inc.; Ford Motor Co.

RA PD 66539

Vehicle illustrated above: Willys-Overland

Classification: Standard

Purpose: To carry personnel, primarily for reconnaissance; to transport light cargo; to tow 37-mm antitank gun. (Popularly known as "THE JEEP").

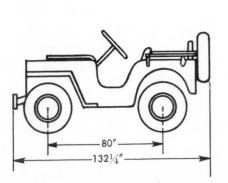

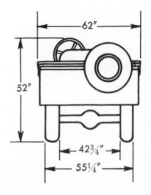

TRUCK, ¼-TON, 4 x 4

GENERAL DATA

Crew, operating 2.........Passenger capacity, including crew   5
Weight.................Net....................(lb)   2,453
                         Payload.................(lb)   800
                         Gross.................(lb)   3,253
Shipping dimensions.......(cu ft) 331............(sq ft) 57
Tires.................Ply ... 6......Size ... 6.00 x 16
Ground clearance.................................(in.)   8¾
Tread, center to center..........................(in.)   49
Electrical system................................(volts)   6
Capacities.............Fuel, 68 octane gasoline....(gal)   15
                         Cooling system............(qt)   11
                         Crankcase (refill)..........(qt)   5
Brakes...............................Hydraulic (Bendix)

PERFORMANCE

Maximum gradability.............................(percent)   60
Turning radius (ft).........Right 17.............Left 18½
Fording depth.......................................(in.)   18
Angle of approach...................................(deg)   45
Angle of departure..................................(deg)   35
Fuel consumption, average conditions.........(miles per gal)   20
Cruising range, average conditions.................(miles)   300
Maximum allowable speed.........................(mph)   65
Number of speeds forward, with transfer case..............   6

ENGINE

Manufacturer......Willys-Overland............Model MB
Type.............In-line, 4 cycle......Number of cylinders   4
Displacement....................................(cu in.)   134.2
Governed speed...........................Not governed
Brake horsepower.....................................   60
Ignition.......................................Battery

ADDITIONAL DATA

....

....

....

TRUCK, CARRYALL, ½-TON, 4 x 2

Technical Manuals: Chevrolet,
TM 10-1305, TM 10-1247.
Dodge, TM 10-1155,
TM 10-1379.

Parts Lists: SNL G-612 (Chev.)
SNL G-613 (Dodge)

Manufacturers: Chevrolet Motor Div. (General Motors Corp.); Dodge
Brothers Corp. (Div. of Chrysler Corp.).

RA PD 308916

Vehicle illustrated above: Chevrolet.

Classification: Standard

Purpose: To transport personnel and light cargo.

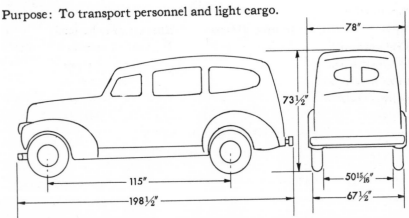

TRUCK, CARRYALL, ½-TON, 4 x 2

Tread, center to center (in.) Front 56½ . . . . Rear 59¼

GENERAL DATA

Crew			2
Weight	Net	(lb)	3,625
	Payload	(lb)	1,000
	Gross	(lb)	4,625
Shipping dimensions . . . . (cu ft) . . . . (sq ft)			
Tires . . . . Ply . . . 6 . . . . . . Size . . . 7.50 x 15			
Ground clearance . . . . (in.)			8½
Electrical system . . . . (volts)			6
Capacities . . . . Fuel, 70 octane gasoline . . . . (gal)			16
	Cooling system . . . . (qt)		
	Crankcase (refill) . . . . (qt)		6
Brakes . . . . Hydraulic			

PERFORMANCE

Maximum gradability . . . . (percent)	32
Turning radius (ft) . . . . Right 19½ . . . . Left 20	
Fording depth . . . . (in.)	
Angle of approach . . . . (deg)	
Angle of departure . . . . (deg)	
Fuel consumption, average conditions . . . . (miles per gal)	11
Cruising range, average conditions . . . . (miles)	176
Maximum allowable speed . . . . (mph)	
Number of speeds forward	3

ENGINE

Manufacturer . . . . . . Chevrolet . . . . Model 1942	
Type . . . . In-line, 4 cycle . . . . . Number of cylinders	6
Displacement . . . . (cu in.)	216.5
Governed speed . . . . (rpm)	
Brake horsepower	
Ignition type . . . . Battery	

ADDITIONAL DATA

. . . .

. . . .

. . . .

. . . .

TRUCK, CANOPY EXPRESS, ½-TON, 4 x 2

Technical Manual: TM 10-1465. Parts List: SNL G-612

Manufacturer: Chevrolet Motor Div. (General Motors Corp.).

RA PD 309122

Classification: Standard

Purpose: To transport light cargo.

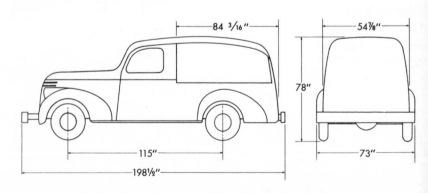

TRUCK, CANOPY EXPRESS, ½-TON, 4 x 2

GENERAL DATA

Crew...			2
Weight..................	Net...................	(lb)	3,395
	Payload.................	(lb)	1,000
	Gross...................	(lb)	4,395
Shipping dimensions........	(cu ft) ....(sq ft)		
Tires....................	Ply...6..... Size...6.50 x 16		
Ground clearance...............................		(in.)	
Electrical system....................................		(volts)	6
Capacities................	Fuel, 70 octane gasoline....(gal)		16
	Cooling system............(qt)		14
	Crankcase (refill)..........(qt)		6
Brakes....................................		Hydraulic	

PERFORMANCE

Maximum gradability............................(percent)	
Turning radius (ft)........Right 19½............Left 20	
Fording depth...............................(in.)	
Angle of approach................................(deg)	
Angle of departure...............................(deg)	
Fuel consumption, average conditions........(miles per gal)	11
Cruising range, average conditions...................(miles)	176
Maximum allowable speed.......................(mph)	
Number of speeds forward............................	

ENGINE

Manufacturer......Chevrolet.....Model 1942 BD 1001 up	
Type.............In-line, 4 cycle.....Number of cylinders	6
Displacement.......................................(cu in.)	216.5
Governed speed.................................(rpm)	
Brake horsepower....................................	
Ignition type ....Battery	

ADDITIONAL DATA

....

....

....

....

TRUCK, PICKUP, ½-TON, 4 x 2

Technical Manuals: Chevrolet,
TM 10-1251, TM 10-1305,
TM 10-1465.
Ford, TM 10-1437.

Parts Lists: SNL G-612 (Chev.)
SNL G-615 (Ford)

Manufacturers: Chevrolet Motor Div. (General Motors Corp.); Ford
Motor Co.

RA PD 66545

Classification: Standard

Purpose: To transport light cargo.

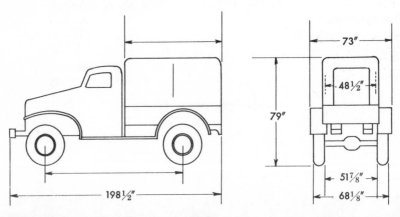

TRUCK, PICKUP, ½-TON, 4 x 2

GENERAL DATA

Crew...			2
Weight.................Net......................(lb)			3,385
	Payload.................(lb)		1,000
	Gross.....................(lb)		4,385
Shipping dimensions.......(cu ft) ....(sq ft)			
Tires.....................Ply...6......Size...7.50 x 16			
Tread, center to center (in.).Front 56½..........Rear 59¼			
Ground clearance...................................(in.)			8½
Electrical system....:.............................(volts)			6
Capacities...............Fuel, 70 octane gasoline....(gal)			18
	Cooling system.............(qt)		14
	Crankcase (refill)..........(qt)		6
Brakes.....................................Hydraulic			

PERFORMANCE

Maximum gradability............................(percent)	33½
Turning radius (ft)........Right 19½.............Left 20	
Fording depth.......................................(in.)	
Angle of approach.................................(deg)	
Angle of departure................................(deg)	
Fuel consumption, average conditions.........(miles per gal)	11
Cruising range, average conditions..................(miles)	198
Maximum allowable speed...........................(mph)	
Number of speeds forward...............................	3

ENGINE

Manufacturer......Chevrolet.....Model 1942 BD 1,000 up	
Type.............In-line, 4 cycle.....Number of cylinders	6
Displacement.......................................(cu in.)	216.5
Governed speed....................................(rpm)	
Brake horsepower.......................................	
Ignition type.......................................Battery	

ADDITIONAL DATA

....

....

....

....

TRUCK, PANEL DELIVERY, ½-TON, 4 x 2

Technical Manuals: Chevrolet,
TM 10-1305, TM 10-1165,
TM 10-1465.
Dodge, TM 10-1155,
TM 10-1379.

Parts Lists: SNL G-612 (Chev.)
SNL G-613 (Dodge)

Manufacturers: Chevrolet Motor Div. (General Motors Corp.); Dodge
Brothers Corp. (Div. of Chrysler Corp.)

RA PD 308915

Vehicle illustrated above: Chevrolet

Classification: Standard

Purpose: To transport light cargo.

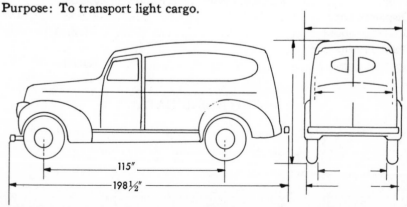

115"
198½"

TRUCK, PANEL DELIVERY, ½-TON, 4 x 2

GENERAL DATA

Crew...			2
Weight................	Net....................	(lb)	3,220
	Payload.................	(lb)	1,180
	Gross...................	(lb)	4,400
Shipping dimensions........	(cu ft) 648..........	(sq ft) 100	
Tires....................	Ply...4......	Size...6.00 x 16	
Tread, center to center (in.)	Front 56½..........	Rear 59¼	
Ground clearance...................................		(in.)	8¼
Electrical system..................................		(volts)	6
Capacities................	Fuel, 70 octane gasoline....	(gal)	16
	Cooling system............	(qt)	14
	Crankcase (refill)..........	(qt)	5
Brakes..................	4 wheel.............	Hydraulic	

PERFORMANCE

Maximum gradability............................	(percent)	
Turning radius (ft)........ Right 19½	Left 20	
Fording depth.....................................	(in.)	18½
Angle of approach.................................	(deg)	30
Angle of departure................................	(deg)	19
Fuel consumption, average conditions........	(miles per gal)	11
Cruising range, average conditions.................	(miles)	176
Maximum allowable speed........................	(mph)	60
Number of speeds forward...............................		

ENGINE

Manufacturer......Chevrolet.....Model 1942 BD 1,000 up		
Type.............In-line, 4 cycle.....Number of cylinders		6
Displacement.......................................	(cu in.)	216.5
Governed speed....................................	(rpm)	3,100
Brake horsepower.......................................		
Ignition type......................................	Battery	

ADDITIONAL DATA

....
....
....
....

TRUCK, CARRYALL, ½-TON, 4 x 4

Technical Manuals: TM 10-1181,
TM 10-1123 (C1),
TM 10-1201 (C1),
TM 10-1153, TM 10-1443.

Parts List: SNL G-505

Manufacturer: Dodge Brothers Corp. (Div. of Chrysler Corp.)

Classification: Limited standard

Purpose: To transport light cargo.

RA PD 309091

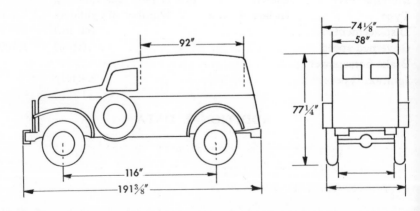

TRUCK, CARRYALL, ½-TON, 4 x 4

GENERAL DATA

Crew.			2
Weight	Net	(lb)	3,595
	Payload	(lb)	1,000
	Gross	(lb)	4,595
Shipping dimensions	(cu ft) 673	(sq ft) 96	
Tires	Ply...8	Size...7.50 x 16	
Ground clearance		(in.)	9
Tread, center to center (in.) Front 59⅜		Rear 61⅜	
Electrical system		(volts)	6
Capacities	Fuel, 70 octane gasoline	(gal)	18
	Cooling system	(qt)	17
	Crankcase (refill)	(qt)	5
Brakes		Hydraulic	

PERFORMANCE

Maximum gradability	(percent)	64
Turning radius (ft) Right 19	Left 24¼	
Fording depth	(in.)	
Angle of approach	(deg)	62½
Angle of departure	(deg)	31½
Fuel consumption, average conditions	(miles per gal)	13
Cruising range, average conditions	(miles)	235
Maximum allowable speed	(mph)	
Number of speeds forward		4

ENGINE

Manufacturer	Dodge	Model T-112	
Type	In-line, 4 cycle	Number of cylinders	6
Displacement		(cu in.)	217.7
Governed speed		(rpm)	1,200-1,900
Brake horsepower			
Ignition type		Battery	

ADDITIONAL DATA

....
....
....
....

TRUCK, COMMAND RECONNAISSANCE, ½-TON, 4 x 4

Technical Manuals: TM 10-1181, TM 10-1195, Parts List: SNL G-505
TM 10-1211, TM 10-1123 (C1),
TM 10-1201 (C1), TM 10-1153,
TM 10-1209, TM 10-1443.

Manufacturer: Dodge Brothers Corp. (Div. of Chrysler Corp.)

RA PD 66337

Classification: Limited standard

Purpose: To provide transportation for staff officers in the field.

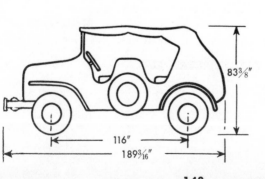

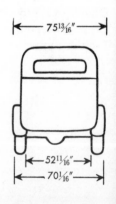

TRUCK, COMMAND RECONNAISSANCE, ½-TON, 4 x 4

GENERAL DATA

Crew, operating 2........	Passenger capacity including crew		5
Weight.................	Net......................	(lb)	4,600*
	Payload.................	(lb)	1,000*
	Gross...................	(lb)	5,600*
Shipping dimensions........	(cu ft)	(sq ft)	
Tires....................	Ply...6...... Size...7.50 x 16		
Ground clearance............		(in.)	9
Electrical system............		(volts)	6
Capacities...............	Fuel, 70 octane gasoline....	(gal)	25
	Cooling system............	(qt)	17
	Crankcase (refill)..........	(qt)	5
Brakes..................		Hydraulic	

PERFORMANCE

Maximum gradability............................	(percent)	62
Turning radius.................................	(ft)	25½
Fording depth.................................	(in.)	
Angle of approach (deg) With winch 45..Without winch 62½		
Angle of departure.............................	(deg)	31½
Fuel consumption, average conditions........	(miles per gal)	12
Cruising range, average conditions.................	(miles)	300
Maximum allowable speed......................	(mph)	56
Number of speeds forward........................		3

ENGINE

Manufacturer......	Dodge.................	Model T-215	
Type.............	In-line, 4 cycle.....	Number of cylinders	6
Displacement.....................................		(cu in.)	230.2
Governed speed...................................		(rpm)	
Brake horsepower.................................			
Ignition type.....................................		Battery	

ADDITIONAL DATA

Winch capacity.......................................	(lb)	5000

*Figures given are for vehicles without winch. For vehicles with winch use the following data:

Weight (lb)..Net 4,900.....Payload 700........Gross 5,600

TRUCK, EMERGENCY REPAIR, ½-TON, 4 x 4

Technical Manual: TM 10-1443.   Parts List: SNL G-505

Manufacturer: Dodge Brothers Corp. (Div. of Chrysler Corp.)

RA PD 66541

Classification: Standard

Purpose: To provide mobile facilities for emergency ordnance repair.

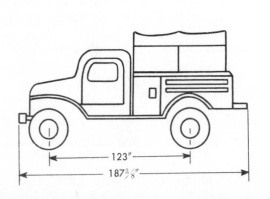

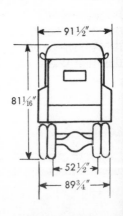

TRUCK, EMERGENCY REPAIR, ½-TON, 4 x 4

GENERAL DATA

Crew			2
Weight	Net	(lb)	5,870
	Payload	(lb)	1,420
	Gross	(lb)	7,290
Shipping dimensions	(cu ft) 804	(sq ft) 119	
Tires	Ply...6	Size...7.50 x 16	
Tread, center to center (in.)	Front 59⅜	Rear 70⅞	
Ground clearance		(in.)	9
Electrical system		(volts)	6
Capacities	Fuel, 70 octane gasoline	(gal)	25
	Cooling system	(qt)	17
	Crankcase (refill)	(qt)	5
Brakes		Hydraulic	

PERFORMANCE

Maximum gradability	(percent)	53
Turning radius	(ft)	27
Fording depth	(in.)	32
Angle of approach	(deg)	62½
Angle of departure	(deg)	33
Fuel consumption, average conditions	(miles per gal)	12
Cruising range, average conditions	(miles)	300
Maximum allowable speed	(mph)	55
Number of speeds forward		3

ENGINE

Manufacturer	Dodge	Models T-211, T-215	
Type	In-line, 4 cycle	Number of cylinders	6
Displacement		(cu in.)	230.2
Governed speed		(rpm)	3,100
Brake horsepower			
Ignition type		Battery	

ADDITIONAL DATA

TRUCK, PANEL DELIVERY, ½-TON, 4 x 4

Technical Manuals: TM 10-1123 (C1),   Parts List: SNL G-505
TM 10-1201 (C1).

Manufacturer: Dodge Brothers Corp. (Div. of Chrysler Corp.)

RA PD 66543

Classification: Limited standard

Purpose: To transport light cargo.

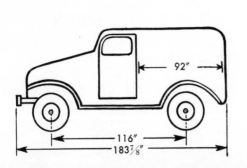

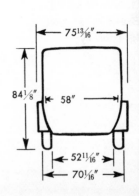

TRUCK, PANEL DELIVERY, ½-TON, 4 x 4

GENERAL DATA

Crew.. 2
Weight.................Net......................(lb) 4,510
                     Payload..................(lb) 1,000
                     Gross....................(lb) 5,510
Shipping dimensions.......(cu ft) 678...........(sq ft) 97
Tires.....................Ply...6......Size...7.50 x 16
Ground clearance..................................(in.) 9
Electrical system..................................(volts) 6
Capacities...............Fuel, 68 octane gasoline....(gal) 25
                     Cooling system............(qt) 17
                     Crankcase (refill)..........(qt) 5
Brakes....................................Hydraulic

PERFORMANCE

Maximum gradability.........................(percent) 6?
Turning radius.......................................(ft) 25½
Fording depth.......................................(in.)
Angle of approach.................................(deg) 6?
Angle of departure................................(deg) 2?
Fuel consumption, average conditions...........(miles per gal) 12
Cruising range, average conditions..................(miles) 300
Maximum allowable speed.........................(mph) 5?
Number of speeds forward............................. 3

ENGINE

Manufacturer......Dodge ....Models T-207, T-211
Type.............In-line, 4 cycle......Number of cylinders 6
Displacement......................................(cu in.) 217.7
Governed speed....................................(rpm) 3,100
Brake horsepower..
Ignition..Battery

ADDITIONAL DATA

. . . .
. . . .
. . . .
. . . .

TRUCK, PICKUP, ½-TON, 4 x 4

Technical Manuals: TM 10-1181, TM 10-1195,   Parts List: SNL G-505
TM 10-1211.

Manufacturer: Dodge Brothers Corp. (Div. of Chrysler Corp.)

RA PD 66545

Classification: Limited standard

Purpose: To transport cargo and personnel.

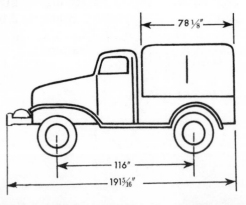

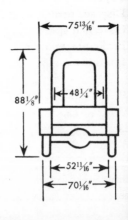

TRUCK, PICKUP, ½-TON, 4x4

GENERAL DATA

Crew... 2
Weight..................Net....................(lb) 4,640*
                 Payload..................(lb) 1,000*
                 Gross....................(lb) 5,640*
Shipping dimensions........(cu ft) 644...........(sq ft) 95
Tires.....................Ply...8......Size...7.50 x 16
Tread, center to center (in.)..Front 59⅜..........Rear 61⅜
Ground clearance...................................(in.) 9
Pintle height (in.).........Loaded 26½......Unloaded 28
Electrical system.................................(volts) 6
Capacities..............Fuel, 68 octane gasoline....(gal) 25
                 Cooling system............(qt) 17
                 Crankcase (refill)..........(qt) 5
Brakes.......................................Hydraulic

PERFORMANCE

Maximum gradability............................(percent) 60
Turning radius..(ft) 25½
Fording depth.......................................(in.) 32
Angle of approach (deg)..With winch 45..Without winch 62½
Angle of departure.................................(deg) 31½
Fuel consumption, average conditions.........(miles per gal) 12
Cruising range, average conditions...................(miles) 300
Maximum allowable speed........................(mph) 55
Number of speeds forward............................. 4

ENGINE

Manufacturer......Dodge............Models T-207, T-211
Type..............In-line, 4 cycle......Number of cylinders 6
Displacement.....................................(cu in.) 217.7
Governed speed....................................(rpm) 3,100
Brake horsepower.......................................
Ignition type....................................Battery

ADDITIONAL DATA

Winch capacity.....................................(lb) 5,000
*Figures given are for vehicles without winch. For vehicles with winch
use the following data:
Weight (lb).....Net 4,940....Payload 700.....Gross 5,640
Model WC-12 after engine No. 42001 and all WC-40 have 230.2
cubic inch displacement. Vehicles so equipped have 65.7
percent maximum gradability.

TRUCK, RADIO, ½-TON, 4 x 4

Technical Manuals: TM 10-1123,
TM 10-1181, TM 10-1211,
TM 10-1201, TM 10-1153,
TM 10-1209, TM 10-1443.

Parts List:

Manufacturer: Dodge Brothers Corp. (Div. of Chrysler Corp.)

RA PD 309119

Classification: Limited standard

Purpose:

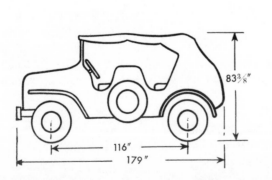

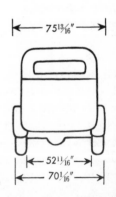

TRUCK, RADIO, ½-TON, 4 x 4

GENERAL DATA

Crew			2
Weight	Net	(lb)	5,070
	Payload	(lb)	1,000
	Gross	(lb)	6,070
Shipping dimensions	(cu ft)	(sq ft)	
Tires	Ply...8	Size...7.50 x 16	
Ground clearance		(in.)	9⅜
Tread, center to center (in.)..Front 59⅜		Rear 61⅜	
Electrical system		(volts)	12
Capacities	Fuel, 70 octane gasoline	(gal)	16
	Cooling system	(qt)	17
	Crankcase (refill)	(qt)	5
Brakes		Hydraulic	

PERFORMANCE

Maximum gradability	(percent)	60
Turning radius	(ft)	24
Fording depth	(in.)	32
Angle of approach	(deg)	45
Angle of departure	(deg)	30
Fuel consumption, average conditions	(miles per gal)	12
Cruising range, average conditions	(miles)	190
Maximum allowable speed	(mph)	
Number of speeds forward		3

ENGINE

Manufacturer......Dodge	Models T-202, T-215	
Type............In-line, 4 cycle	Number of cylinders	6
Displacement	(cu in.)	230.2
Governed speed	(rpm)	
Brake horsepower		
Ignition type	Battery	

ADDITIONAL DATA

. . . .

. . . .

. . . .

. . . .

TRUCK, WEAPONS CARRIER, ½-TON, 4x4

Technical Manuals: TM 10-1123, TM 10-1153, TM 10-1443.

Parts List: SNL G-505

Manufacturer: Dodge Brothers Corp. (Div. of Chrysler Corp.)

RA PD 66549

Classification: Limited standard

Purpose: To transport weapons, personnel, and cargo.

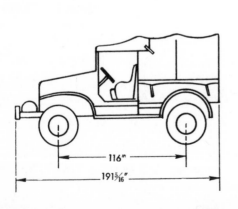

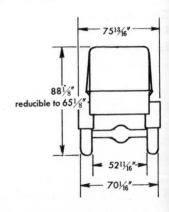

158

TRUCK, WEAPONS CARRIER, ½-TON, 4 x 4

GENERAL DATA

Crew... 2
Weight..................Net........................... 4,240*
                Payload..................(lb) 1,000*
                Gross....................(lb) 5,240*
Shipping dimensions.......(cu ft) 517............(sq ft) 95
Tires....................Ply...8......Size...7.50 x 16
Ground clearance...................................(in.) 9
Ground pressure.......................(lb per sq in.)
Electrical system..................................(volts) 6
Capacities..............Fuel, 70 octane gasoline....(gal) 25
                Cooling system.............(qt) 17
                Crankcase (refill)..........(qt) 5
Brakes.....................................Hydraulic

PERFORMANCE

Maximum gradability...........................(percent) 62
Turning radius.....................................(ft) 25½
Fording depth.....................................(in.) 32
Angle of approach.................................(deg) 62
Angle of departure................................(deg) 31
Fuel consumption, average conditions........(miles per gal) 12
Cruising range, average conditions.................(miles) 250
Maximum allowable speed.......................(mph) 55
Number of speeds forward............................. 4

ENGINE

Manufacturer......Dodge.............Models T-207, T-211
Type.............In-line, 4 cycle.....Number of cylinders 6
Displacement.......Model WC-3...................(cu in.) 217.7
Governed speed ....(rpm) 3,100
Brake horsepower..
Ignition type...................................Battery

ADDITIONAL DATA

Model WC-13 after engine No. 42001 and all Model WC-21 have 230.2 cubic inch displacement. Vehicles so equipped have 67.9 percent maximum gradability.

*Figures given are for vehicles without winch. For vehicles with winch use the following data: Weight (lb)...Net 4,775...Payload 1,000...Gross 5,775. Shipping dimensions....(cu ft) 546....(sq ft) 100.

TRUCK, PANEL DELIVERY, ¾-TON, 4 x 2

Technical Manual: TM 10-1287   Parts List: SNL G-616

Manufacturer: Chevrolet Motor Div. (General Motors Corp.)

Classification: Limited standard   RA PD 308931

Purpose: To transport light cargo.

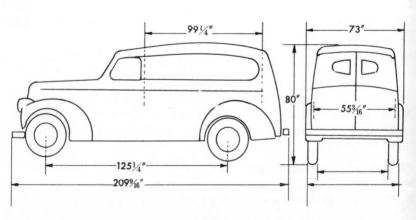

TRUCK, PANEL DELIVERY, ¾-TON, 4 x 2

GENERAL DATA

Crew			2
Weight	Net	(lb)	3,600
	Payload	(lb)	1,650
	Gross	(lb)	5,250
Shipping dimensions	(cu ft)	(sq ft)	
Tires	Ply...8...Size...Comm. 15 in.		
Tread, center to center		(in.)	60⅜
Ground clearance		(in.)	
Electrical system		(volts)	6
Capacities	Fuel, 70 octane gasoline	(gal)	18
	Cooling system	(qt)	18
	Crankcase (refill)	(qt)	6
Brakes		Hydraulic	

PERFORMANCE

Maximum gradability	(percent)	
Turning radius	(ft)	21¼
Fording depth	(in.)	
Angle of approach	(deg)	
Angle of departure	(deg)	
Fuel consumption, average conditions	(miles per gal)	10
Cruising range, average conditions	(miles)	180
Maximum allowable speed	(mph)	
Number of speeds forward		3

ENGINE

Manufacturer......Chevrolet............Model 1942 **ABF**		
Type.............In-line, 4 cycle.....Number of cylinders		6
Displacement	(cu in.)	216.5
Governed speed	(rpm)	
Brake horsepower		90
Ignition type	Battery	

ADDITIONAL DATA

. . . .

. . . .

. . . .

. . . .

TRUCK, PICKUP, ¾-TON, 4 x 2

Technical Manuals: TM 10-1163, TM 10-1167, Parts List: SNL G-616
TM 10-1305.

Manufacturer: Chevrolet Motor Div. (General Motors Corp.)

RA PD 308930

Classification: Limited standard

Purpose: To transport general cargo.

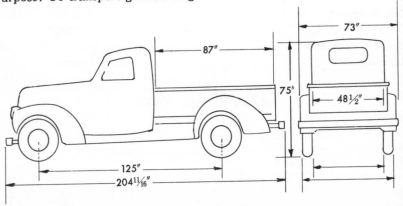

TRUCK, PICKUP, ¾-TON, 4 x 2

GENERAL DATA

Crew..		2
Weight................Net................................(lb)		3,375
Payload, includes 160 lb driver..(lb)		1,660
Gross........................(lb)		5,035
Shipping dimensions......(cu ft) ....(sq ft)		
Tires..................Ply...6.....Size...Comm. 15 in.		
Ground clearance.....................................(in.)		8
Tread, center to center...........................(in.)		60⅜
Electrical system...................................(volts)		6
Capacities.............Fuel, 70 octane gasoline......(gal)		18
Cooling system..............(qt)		14
Crankcase (refill)............(qt)		6
Brakes..Hydraulic		

PERFORMANCE

Maximum gradability...........................(percent)	32
Turning radius....................................(ft)	21½
Fording depth....................................(in.)	
Angle of approach................................(deg)	31
Angle of departure...............................(deg)	15
Fuel consumption, average conditions........(miles per gal)	10
Cruising range, average conditions.................(miles)	180
Maximum allowable speed........................(mph)	60
Number of speeds forward............................	3

ENGINE

Manufacturer......Chevrolet................Model **ABF**	
Type.............In-line, 4 cycle.....Number of cylinders	6
Displacement.....................................(cu in.)	216.5
Governed speed....................................(rpm)	
Brake horsepower....................................	90
Ignition type...................................Battery	

ADDITIONAL DATA

....
....
....
....

TRUCK, CARRYALL, ¾-TON, 4 x 4

Technical Manuals: TM 9-808, TM 9-1808A,   Parts List: SNL G-502
TM 9-1808B.

Manufacturer: Dodge Brothers Corp. (Div. of Chrysler Corp.)

RA PD 308966

Classification: Limited standard

Purpose: To transport light cargo.

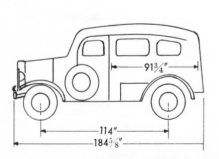
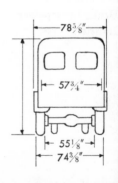

TRUCK, CARRYALL, ¾-TON, 4 x 4

GENERAL DATA

Crew...			2
Weight....................	Net.....................	(lb)	5,750
	Payload.................	(lb)	1,800
	Gross...................	(lb)	7,550
Shipping dimensions........	(cu ft)	...........(sq ft)	
Tires....................	Ply...8......	Size...9.00 x 16	
Tread, center to center............................		(in.)	64¾
Ground clearance.................................		(in.)	10⅝
Electrical system...............................		(volts)	6
Capacities................	Fuel, 70 octane gasoline....	(gal)	30
	Cooling system............	(qt)	18
	Crankcase (refill)..........	(qt)	5
Brakes...................................		Hydraulic	

PERFORMANCE

Maximum gradability...........................	(percent)	55
Turning radius.................................	(ft)	24½
Fording depth.................................	(in.)	34
Angle of approach.............................	(deg)	53
Angle of departure............................	(deg)	28
Fuel consumption, average conditions..........	(miles per gal)	8
Cruising range, average conditions................	(miles)	240
Maximum allowable speed......................	(mph)	54
Number of speeds forward........................		4

ENGINE

Manufacturer.....	Dodge..................	Model T-214	
Type.............	In-line, 4 cycle......	Number of cylinders	6
Displacement.......................................		(cu in.)	230.2
Governed speed..................................		(rpm)	3,200
Brake horsepower...................................			76
Ignition type...................................		Battery	

ADDITIONAL DATA

....

....

....

....

TRUCK, COMMAND, ¾-TON, 4 x 4

Technical Manuals: TM 9-808, TM 9-1808A, Parts List: SNL G-502
TM 9-1808B.

Manufacturer: Dodge Brothers Corp. (Div. of Chrysler Corp.)

RA PD 66341

Classification: Standard

Purpose: To provide transportation for command officers in the field.

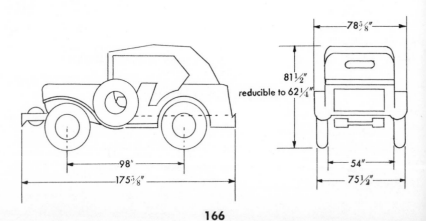

TRUCK, COMMAND, ¾-TON, 4 x 4

GENERAL DATA

Crew.. 2
Weight.................Net.....................(lb) 5,375*
                      Payload.................(lb) 1,500*
                      Gross...................(lb) 6,875*
Shipping dimensions.......(cu ft) 442*.........(sq ft) 85*
Tires.....................Ply...8......Size...9.00 x 16
Ground clearance......................................(in.) $10\frac{5}{8}$
Electrical system.....................................(volts) 12
Capacities...............Fuel, 70 octane gasoline....(gal) 30
                        Cooling system............(qt) 17
                        Crankcase (refill)..........(qt) 5
Brakes....................................Hydraulic

PERFORMANCE

Maximum gradability...........................(percent) 60
Turning radius.......................................(ft) $21\frac{2}{3}$
Fording depth..(in.) 34
Angle of approach (deg)......w/winch $36\frac{1}{2}$, w/o winch $53\frac{1}{2}$
Angle of departure...................................(deg) 31
Fuel consumption, average conditions.........(miles per gal) 8
Cruising range, average conditions.................(miles) 210
Maximum allowable speed..........................(mph) 54
Number of speeds forward.................................

ENGINE

Manufacturer......Dodge..................Model T-214
Type.............In-line, 4 cycle......Number of cylinders 6
Displacement..(cu in.) 230.2
Governed speed.......................................(rpm) 3,200
Brake horsepower... 76
Ignition type...................................Battery

ADDITIONAL DATA

Winch capacity.......................................(lb) 5,000
*Figures given are for vehicles without winch. For vehicles with winch use the following data:
Weight (lb)....Net 5,675.....Payload 1,500.....Gross 7,175
Shipping dimensions........(cu ft) 500............(sq ft) 96

TRUCK, EMERGENCY REPAIR, ¾-TON, 4 x 4

Technical Manuals: TM 9-808, TM 9-1808A,   Parts List: SNL G-502
TM 9-1808B.

Manufacturer: Dodge Brothers Corp. (Div. of Chrysler Corp.)

RA PD 309020

Classification: Limited standard

Purpose: To provide mobile facilities for emergency repair.

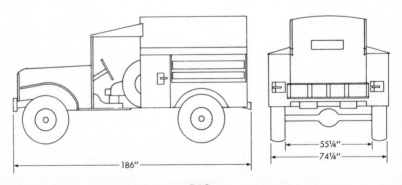

TRUCK, EMERGENCY REPAIR, ¾-TON, 4 x 4

GENERAL DATA

Crew... 5
Weight..................Net......................(lb) 5,350
                       Payload.................(lb) 2,170
                       Gross....................(lb) 7,520
Shipping dimensions.......(cu ft) ....(sq ft)
Tires....................Ply...8......Size...9.00 x 16
Tread, center to center............................(in.) 64¾
Ground clearance..................................(in.) 10¾
Electrical system..................................(volts) 6
Capacities..............Fuel, 72 octane gasoline....(gal) 30
                       Cooling system.............(qt) 17
                       Crankcase (refill)..........(qt) 5
Brakes....................................Hydraulic

PERFORMANCE

Maximum gradability..........................(percent) 52
Turning radius......................................(ft) 26
Fording depth......................................(in.) 34
Angle of approach................................(deg) 53
Angle of departure...............................(deg) 32
Fuel consumption, average conditions........(miles per gal) 8
Cruising range, average conditions.................(miles) 240
Maximum allowable speed.........................(mph) 55
Number of speeds forward.............................. 4

ENGINE

Manufacturer......Dodge...................Model T-214
Type.............In-line, 4 cycle......Number of cylinders 6
Displacement...................................(cu in.) 230.2
Governed speed.....................................(rpm) 3,200
Brake horsepower...........................at 3,200 rpm 76
Ignition type...................................Battery

ADDITIONAL DATA

....
....
....
....

TRUCK, LIGHT MAINTENANCE AND INSTALLATION
¾-TON, 4 x 4, K-50

Technical Manuals: Parts List:

Manufacturer: Dodge Brothers Corp. (Div. of Chrysler Corp.)

RA PD 66551

Classification: Limited standard

Purpose: Used by Signal Corps to transport equipment for light installation and maintenance.

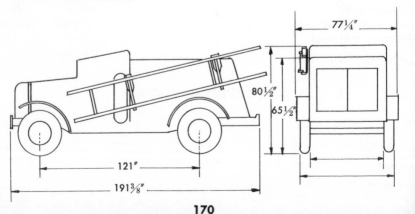

TRUCK, LIGHT MAINTENANCE AND INSTALLATION
¾-TON, 4 x 4, K-50

GENERAL DATA

Crew		2
Weight	Net (lb)	5,250
	Payload (lb)	500
	Gross (lb)	5,750
Shipping dimensions	(cu ft) 708 (sq ft) 105	
Tires	Ply...8......Size...9.00 x 16	
Tread, center to center	(in.)	64¼
Ground clearance	(in.)	10⅝
Electrical system	(volts)	6
Capacities	Fuel, 70 octane gasoline....(gal)	30
	Cooling system (qt)	17
	Crankcase (refill) (qt)	5
Brakes	Hydraulic	

PERFORMANCE

Maximum gradability	(percent)	53
Turning radius	(ft)	26¼
Fording depth	(in.)	34
Angle of approach	(deg)	53
Angle of departure	(deg)	28
Fuel consumption, average conditions	(miles per gal)	12
Cruising range, average conditions	(miles)	300
Maximum allowable speed	(mph)	55
Number of speeds forward		3

ENGINE

Manufacturer......Dodge......Model T214		
Type............In-line, 4 cycle......Number of cylinders		6
Displacement	(cu in.)	230.2
Governed speed	(rpm)	3,200
Brake horsepower		76
Ignition type	Battery	

ADDITIONAL DATA

. . . .

. . . .

. . . .

. . . .

TRUCK, WEAPONS CARRIER, ¾-TON, 4 x 4

Technical Manuals: TM 9-808, TM 9-1808A,   Parts List: SNL G-502
                          TM 9-1808B.

Manufacturer: Dodge Brothers Corp. (Div. of Chrysler Corp.)

RA PD 66555

Classification: Standard

Purpose: To transport weapons, tools and equipment.

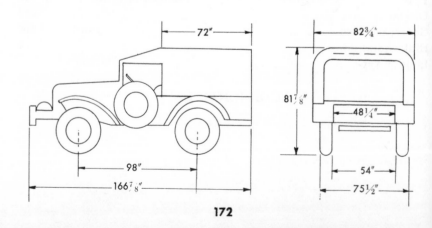

172

TRUCK, WEAPONS CARRIER, ¾-TON, 4 x 4

GENERAL DATA

Crew.. 2
Weight................Net....................(lb) 5,250*
                     Payload.................(lb) 1,500*
                     Gross....................(lb) 6,750*
Shipping dimensions.......(cu ft) 529..........(sq ft) 102
Tires....................Ply...8......Size...9.00 x 16
Tread, center to center............................(in.) 64¾
Ground clearance...................................(in.) 10⅝
Electrical system..................................(volts) 6
Capacities..............Fuel, 70 octane gasoline....(gal) 30
                        Cooling system............(qt) 18
                        Crankcase (refill)..........(qt) 5
Brakes...Hydraulic

PERFORMANCE

Maximum gradability..........................(percent) 60
Turning radius.....................................(ft) 22
Fording depth....................................(in.) 34
Angle of approach (deg)...With winch 36...Without winch 53
Angle of departure................................(deg) 31
Fuel consumption, average conditions.........(miles per gal) 8
Cruising range, average conditions.................(miles) 240
Maximum allowable speed.........................(mph) 54
Number of speeds forward............................. 4

ENGINE

Manufacturer......Dodge..................Model T-214
Type............In-line, 4 cycle.....Number of cylinders 6
Displacement.....................................(cu in.) 230.2
Governed speed..................................(rpm) 3,200
Brake horsepower.................................... 76
Ignition type.....................................Battery

ADDITIONAL DATA

Winch capacity.....................................(lb) 5,000

*Figures given are for vehicles without winch. For vehicles with
   winch use the following data:

Weight (lb)....Net 5,550 .... Payload 1,500.....Gross 7,050

TRUCK, CANOPY EXPRESS, 1-TON, 4 x 2

Technical Manual: TM 10-1305.   Parts List:

Manufacturer: Chevrolet Motor Div. (General Motors Corp.)

RA PD 308942

Classification: Standard

Purpose: To transport light cargo.

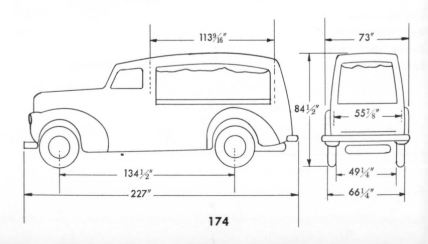

TRUCK, CANOPY EXPRESS, 1-TON, 4 x 2

GENERAL DATA

Crew. 2
Weight. . . . . .Net. . . . .(lb)   4,780
                        Payload. . . . .(lb)   2,000
                        Gross. . . . .(lb)   6,780
Shipping dimensions. . . . .(cu ft)   . . . .(sq ft)
Tires. . . . . .Ply. . . 8. . . . . .Size . . . 7.50 x 20
Electrical system. . . . .(volts)   6
Capacities. . . . . .Fuel, 70 octane gasoline. . . .(gal)   18
                        Cooling system. . . . .(qt)   16
                        Crankcase (refill). . . . .(qt)   6
Brakes. . . . . .Hydraulic

PERFORMANCE

Maximum gradability. . . . .(percent)
Turning radius. . . . .(ft)   26
Fording depth. . . . .(in.)
Angle of approach. . . . .(deg)
Angle of departure. . . . .(deg)
Fuel consumption, average conditions. . . . .(miles per gal)   9
Cruising range, average conditions. . . . .(miles)   162
Maximum allowable speed. . . . .(mph)
Number of speeds forward.   4

ENGINE

Manufacturer. . . . . . .Chevrolet. . . . . . .Model 1942 BF 1001 up
Type. . . . . .In-line, 4 cycle. . . . . .Number of cylinders   6
Displacement. . . . .(cu in.)   216.5
Governed speed. . . . .(rpm)
Brake horsepower. . . . .
Ignition type. . . . . .Battery

ADDITIONAL DATA

. . . .
. . . .
. . . .
. . . .

TRUCK, PICKUP, 1-TON, 4 x 2

Technical Manual: TM 10-1305.   Parts List:

Manufacturer: Chevrolet Motor Div. (General Motors Corp.)

RA PD 309128

Classification: Standard

Purpose: To transport cargo and personnel.

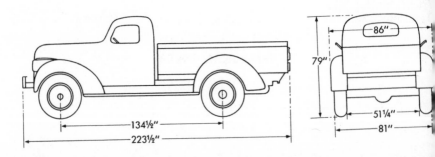

TRUCK, PICKUP, 1-TON, 4 x 2

GENERAL DATA

Crew...

Weight	Net		(lb)	4,825
	Payload		(lb)	3,150
	Gross		(lb)	7,975

Shipping dimensions........(cu ft) ....(sq ft)

Tires.....................Ply...8......Size...6.50 x 20

Ground clearance.....................................(in.)   9

Electrical system.....................................(volts)   6

Capacities	Fuel, 72 octane gasoline....(gal)	18
	Cooling system............(qt)	16
	Crankcase (refill)..........(qt)	5

Brakes.....................................Hydraulic

PERFORMANCE

Maximum gradability............................(percent)   66

Turning radius.......................................(ft)   26

Fording depth.......................................(in.)

Angle of approach................................(deg)   37

Angle of departure...............................(deg)   20

Fuel consumption, average conditions........(miles per gal)   9

Cruising range, average conditions.................(miles)   150

Maximum allowable speed.........................(mph)   48

Number of speeds forward..............................   4

ENGINE

Manufacturer......Chevrolet....................Model BQ

Type.............In-line, 4 cycle......Number of cylinders   6

Displacement......................................(cu in.)   216.5

Governed speed......................................(rpm)

Brake horsepower.....................................   90

Ignition type....................................Battery

ADDITIONAL DATA

....

....

....

....

TRUCK, COMBINATION, STAKE AND PLATFORM, 1½-TON, 4 x 2

Technical Manuals:
Ford, TM 10-1139, TM 10-1329,
TM 10-1433, TM 10-1541.
Chevrolet, TM 10-1305, TM 10-1341,
TM 10-1557.

Parts Lists: SNL G-540 (Ford)
SNL G-617 (Chev.)

Manufacturers: Chevrolet Motor Div. (General Motors Corp.);
Ford Motor Co.

Vehicle illustrated above: Chevrolet

RA PD 308946

Classification: Standard

Purpose: To transport general cargo.

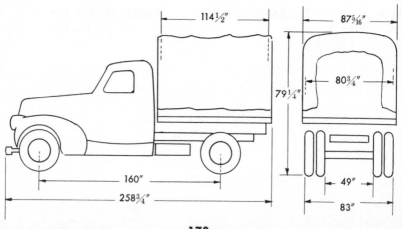

TRUCK, COMBINATION, STAKE AND PLATFORM, 1½-TON, 4 x 2

GENERAL DATA

Crew.			2
Weight. . . . . .Net. . . . .(lb)			4,985
	Payload. . . . .(lb)		4,515
	Gross. . . . .(lb)		9,500
Shipping dimensions. . . . . . . (cu ft) . . . . (sq ft)			
Tires. . . . . .Ply . . . 10 . . . . . Size . . . 7.00 x 20			
Tread, center to center (in.). .Front 56$\frac{1}{16}$. . . . . .Rear 66			
Ground clearance. . . . .(in.)			9
Electrical system. . . . .(volts)			6
Capacities. . . . . .Fuel, 70 octane gasoline. . . .(gal)			18
	Cooling system. . . . .(qt)		16
	Crankcase (refill). . . . .(qt)		5
Brakes. . . . . .Hydraulic			

PERFORMANCE

Maximum gradability. . . . .(percent)	63
Turning radius (ft). . . . . .Right 28. . . . . .Left 30	
Fording depth. . . . .(in.)	33
Angle of approach. . . . .(deg)	33
Angle of departure. . . . .(deg)	16
Fuel consumption, average conditions. . . . .(miles per gal)	12
Cruising range, average conditions. . . . .(miles)	216
Maximum allowable speed. . . . .(mph)	35
Number of speeds forward.	4

ENGINE

Manufacturer. . . . . . .Chevrolet. . . . . .Model, Loadmaster	
Type. . . . . .In-line, 4 cycle. . . . . .Number of cylinders	6
Displacement. . . . .(cu in.)	235.5
Governed speed. . . . .(rpm)	2,115
Brake horsepower.	81
Ignition type. . . . . .Battery	

ADDITIONAL DATA

. . . .

. . . .

. . . .

. . . .

TRUCK, CARGO, 1½-TON, 4 x 2

Technical Manuals:
    Ford, TM 10-1433, TM 10-1539,
               TM 10-1347.
Chevrolet, TM 10-1305, TM 10-1489.
        Dodge, TM 10-1157.

Parts Lists: SNL G-540 (Ford)
          SNL G-617 (Chev.)
          SNL G-618 (Dodge)

Manufacturers: Chevrolet Motor Div. (General Motors Corp.); Dodge Brothers Corp. (Div. of Chrysler Corp.); Ford Motor Co.

RA PD 308945

Vehicle illustrated above: Ford

Classification: Standard

Purpose: To transport general cargo.

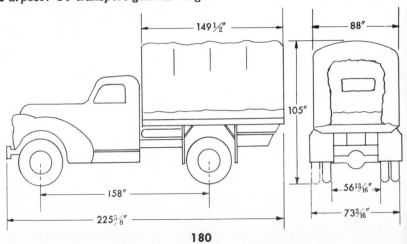

TRUCK, CARGO, 1½-TON, 4 x 2

GENERAL DATA

Crew..			2
Weight...................Net.......................(lb)			6,514
	Payload..................(lb)		3,150
	Gross...................(lb)		9,664
Shipping dimensions.......(cu ft) ....(sq ft)			
Tires....................Ply...8......Size...7.50 x 20			
Tread, center to center (in.)..Front 57.8............Rear 65			
Ground clearance.................................(in.)			9¼
Electrical system...........................(volts)			6
Capacities..............Fuel, 70 octane gasoline....(gal)			49
	Cooling system...........(qt)		17
	Crankcase (refill)..........(qt)		5
Brakes.................................Hydraulic			

PERFORMANCE

Maximum gradability...........................(percent)	47
Turning radius....................................(ft)	29½
Fording depth....................................(in.)	25
Angle of approach................................(deg)	35
Angle of departure...............................(deg)	20
Fuel consumption, average conditions, with towed load.........................(miles per gal)	10
Cruising range, average conditions, with towed load...(miles)	400
Maximum allowable speed........................(mph)	45
Number of speeds forward...............................	3

ENGINE

Manufacturer......Ford....................Model 2 GT	
Type.............In-line, 4 cycle......Number of cylinders	6
Displacement.....................................(cu in.)	225.7
Governed speed.....................................(rpm)	3400
Brake horsepower.......................................	81
Ignition type.....................................Battery	

ADDITIONAL DATA

. . . .

. . . .

. . . .

. . . .

TRUCK, CANOPY EXPRESS, 1½-TON, 4 x 2

Technical Manuals: TM 10-1305, TM 10-1465.   Parts List: SNL G-617
Manufacturer: Chevrolet Motor Div. (Division of General Motors Corp.).

Classification: Standard

Purpose: To transport cargo.   RA PD 308942

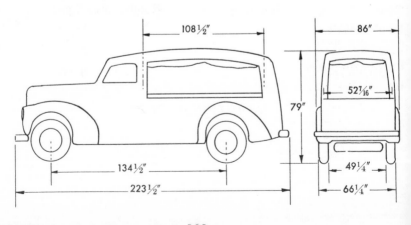

TRUCK, CANOPY EXPRESS, 1½-TON, 4 x 2

GENERAL DATA

Crew..			1
Weight...................Net....................(lb)			4,825
	Payload..................(lb)		3,150
	Gross....................(lb)		7,975
Tires....................Ply...8......Size...6.50 x 20			
Tread, center to center (in.)..Front ....Rear			
Ground clearance...................................(in.)			
Electrical system....................................(volts)			6
Capacities..............Fuel, 70 octane gasoline....(gal)			18
	Cooling system.............(qt)		16
	Crankcase (refill)..........(qt)		6
Brakes...Hydraulic			

PERFORMANCE

Maximum gradability............................(percent)	
Turning radius.......................................(ft)	26
Fording depth.......................................(in.)	
Angle of approach..................................(deg)	
Angle of departure.................................(deg)	
Fuel consumption, average conditions.........(miles per gal)	9
Cruising range, average conditions...................(miles)	162
Maximum allowable speed...........................(mph)	
Number of speeds forward.............................	4

ENGINE

Manufacturer......Chevrolet......Model 1942 BQ 1001 up	
Type.............In-line, 4 cycle.....Number of cylinders	6
Displacement......................................(cu in.)	216
Governed speed...............................(rpm) 1,200-2,000	
Brake horsepower.......................................	90
Ignition type...................................Battery	

ADDITIONAL DATA

....

....

....

....

TRUCK, DUMP, 1½-TON, 4 x 2

Technical Manuals: Chevrolet, TM 10-1305, TM 10-1329. Ford, TM 10-1139, TM 10-1329.

Parts Lists: SNL G-620 (GMC) SNL G-540 (Ford) SNL G-617 (Chev.)

Manufacturers: Chevrolet Motor Div. (General Motors Corp.); Ford Motor Co.

RA PD 308950

Vehicle illustrated above: Chevrolet

Classification: Standard

Purpose: To transport and dump stone, sand, gravel, etc., and to transport general cargo.

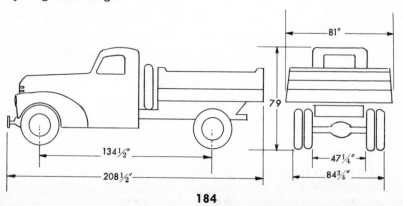

TRUCK, DUMP, 1½-TON, 4 x 2

GENERAL DATA

Crew.. 2
Weight................Net....................(lb) 5,975
                     Payload.................(lb) 3,150
                     Gross...................(lb) 9,125
Shipping dimensions........(cu ft) ....(sq ft)
Tires....................Ply...8......Size...6.50 x 20
Tread, center to center (in.).Front ....Rear
Ground clearance....................................(in.)
Electrical system....................................(volts) 6
Capacities..............Fuel, 70 octane gasoline....(gal) 18
                       Cooling system...........(qt) 16
                       Crankcase (refill)..........(qt) 6
Brakes......................................Hydraulic

PERFORMANCE

Maximum gradability..........................(percent)
Turning radius...................................(ft) 26
Angle of approach................................(deg)
Angle of departure...............................(deg)
Fuel consumption, average conditions........(miles per gal) 9
Cruising range, average conditions.................(miles) 162
Maximum allowable speed.....................(mph)
Number of speeds forward............................. 4

ENGINE

Manufacturer......Chevrolet......Model 1942 BQ 1001 up
Type.............In-line, 4 cycle....Number of cylinders 6
Displacement.....................................(cu in.) 216.5
Governed speed....................................(rpm)
Brake horsepower..................................... 90
Ignition type....................................Battery

ADDITIONAL DATA

....
....
....
....

TRUCK, FIRE, 1½-TON, 4 x 2

Technical Manuals: Parts List:

Manufacturers: Ward-LaFrance; Ford.

RA PD 66577

Classification: Standard

Purpose: Used by Corps of Engineers to transport fire-fighting and pumping equipment.

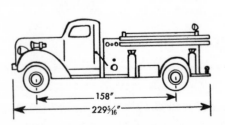

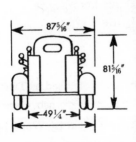

TRUCK, FIRE, 1½-TON, 4 x 2

GENERAL DATA

Crew... 8
Weight................... Gross.....................(lb) 10,670
Shipping dimensions........ (cu ft) 934...........(sq ft) 138
Tires.....................Ply...8......Size...6.50 x 20
Ground clearance.......................................(in.) 9¼
Tread, center to center.....Front ....Rear
Electrical system....................................(volts) 6
Capacities...............Fuel, 70 octane gasoline....(gal) 37
                        Cooling system............(qt) 17½
                        Crankcase (refill)..........(qt) 5
Brakes..Hydraulic

PERFORMANCE

Maximum gradability...........................(percent)
Turning radius.......................................(ft) 29½
Fording depth.......................................(in.)
Angle of approach................................(deg) 35
Angle of departure................................(deg) 20
Fuel consumption, average conditions........(miles per gal) 8
Cruising range, average conditions.................(miles) 150
Maximum allowable speed.........................(mph) 53
Number of speeds forward.............................

ENGINE

Manufacturer......Ford..................Model
Type.............V-8, 4 cycle.......Number of cylinders 8
Displacement.....................................(cu in.) 221
Governed speed...................................(rpm)
Brake horsepower....................................
Ignition type...................................Battery

ADDITIONAL DATA

This vehicle used as Truck, fire pumper, type "A", overseas, class 325 and
    Truck, fire crash, class 125.

Pump driven by Ward-LaFrance Model WLF-F6, 6 cylinder, 225.7 cubic
    inch displacement.

TRUCK, PANEL DELIVERY, 1½-TON, 4 x 2

Technical Manuals: Chevrolet,
TM 10-1305, TM 10-1403,
TM 10-1461.
Ford, TM 10-1257,
TM 10-1329.

Parts Lists: SNL G-540 (Ford)
SNL G-620 (Chev.)

Manufacturers: Chevrolet Motor Div. (General Motors Corp.); Ford
Motor Co.

Vehicle illustrated above: Chevrolet

Classification: Standard

Purpose: To transport light cargo.

RA PD 308943

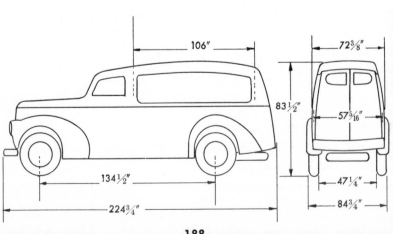

TRUCK, PANEL DELIVERY, 1½-TON, 4 x 2

GENERAL DATA

Crew			2
Weight	Net	(lb)	4,275
	Payload	(lb)	3,425
	Gross	(lb)	7,700
Shipping dimensions	(cu ft)	(sq ft)	
Tires	Ply: Front 6	Rear 8	
	Size: Front	6.00 x 20	
	Rear	6.50 x 20	
Ground clearance		(in.)	
Electrical system		(volts)	6
Capacities	Fuel, 70 octane gasoline	(gal)	18
	Cooling system	(qt)	14
	Crankcase (refill)	(qt)	5
Brakes		Hydraulic	

PERFORMANCE

Maximum gradability	(percent)	
Turning radius	(ft)	26
Angle of approach	(deg)	
Angle of departure	(deg)	
Fuel consumption, average conditions	(miles per gal)	12
Cruising range, average conditions	(miles)	216
Maximum allowable speed	(mph)	
Number of speeds forward		3

ENGINE

Manufacturer	Chevrolet	Model	
Type	In-line, 4 cycle	Number of cylinders	6
Displacement		(cu in.)	216.5
Governed speed		(rpm)	
Brake horsepower			

ADDITIONAL DATA

. . . .

. . . .

. . . .

. . . .

TRUCK, PICKUP, 1½-TON, 4 x 2

Technical Manuals: TM 10-1305, TM 10-1465.   Parts List: SNL G-617
Manufacturer: Chevrolet Motor Div. (General Motors Corp.).

Classification: Standard

Purpose: To transport cargo.

RA PD 308944

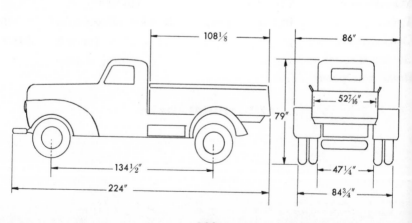

TRUCK, PICKUP, 1½-TON, 4 x 2

GENERAL DATA

Crew...				1
Weight..................	Net....................		(lb)	4,965
	Payload..................		(lb)	3,150
	Gross....................		(lb)	8,015
Shipping dimensions.......	(cu ft)	.........(sq ft)		
Tires.....................	Ply...8......	Size...6.50 x 20		
Ground clearance...........................			(in.)	9
Electrical system..................................			(volts)	6
Capacities..............	Fuel, octane gasoline....		(gal)	18
	Cooling system............		(qt)	16
	Crankcase (refill)..........		(qt)	5
Brakes..		Hydraulic		

PERFORMANCE

Maximum gradability............................	(percent)	
Turning radius (ft)........	Right ....Left	
Fording depth...............................	(in.)	
Angle of approach................................	(deg)	
Angle of departure...............................	(deg)	
Fuel consumption, average conditions.........	(miles per gal)	
Cruising range, average conditions..................	(miles)	150
Maximum allowable speed.........................	(mph)	
Number of speeds forward............................		4

ENGINE

Manufacturer......	Chevrolet.................	Model	
Type.............	In-line, 4 cycle.....	Number of cylinders	6
Displacement...........................		(cu in.)	216.5
Governed speed..................................		(rpm)	
Brake horsepower.......................................			

ADDITIONAL DATA

....
....
....
....

TRUCK, AIRFIELD CRASH, 1½-TON, 4 x 4

Technical Manual: TM 10-1127 (C1).   Parts List:

Manufacturer: Chevrolet Motor Div. (General Motors Corp.).

RA PD 66561

Classification: Standard

Purpose: To provide mobile fire-fighting and crash equipment for airfields.

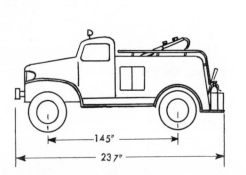

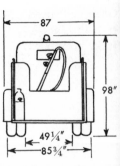

TRUCK, AIRFIELD CRASH, 1½-TON, 4 x 4

GENERAL DATA

Crew. . . . .
Weight. . . . . Net. . . . . (lb)
Payload. . . . . (lb)
Gross. . . . . (lb)   9,000
Shipping dimensions. . . . . (cu ft) 937. . . . . (sq ft) 129
Tires. . . . . Ply. . . 8. . . . . . . Size . . . 7.50 x 20
Ground clearance. . . . . (in.)
Electrical system. . . . . (volts)   6
Capacities. . . . . Fuel, 70 octane gasoline. . . . (gal)   30
Cooling system. . . . . (qt)   17
Crankcase. . . . . (qt)   7½
Brakes. . . . . (Hydrovac) Hydraulic

PERFORMANCE

Maximum gradability. . . . . (percent)   65
Turning radius. . . . . (ft)   29½
Fording depth. . . . . (in.)   32
Angle of approach. . . . . (deg)   45
Angle of departure. . . . . (deg)
Fuel consumption, average conditions. . . . . (miles per gal)   9
Cruising range, average conditions. . . . . (miles)   270
Maximum allowable speed. . . . . (mph)   48
Number of speeds forward.   4

ENGINE

Manufacturer. . . . . . . Chevrolet. . . . . Model BU-1001 up
Type. . . . . In-line, 4 cycle. . . . . Number of cylinders   6
Displacement. . . . . (cu in.)   235.5
Governed speed. . . . . (rpm)   3,100
Brake horsepower.   83
Ignition type. . . . . Battery

ADDITIONAL DATA

. . . .
. . . .
. . . .
. . . .

TRUCK, BOMB SERVICE, M6, 1½-TON, 4 x 4

Technical Manuals: TM 9-765, TM 9-1765A,   Parts List: SNL G-85
TM 9-1765B.

Manufacturer: Chevrolet Motor Div. (General Motors Corp.), (Model
G 7128).

RA PD 66563

Classification: Standard

Purpose: To tow bomb trailers and lift bombs on and off trailers.

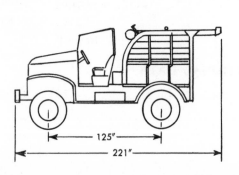

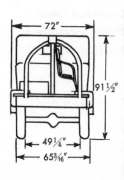

TRUCK, BOMB SERVICE, M6, 1½-TON, 4 x 4

GENERAL DATA

Crew			5
Weight	Net	(lb)	6,325
	Payload	(lb)	2,050
	Gross	(lb)	8,375
Shipping dimensions	(cu ft) 845	(sq ft) 111	
Tires	Ply . . . 8	Size . . . 7.50 x 20	
Tread, center to center (in.)	Front $60\frac{5}{16}$	Rear $57\frac{1}{4}$	
Ground clearance		(in.)	$9\frac{7}{8}$
Electrical system		(volts)	6
Capacities	Fuel, 70 octane gasoline	(gal)	30
	Cooling system	(qt)	$17\frac{1}{4}$
	Crankcase (refill)	(qt)	5
Brakes		Hydraulic	

PERFORMANCE

Maximum gradability	(percent)	65
Turning radius	(ft)	26
Angle of approach	(deg)	45
Angle of departure	(deg)	38
Fuel consumption, average conditions	(miles per gal)	$8\frac{1}{2}$
Cruising range, average conditions	(miles)	250
Maximum allowable speed	(mph)	55

	1st	2nd	3rd	4th
Cruising speed	6	14	28	48

ENGINE

Manufacturer . . . . . . Chevrolet	Model BV 1001 up	
Type . . . . In-line, 4 cycle	Number of cylinders	6
Displacement	(cu in.)	235.5
Governed speed	Not governed	
Brake horsepower		83
Ignition type	Battery	

ADDITIONAL DATA

Winch capacity . . . . . (Mounted on bomb handling hoist) . . . (lb)		2,000

. . . .

. . . .

. . . .

TRUCK, CARGO, 1½-TON, 4 x 4

Technical Manuals: Chevrolet,   Parts Lists: SNL G-621 (Dodge)
TM 10-1431, TM 10-1127 (C1),   SNL G-622 (Ford)
TM 10-1203.   SNL G-506 (Chev.)
Ford, TM 10-1435.
Dodge, TM 10-1179, TM 10-1193.

Manufacturers: Chevrolet Motor Div. (General Motors Corp.); Dodge
Brothers Corp. (Div. Chrysler Corp.); Ford Motor Co.

RA PD 66567

Vehicle illustrated above: Chevrolet

Classification: Standard

Purpose: To transport general cargo and personnel.

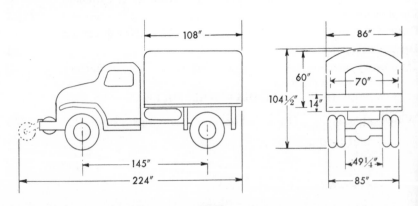

TRUCK, CARGO, 1½-TON, 4 x 4

GENERAL DATA

Crew, operating. 2
Weight. . . . . .Net. . . . .(lb)   7,545*
. . . . Payload. . . . .(lb)   3,000*
. . . . Gross. . . . .(lb)   10,545*
Shipping dimensions†. . . . . . (cu ft) 1,001. . . . . (sq ft) 138
Tires. .Ply. . . 8. . . . . . Size . . . 7.50 x 20
Tread, center to center (in.).Front 60½. . . . . .Rear 67½
Ground clearance. . . . .(in.)   9⅞
Electrical system. . . . .(volts)   6
Capacities. . . . . .Fuel, 70 octane gasoline. . . .(gal)   30
. . . . Cooling system. . . . .(qt)   17
. . . . Crankcase (refill). . . . .(qt)   5
Brakes. . . . . .Hydraulic

PERFORMANCE

Maximum gradability. . . . .(percent)   65
Turning radius (ft). . . . . . . .Right 29. . . . . .Left 28½
Fording depth. . . . .(in.)   32
Angle of approach (deg). . . .with winch 39.without winch 45
Angle of departure. . . . .(deg)   30
Fuel consumption, average conditions. . . . .(miles per gal)   9
Cruising range, average conditions. . . . .(miles)   270
Maximum allowable speed. . . . .(mph)   48
Number of speeds forward.   4

ENGINE

Manufacturer. . . . . . .Chevrolet. . . . . .Model 1942, BV-1001 up
Type. . . . . .In-line, 4 cycle. . . . . .Number of cylinders   6
Displacement. . . . .(cu in.)   235.5
Governed speed. . . . .(rpm)   3,100
Brake horsepower.   83
Ignition type. . . . . .Battery

ADDITIONAL DATA

Winch capacity. . . . .(lb)   10,000
*Figures given are for vehicle without winch. For vehicles with winch
    use the following data:
      Weight (lb). . . . . .Net—8,215; Payload—3,000; Gross   11,215
†Data on wood body model same as above data on steel body model,
    except as follows:
      Height (top up). . . . .(in.)   106½
      Width. . . . .(in.)   69¾
      Top up. . . . .(cu ft)   1,225
      Top down. . . . .(cu ft)   1,005

TRUCK, COMBINATION STAKE AND PLATFORM, 15 FT, 1½-TON, 4 x 4

Technical Manuals: TM 10-1131, TM 10-1203, Parts List: SNL G-506
TM 10-1559.

Manufacturer: Chevrolet Motor Div. (General Motors Corp.)

RA PD 66569

Classification: Standard

Purpose: To transport general cargo and personnel.

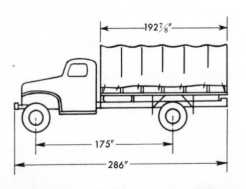

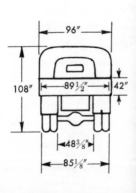

TRUCK, COMBINATION STAKE AND PLATFORM, 15 FT, 1½-TON, 4 x 4

GENERAL DATA

Crew...			2
Weight.................	Net.....................(lb)		8,965
	Payload..................(lb)		3,000
	Gross....................(lb)		11,965
Shipping dimensions........(cu ft) 1,276.........(sq ft) 177			
Tires, type.............Ply...8......Size...7.50 x 20			
Tread, center to center (in.) Front 60½..........Rear 67½			
Ground clearance...............................(in.)			9⅞
Pintle height..................................(in.)			30³⁄₁₆
Electrical system..............................(volts)			6
Capacities.............Fuel, 72 octane gasoline....(gal)			30
	Cooling system...........(qt)		16
	Crankcase (refill).........(qt)		5
Brakes.......................................Hydraulic			

PERFORMANCE

Maximum gradability............................(percent)	65
Turning radius.......................................(ft)	31
Fording depth.......................................(in.)	32
Angle of approach.................................(deg)	41
Angle of departure................................(deg)	29
Fuel consumption, average conditions.......(miles per gal)	9
Cruising range, average conditions.................(miles)	270
Maximum allowable speed..........................(mph)	48
Number of speeds forward................................	4

ENGINE

Manufacturer......Chevrolet.........Model BVA-1001 up	
Type.............In-line, 4 cycle.....Number of cylinders	6
Displacement...................................(cu in.)	235.5
Governed speed...................................(rpm)	3,100
Brake horsepower.......................................	80
Ignition type...................................Battery	

ADDITIONAL DATA

....

....

....

....

....

TRUCK, COMBINATION STAKE AND PLATFORM, C.O.E., 1½-TON, 4 x 4

Technical Manuals: TM 10-1203, TM 10-1131, TM 10-1559.

Parts List: SNL G-506

Manufacturer: Chevrolet Motor Div. (General Motors Corp.)

RA PD 66587

Classification: Limited standard

Purpose: To transport general cargo.

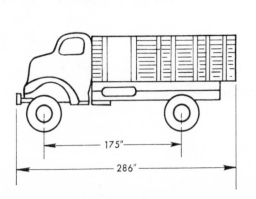

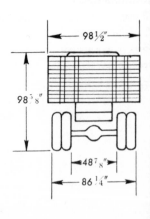

TRUCK, COMBINATION STAKE AND PLATFORM, C.O.E., 1½-TON, 4 x 4

GENERAL DATA

Crew			2
Weight	Net	(lb)	8,890
	Payload	(lb)	3,000
	Gross	(lb)	11,890
Shipping dimensions	(cu ft)	(sq ft)	
Tires	Ply...8	Size...7.50 x 20	
Tread, center to center (in.)	Front 60½	Rear 67½	
Ground clearance		(in.)	10
Electrical system		(volts)	6
Capacities	Fuel, 72 octane gasoline	(gal)	30
	Cooling system	(qt)	16
	Crankcase (refill)	(qt)	5
Brakes		Hydraulic	

PERFORMANCE

Maximum gradability	(percent)	65
Turning radius	(ft)	31
Fording depth	(in.)	
Angle of approach	(deg)	41½
Angle of departure	(deg)	29
Fuel consumption, average conditions	(miles per gal)	8
Cruising range, average conditions	(miles)	240
Maximum allowable speed	(mph)	43
Number of speeds forward		4

ENGINE

Manufacturer	Chevrolet	Model BVA-1001 up	
Type	In-line, 4 cycle	Number of cylinders	6
Displacement		(cu in.)	235.5
Governed speed		(rpm)	2,850
Brake horsepower			90
Ignition type		Battery	

ADDITIONAL DATA

TRUCK, COMBINATION STAKE AND PLATFORM, C.O.E., 1½-TON, 4 x 4, K-33 AND K-54

Technical Manuals: Parts List:

Manufacturer: Chevrolet Motor Div. (General Motors Corp.)

RA PD 66587

Classification: K-33 limited standard; K-54 standard

Purpose: Used by Signal Corps to transport general cargo.

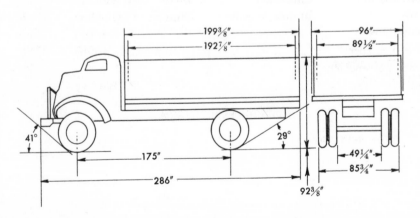

TRUCK, COMBINATION STAKE AND PLATFORM, C.O.E. 1½-TON, 4 x 4, K-33 AND K-54

GENERAL DATA

Crew... 2
Weight................... Net....................(lb) 8,570
                        Payload.................(lb) 3,000
                        Gross...................(lb) 11,570
Shipping dimensions.......(cu ft) 1,963........(sq ft) 191
Tires....................Ply...8......Size...7.50 x 20
Tread, center to center...........................(in.) 68
Ground clearance..................................(in.) 9½
Electrical system................................(volts) 6
Capacities..............Fuel, 70 octane gasoline....(gal) 30
                        Cooling system.............(qt) 16
                        Crankcase (refill)..........(qt) 7½
Brakes.......................(Hydrovac) Hydraulic

PERFORMANCE

Maximum gradability............................(percent) 65
Turning radius......................................(ft) 31
Fording depth......................................(in.) 32
Angle of approach..................................(deg) 41
Angle of departure.................................(deg) 23
Fuel consumption, average conditions.........(miles per gal) 8
Cruising range, average conditions..................(miles) 240
Maximum allowable speed...........................(mph) 43
Number of speeds forward............................. 4

ENGINE

Manufacturer......Chevrolet.........Model BVA-1001 up
Type..............In-line, 4 cycle.....Number of cylinders 6
Displacement....................................(cu in.) 235.5
Governed speed....................................(rpm) 2,850
Brake horsepower..................................... 83
Ignition type.......................................Battery

ADDITIONAL DATA

K-33 is the same as K-54.

....
....
....

TRUCK, DUMP, 1½-TON, 4 x 4

Technical Manuals: Chevrolet,   Parts Lists: SNL G-621 (Dodge)
     TM 10-1557, TM 10-1127 (C1),   SNL G-506 (Chev.)
     TM 10-1203, TM 10-1431.
Dodge, TM 10-1179, TM 10-1193.

Manufacturers: Chevrolet Motor Div. (General Motors Corp.); Dodge
  Brothers (Div. of Chrysler Corp.).

RA PD 66571

Vehicle illustrated above: Chevrolet

Classification: Limited standard

Purpose: To transport and dump earth, sand, gravel, coal, etc., and to
  carry general cargo.

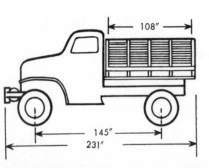
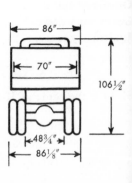

TRUCK, DUMP, 1½-TON, 4 x 4

GENERAL DATA

Crew. 2
Weight. . . . . .Net. . . . .(lb)   8,300*
                     Payload. . . . .(lb)   3,000*
                     Gross. . . . .(lb) 11,300*
Shipping dimensions. . . . .(cu ft)   . . . .(sq ft)
Tires. . . . . .Ply. . . 8. . . . . . .Size . . . 7.50 x 20
Tread, center to center (in.).Front 60½. . . . . .Rear 67½
Ground clearance. . . . .(in.)   10
Pintle height. . . . .(in.) $30\frac{3}{16}$
Electrical system. . . . .(volts)   6
Capacities. . . . . .Fuel, 72 octane gasoline. . . .(gal)   30
                     Cooling system. . . . .(qt)   17
                     Crankcase (refill). . . . .(qt)   5
Brakes. . . . . .Hydraulic

PERFORMANCE

Maximum gradability. . . . .(percent)   65
Turning radius. . . . .(ft)   29½
Fording depth. . . . .(in.)   32
Angle of approach (deg) . . . .with winch 39. .without winch 45
Angle of departure. . . . .(deg)   30
Fuel consumption, average conditions. . . . .(miles per gal)   9
Cruising range, average conditions. . . . .(miles)   270
Maximum allowable speed. . . . .(mph)   48
Number of speeds forward.   4

ENGINE

Manufacturer. . . . . . .Chevrolet. . . . . . .Model 1941 BV-1001 up
Type. . . . . .In-line, 4 cycle. . . . .Number of cylinders   6
Displacement. . . . .(cu in.)   235.5
Governed speed. . . . .(rpm)   3,100
Brake horsepower.   83
Ignition type. . . . . .Battery

ADDITIONAL DATA

Winch capacity. . . . .(lb)   10,000
*Figures given are for vehicles without winch. For vehicles with winch
    use the following data:
        Weight (lb). . . . . .Net 9,130. . . . . .Payload 3,000. . . . . .Gross 12,130

TRUCK, EARTH AUGER, 1½-TON, 4 x 4, M1

Technical Manuals: Chevrolet,   Parts Lists:
    TM 10-1127, TM 10-1203.

Manufacturers: Chevrolet Motor Div. (General Motors Corp.); Ford
    Motor Co.

RA PD 66573

Vehicle illustrated above: Chevrolet

Classification: Limited standard

Purpose: Used by Corps of Engineers to provide mobile equipment for
    earth boring and telephone pole setting.

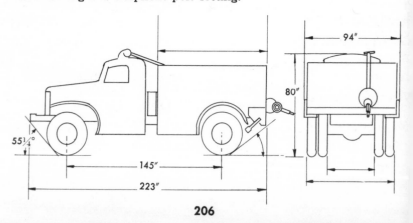

TRUCK, EARTH AUGER, 1½-TON, 4 x 4, M1

GENERAL DATA

Crew... 2

Weight...................Net.......................(lb) 7,200

Payload..................(lb) 3,000

Gross....................(lb) 10,200

Shipping dimensions........(cu ft) 1,419.........(sq ft) 164

Tires.....................Ply..8.........Size..7.50 x 20

Ground clearance.....................................(in.) 9⅞

Electrical system................................(volts) 6

Capacities................Fuel, 70 octane gasoline....(gal) 35

Cooling system............(qt) 17

Crankcase (refill)..........(qt) 7½

Transmission w/o P.T.O.....(pt) 5½

Brakes.....................................Hydraulic

PERFORMANCE

Maximum gradability..........................(percent) 65

Turning radius.......................................(ft) 29½

Fording depth..(in.) 32

Angle of approach..................................(deg) 45

Angle of departure.................................(deg) 30

Fuel consumption, average conditions.........(miles per gal) 9

Cruising range, average conditions...................(miles) 315

Maximum allowable speed..........................(mph) 48

Number of speeds forward..............................

ENGINE

Manufacturer.......Chevrolet...........Model BV-1001 up

Type.............In-line, 4 cycle......Number of cylinders 6

Displacement......................................(cu in.) 235

Governed speed.......................................(rpm) 3,100

Brake horsepower...................................... 83

Ignition type....................................Battery

ADDITIONAL DATA

Winch capacity.......................................(lb) 10,000

....

....

....

....

....

TRUCK, EARTH BORER AND POLESETTER, 1½-TON, 4 x 4, K-44

Technical Manuals: Parts List:

Manufacturer: Chevrolet Motor Div. (General Motors Corp.)

RA PD 66573

Classification: Standard

Purpose: Used by Signal Corps to provide mobile equipment for earth boring and telephone pole-setting.

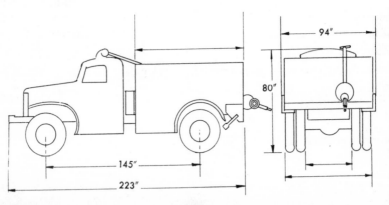

TRUCK, EARTH BORER AND POLESETTER, 1½-TON, 4 x 4, K-44

GENERAL DATA

Crew			2
Weight	Net	(lb)	7,200
	Payload	(lb)	3,000
	Gross	(lb)	10,200
Shipping dimensions	(cu ft) 1,438	(sq ft)	164
Tires	Ply ... 8	Size ... 7.50 x 20	
Ground clearance		(in.)	9⅞
Electrical system		(volts)	6
Capacities	Fuel, 70 octane gasoline	(gal)	35
	Cooling system	(qt)	17
	Crankcase (refill)	(qt)	7½
Brakes	Hydraulic		

PERFORMANCE

Maximum gradability	(percent)	65
Turning radius	(ft)	29½
Fording depth	(in.)	32
Angle of approach	(deg)	55
Angle of departure	(deg)	39
Fuel consumption, average conditions	(miles per gal)	9
Cruising range, average conditions	(miles)	315
Maximum allowable speed	(mph)	48
Number of speeds forward		4

ENGINE

Manufacturer	Chevrolet	Model BV-1001 up	
Type	In-line, 4 cycle	Number of cylinders	6
Displacement		(cu in.)	235.5
Governed speed		(rpm)	3,100
Brake horsepower			83
Ignition type	Battery		

ADDITIONAL DATA

Winch capacity	(lb)	10,000

TRUCK, FIELD LIGHTING, 1½-TON, 4 x 4, J-3 AND J-4

Technical Manuals: Parts List:

Manufacturers: Chevrolet Motor Div. (General Motors Corp.);
  Equipment—American Gas Accumulator Co., Models J-3, J-4.

RA PD 309024

Classification: Standard

Purpose: Used by Army Air Forces to transport lighting equipment for airfields.

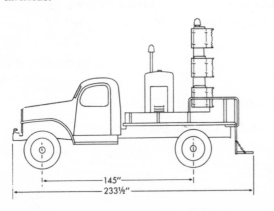
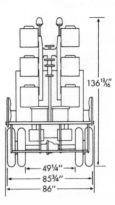

TRUCK, FIELD LIGHTING, 1½-TON, 4 x 4, J-3 AND J-4

GENERAL DATA

Crew			2
Weight	Net	(lb)	7,200
	Payload	(lb)	3,000
	Gross	(lb)	10,200
Shipping dimensions	(cu ft) 1,430	(sq ft) 130	
Tires	Ply ... 8	Size ... 7.50 x 20	
Tread, center to center (in.)	Front	Rear	
Ground clearance		(in.)	9⅞
Electrical system		(volts)	6
Capacities	Fuel, 70 octane gasoline	(gal)	30
	Cooling system	(qt)	17
	Crankcase (refill)	(qt)	7½
Brakes		Hydraulic	

PERFORMANCE

Maximum gradability	(percent)	65
Turning radius	(ft)	28
Fording depth	(in.)	32
Angle of approach	(deg)	45
Angle of departure	(deg)	30
Fuel consumption, average conditions	(miles per gal)	9
Cruising range, average conditions	(miles)	195
Maximum allowable speed	(mph)	48
Number of speeds forward		

ENGINE

Manufacturer ... Chevrolet	Model BV-1001 up	
Type ... In-line, 4 cycle	Number of cylinders	6
Displacement	(cu in.)	235.5
Governed speed	(rpm)	3,100
Brake horsepower		83
Ignition type	Battery	

ADDITIONAL DATA

Difference between J-3 and J-4 is power plant for electrical supply.

TRUCK, FIELD LIGHTING, 1½-TON, 4 x 4, J-5

Technical Order: T.O. 19-10-7.　　　　　Parts List:

Manufacturers: Chevrolet Motor Div. (General Motors Corp.);
　Equipment—Davey Compressor Co., Model J-5.

RA PD 309028

Classification: Standard

Purpose: Used by Army Air Forces to transport lighting equipment for
　airfields.

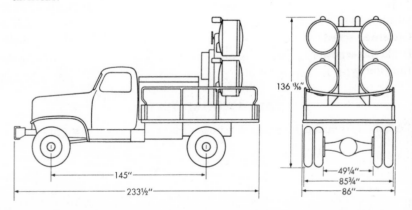

TRUCK, FIELD LIGHTING, J-5, 1½-TON, 4 x 4

GENERAL DATA

Crew...			2
Weight....................Net.......................(lb)			7,200
	Payload..................(lb)		3,000
	Gross....................(lb)		10,200
Shipping dimensions.......(cu ft) 1,430.........(sq ft) 130			
Tires......................Ply...8......Size...7.50 x 20			
Tread, center to center (in.).Front ....Rear			
Ground clearance....................................(in.)			9⅞
Electrical system...................................(volts)			6
Capacities...............Fuel, 70 octane gasoline....(gal)			30
	Cooling system............(qt)		17
	Crankcase (refill)..........(qt)		7½
Brakes....................................Hydraulic			

PERFORMANCE

Maximum gradability...........................(percent)	65
Turning radius.....................................(ft)	28
Fording depth....................................(in.)	32
Angle of approach................................(deg)	45
Angle of departure...............................(deg)	30
Fuel consumption, average conditions.........(miles per gal)	9
Cruising range, average conditions..................(miles)	195
Maximum allowable speed.........................(mph)	48
Number of speeds forward................................	

ENGINE

Manufacturer......Chevrolet..........Model BV-1001 up	
Type.............In-line, 4 cycle....Number of cylinders	6
Displacement.....................................(cu in.)	235.5
Governed speed....................................(rpm)	3,100
Brake horsepower..	83
Ignition type....................................Battery	

ADDITIONAL DATA

Chassis is equipped with power take-off for generator.

....
....
....

TRUCK, PANEL DELIVERY, 1½-TON, 4 x 4

Technical Manuals: TM 10-1203,
TM 10-1127 (C1), TM 10-1431.

Parts List: SNL G-506

Manufacturer: Chevrolet Motor Div. (General Motors Corp.)

Classification: Standard

Purpose: To transport general cargo.

RA PD 309098

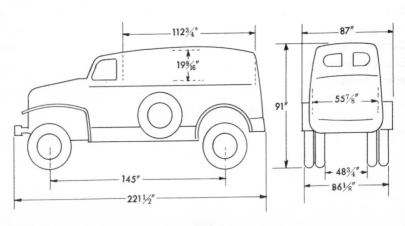

TRUCK, PANEL DELIVERY, 1½-TON, 4 x 4

GENERAL DATA

Crew...			2
Weight....................	Net....................	(lb)	6,760
	Payload..................	(lb)	3,000
	Gross....................	(lb)	9,760
Shipping dimensions........	(cu ft)	.........(sq ft)	
Tires....................	Ply...8......	Size...7.50 x 20	
Tread, center to center (in.).	Front 60½..........	Rear 67½	
Ground clearance.................................		(in.)	9⅞
Electrical system.................................		(volts)	6
Capacities.................	Fuel, 72 octane gasoline....	(gal)	30
	Cooling system.............	(qt)	17
	Crankcase (refill)..........	(qt)	5
Brakes....................................		Hydraulic	

PERFORMANCE

Maximum gradability............................	(percent)	65
Turning radius.................................	(ft)	28
Fording depth..................................	(in.)	32
Angle of approach..............................	(deg)	45
Angle of departure.............................	(deg)	30
Fuel consumption, average conditions........	(miles per gal)	9
Cruising range, average conditions..............	(miles)	270
Maximum allowable speed......................	(mph)	48
Number of speeds forward......................		4

ENGINE

Manufacturer......	Chevrolet......	Model 1942 BV-1001 up	
Type.............	In-line, 4 cycle.....	Number of cylinders	6
Displacement................................		(cu in.)	235.5
Governed speed..............................		(rpm)	3,100
Brake horsepower............................			83
Ignition type.................................		Battery	

ADDITIONAL DATA

. . . .

. . . .

. . . .

. . . .

TRUCK, PANEL DELIVERY, 1½-TON, 4 x 4, K-51

Technical Manuals: TM 10-1203,   Parts List:
 TM 10-1127 (C1), TM 10-1431.

Manufacturer: Chevrolet Motor Div. (General Motors Corp.), (Model
 G 7107).

RA PD 66581

Classification: Limited standard

Purpose: Used by the Signal Corps to transport light general cargo.

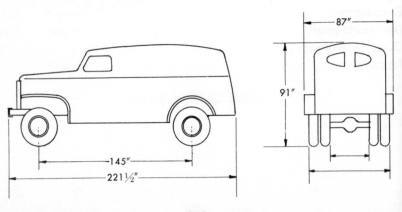

TRUCK, PANEL DELIVERY, 1½-TON, 4 x 4, K-51

GENERAL DATA

Crew..			2
Weight.................	Net........................(lb)		6,760
	Payload..................(lb)		3,000
	Gross.....................(lb)		9,760
Shipping dimensions........(cu ft) 1,541.........(sq ft) 133			
Tires.....................	Ply...8......Size...7.50 x 20		
Ground clearance.......................................(in.)			9⅞
Tread, center to center................................(in.)			67¾
Electrical system....................................(volts)			6
Capacities..............	Fuel, 70 octane gasoline....(gal)		30
	Cooling system............(qt)		17
	Crankcase (refill)..........(qt)		7½
Brakes...Hydraulic			

PERFORMANCE

Maximum gradability...........................(percent)	65
Turning radius......................................(ft)	29½
Fording depth......................................(in.)	32
Angle of approach.................................(deg)	53
Angle of departure................................(deg)	40
Fuel consumption, average conditions.........(miles per gal)	9
Cruising range, average conditions...................(miles)	270
Maximum allowable speed...........................(mph)	48
Number of speeds forward................................	

ENGINE

Manufacturer......Chevrolet..........Model BV-1001 up	
Type.............In-line, 4 cycle.....Number of cylinders	6
Displacement...................................(cu in.)	235.5
Governed speed...................................(rpm)	3,100
Brake horsepower.....................................	83
Ignition type....................................Battery	

ADDITIONAL DATA

....

....

....

....

TRUCK, TELEPHONE CONSTRUCTION AND MAINTENANCE, 1½-TON, 4 x 4, K-43

Technical Manual: TM 10-1203. Parts List:

Manufacturer: Chevrolet Motor Div. (General Motors Corp.)

RA PD 66589

Classification: Limited standard

Purpose: Used by Signal Corps to provide mobile facilities for telephone maintenance and construction.

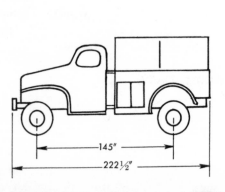

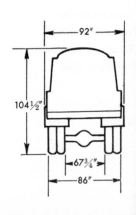

TRUCK, TELEPHONE CONSTRUCTION AND MAINTENANCE, 1½-TON, 4 x 4, K-43

GENERAL DATA

Crew.. 2
Weight...................Net......................(lb) 10,215
                    Payload...................(lb) 1,035
                    Gross....................(lb) 11,250
Shipping dimensions.......(cu ft) 3,070.........(sq ft) 140
Tires....................Ply...8.......Size...7.50 x 20
Ground clearance....................................(in.) 9⅞
Electrical system...................................(volts) 6
Capacities............Fuel, 70 octane gasoline....(gal) 35
                    Cooling system............(qt) 17
                    Crankcase.................(qt) 7½
Brakes..Hydraulic

PERFORMANCE

Maximum gradability.............................(percent) 65
Turning radius.......................................(ft) 29½
Fording depth.......................................(in.) 32
Angle of approach...................................(deg) 54
Angle of departure..................................(deg) 35
Fuel consumption, average conditions........(miles per gal) 9
Cruising range, average conditions (approx)..........(miles) 315
Maximum allowable speed.............................(mph) 48
Number of speeds forward.................................. 4

ENGINE

Manufacturer......Chevrolet...........Model BV-1001 up
Type.............In-line, 4 cycle....Number of cylinders 6
Displacement.......................................(cu in.) 235.5
Governed speed......................................(rpm) 3,100
Brake horsepower.. 83
Ignition type.....................................Battery

ADDITIONAL DATA

Winch capacity..(lb)

. . . .

. . . .

. . . .

TRUCK, TURRET TRAINER, 1½-TON, 4 x 4, E-5

Technical Order: T.O. 11-65-1   Parts List:

Manufacturers: Chevrolet Motor Div. (General Motors Corp.)
  Equipment—Herman Body Co.

RA PD 309026

Classification: Standard

Purpose: Used by Army Air Forces to provide mobile facilities for aerial
  gunnery training.

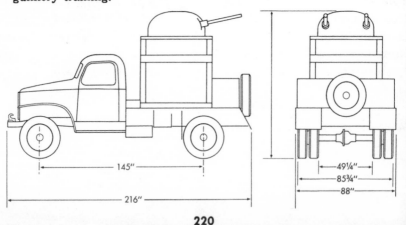

TRUCK, TURRET TRAINER, 1½-TON, 4 x 4, E-5

GENERAL DATA

Crew..			
Weight.................	Net...................	(lb)	6,775
	Payload.................	(lb)	3,000
	Gross..................	(lb)	9,775
Shipping dimensions........	(cu ft) 1,294........	(sq ft) 132	
Tires................	Ply...8.......	Size...7.50 x 20	
Tread, center to center (in.).Front	..........Rear		
Ground clearance...................................		(in.)	9⅞
Electrical system..................................		(volts)	6
Capacities..............	Fuel, 70 octane gasoline....(gal)		30
	Cooling system............(qt)		17
	Crankcase (refill)..........(qt)		7½
Brakes.......................(Hydrovac) Hydraulic			

PERFORMANCE

Maximum gradability........................(percent)		65
Turning radius..(ft)		29½
Fording depth..(in.)		32
Angle of approach..................................(deg)		45
Angle of departure..................................(deg)		
Fuel consumption, average conditions........(miles per gal)		9
Cruising range, average conditions.................(miles)		270
Maximum allowable speed......................(mph)		48
Number of speeds forward................................		

ENGINE

Manufacturer......Chevrolet..........Model BV-1001 up		
Type.............In-line, 4 cycle.....Number of cylinders		6
Displacement....................................(cu in.)		235.5
Governed speed...................................(rpm)		3,100
Brake horsepower...		83
Ignition type....................................Battery		

ADDITIONAL DATA

. . . .

. . . .

. . . .

. . . .

TRUCK, CARGO AND PERSONNEL CARRIER,
1½-TON, 6 x 6

Technical Manuals: TM 9-810, TM 9-1808A.   Parts List: SNL G-507

Manufacturer: Dodge Brothers Corp. (Div. of Chrysler Corp.)

RA PD 66585

Classification: Standard

Purpose: To transport personnel and general cargo.

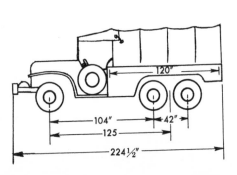

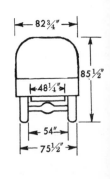

TRUCK, CARGO AND PERSONNEL CARRIER, 1½-TON, 6 x 6

GENERAL DATA

Crew, operating.....2......Passenger capacity, including crew

Weight...............	Net.........................(lb)	6,925*
	Payload..................(lb)	3,000*
	Gross....................(lb)	9,925*

Shipping dimensions.......(cu ft) ....(sq ft)

Tires...............Ply...8.......Size...9.00 x 16

Tread, center to center.......................(in.)   64¾

Ground clearance.............................(in.)   10⅝

Pintle height (in.).........Loaded 26¾.....Unloaded 27⁵⁄₁₆

Electrical system.............................(volts)   6

Capacities..............Fuel, 70 octane gasoline....(gal)   30

                        Cooling system............(qt)   18

                        Crankcase................(qt)   5

Brakes.....................................Hydraulic

PERFORMANCE

Maximum gradability...........................(percent)   60

Turning radius................................(ft)   26½

Fording depth.................................(in.)   34

Angle of approach (deg)..with winch 37½...without winch 54

Angle of departure............................(deg)   31

Fuel consumption, average conditions........(miles per gal)   8

Cruising range, average conditions.................(miles)   240

Maximum allowable speed.........................(mph)   54

Number of speeds forward...............................   4

ENGINE

Manufacturer......Dodge...................Model T-223

Type..............In-line, 4 cycle.....Number of cylinders   6

Displacement.................................(cu in.)   230.2

Governed speed..............................(rpm)   3,200

Brake horsepower.......................................   92

Ignition type.................................Battery

ADDITIONAL DATA

Winch capacity.....................................(lb)   5,000

*Figures given are for vehicles without winch. For vehicles with winch use the following data:

    Weight (lb)......Net 7,375; Payload 3,000; Gross 10,375

TRUCK, ORDNANCE MAINTENANCE, 1½-3 TON, 4 x 4

Technical Manuals: TM 10-1231, TM 10-1401, TM 10-1136, TM 10-1215.

Parts Lists: SNL G-57, SNL G-58, SNL G-59, SNL G-72, SNL G-82, SNL G-83, SNL G-84, SNL G-91. SNL G-92.

Manufacturer: General Motors Truck and Coach Div. of Yellow Truck and Coach Mfg. Co.

Classification: Limited standard

RA PD 309096

Purpose: To provide mobile facilities for small arms repair.

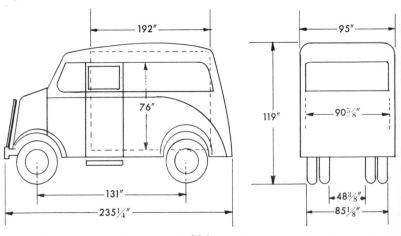

TRUCK, ORDNANCE MAINTENANCE, 1½-3 TON, 4 x 4

GENERAL DATA

Crew			2
Weight	Net	(lb)	9,710
	Payload	(lb)	3,290
	Gross	(lb)	13,000
Shipping dimensions	(cu ft)	(sq ft)	
Tires	Ply . . . 8	Size . . . 7.50 x 20	
Tread, center to center (in.)	Front 62¼	Rear 66¾	
Ground clearance		(in.)	9⅞
Electrical system		(volts)	6
Capacities	Fuel, 68 octane gasoline	(gal)	30
	Cooling system	(qt)	23
	Crankcase (refill)	(qt)	10
Brakes		Hydraulic	

PERFORMANCE

Maximum gradability		(percent)	
Turning radius (ft)	Right 27	Left 28	
Fording depth		(in.)	
Angle of approach		(deg)	45
Angle of departure		(deg)	21
Fuel consumption, average conditions		(miles per gal)	7.5
Cruising range, average conditions		(miles)	225
Maximum allowable speed		(mph)	45
Number of speeds forward			

ENGINE

Manufacturer	GMC	Model 278	
Type	In-line, 4 cycle	Number of cylinders	
Displacement		(cu in.)	248.5
Governed speed		(rpm)	2,870
Brake horsepower			
Ignition type		Battery	

ADDITIONAL DATA

Data given is for Truck, small arms repair, M1. The same basic vehicle with different equipment is used as: Truck, artillery repair, M1 and M2; Truck, automotive repair, M1 and M2; Truck, instrument repair, M1; Truck, light machine shop, M3; Truck, machine shop, M4; Truck, small arms repair, M1; Truck, spare parts, M1 and M2; Truck, tank maintenance, M1; Truck, tool and bench, M2.

TRUCK, CARGO, 2½-TON, 4 x 2

Technical Manuals: General Motors,   Parts Lists: SNL G-541 (IHC)
TM 10-1261 (C1).   SNL G-623 (GMC)
International Harvester, TM 10-1115,   SNL G-624 (Mack)
TM 10-1141, TM 10-1345.

Manufacturers: General Motors Truck & Coach Div. of Yellow Truck & Coach Mfg. Co.; International Harvester Co.; Mack Mfg. Co.

RA PD 308948

Vehicle illustrated above: GMC

Classification: Standard

Purpose: To transport general cargo.

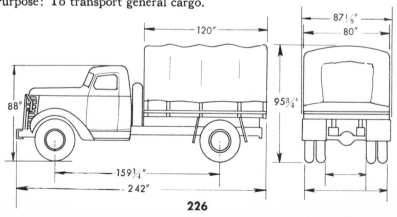

TRUCK, CARGO, 2½-TON, 4 x 2

GENERAL DATA

Crew...			2
Weight...............Net.........................(lb)			7,318
Payload...................(lb)			5,000
Gross.....................(lb)			12,318
Tires.....................Ply...10.....Size...8.25 x 20			
Tread, center to center.............................(in.)			67¾
Ground clearance....................................(in.)			
Electrical system..................................(volts)			6
Capacities...............Fuel, octane gasoline....(gal)			30
Cooling system............(qt)			23
Crankcase (refill)..........(qt)			10
Brakes......................................Hydraulic			

PERFORMANCE

Maximum gradability..............................(percent)	
Turning radius......................................(ft)	27
Fording depth.......................................(in.)	
Angle of approach..................................(deg)	36
Angle of departure.................................(deg)	25
Fuel consumption, average conditions.........(miles per gal)	9
Cruising range, average conditions..................(miles)	270
Maximum allowable speed..........................(mph)	
Number of speeds forward................................	

ENGINE

Manufacturer......GMC.....................Model 270	
Type.............In-line, 4 cycle.....Number of cylinders	6
Displacement.......................................(cu in.)	269.5
Governed speed......................................(rpm)	
Brake horsepower..	104
Ignition type....................................Battery	

ADDITIONAL DATA

....

....

....

....

TRUCK, COMBINATION STAKE AND PLATFORM, 2½-TON, 4 x 2

Technical Manuals:
   IHC, TM 10-1141, TM 10-1115,
          TM 10-1173 (C1).
       Mack, TM 10-1273.
   GMC, TM 10-1261 (C1),
          TM 10-1515.

Parts Lists: SNL G-623 (GMC)
SNL G-541 (IHC)
SNL G-624 (Mack)

Manufacturers: General Motors Truck and Coach Div. of Yellow Truck & Coach Mfg. Co.; International Harvester Co.; Mack Mfg. Corp.

RA PD 308971

Vehicle illustrated above: International Model K-7

Classification: Standard

Purpose: To transport general cargo.

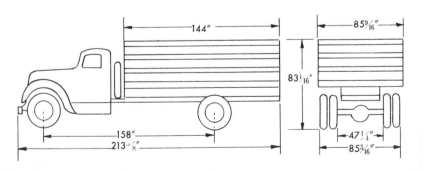

TRUCK, COMBINATION STAKE AND PLATFORM, 2½-TON, 4 x 2

GENERAL DATA

Crew, operating.......... .....Passenger capacity, including crew		
Weight................... Net....................(lb)		8,521
Payload..................(lb)		5,000
Gross....................(lb)		13,521
Shipping dimensions.......(cu ft) ....(sq ft)		
Tires.....................Ply...10......Size...8.25 x 20		
Tread, center to center............................(in.)		65⁷⁄₁₆
Ground clearance.................................(in.)		10¹⁄₁₆
Electrical system................................(volts)		6
Capacities...............Fuel, 70 octane gasoline....(gal)		21
Cooling system............(qt)		18½
Crankcase (refill)..........(qt)		6½
Brakes...Hydraulic		

Crew, operating.....   .....Passenger capacity, including crew
Weight...................Net....................(lb)   8,521
                         Payload..................(lb)   5,000
                         Gross....................(lb)   13,521
Shipping dimensions.......(cu ft)   ....(sq ft)
Tires.....................Ply...10......Size...8.25 x 20
Tread, center to center............................(in.) $65\frac{7}{16}$
Ground clearance.................................(in.) $10\frac{1}{16}$
Electrical system................................(volts)   6
Capacities...............Fuel, 70 octane gasoline....(gal)   21
                         Cooling system............(qt) $18\frac{1}{2}$
                         Crankcase (refill)..........(qt) $6\frac{1}{2}$
Brakes...Hydraulic

PERFORMANCE

Maximum gradability............................(percent)   43
Turning radius.......................................(ft) $27\frac{1}{2}$
Fording depth.......................................(in.) $26\frac{3}{16}$
Angle of approach...............................(deg)   31
Angle of departure..............................(deg)
Fuel consumption, average conditions.........(miles per gal)   9
Cruising range, average conditions.................(miles)   180
Maximum allowable speed.......................(mph)   54
Number of speeds forward.................................   5

ENGINE

Manufacturer......IHC.................Model FAC-269
Type.............In-line, 4 cycle.....Number of cylinders   6
Displacement.....................................(in.)   269
Governed speed....................................(rpm)   3,000
Brake horsepower...   88
Ignition type.....................................Battery

ADDITIONAL DATA

....

....

....

....

TRUCK, DUMP, 2½-TON, 4 x 2

Technical Manuals: TM 10-1115, TM 10-1141, Parts List: SNL G-541
TM 10-1345, TM 10-1511, TM 10-1685.

Manufacturer: International Harvester Co.

RA PD 308949

Classification: Standard

Purpose: To transport and dump earth, sand, gravel, etc., and to transport general cargo.

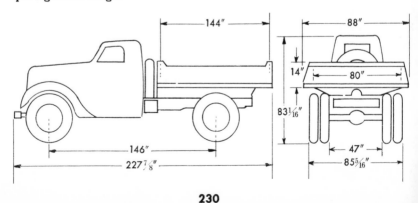

TRUCK, DUMP, 2½-TON, 4 x 2

GENERAL DATA

Crew, operating.....2.....Passenger capacity, including crew	4
Weight..................Net.....................(lb)	11,000
Payload..................(lb)	5,000
Gross....................(lb)	16,000
Shipping dimensions.......(cu ft) ....(sq ft)	
Tires.....................Ply...10.....Size...8.25 x 20	
Tread, center to center (in.).Front 65½..........Rear 66⅛	
Ground clearance.................................(in.)	10¹⁄₁₆
Pintle height............Loaded 27⅝.....Unloaded 31⅝	
Electrical system.................................(volts)	6
Capacities................Fuel, 70 octane gasoline....(gal)	31
Cooling system............(qt)	23
Crankcase (refill)..........(qt)	5½
Brakes...........................(Wagner) Hydraulic	

PERFORMANCE

Maximum gradability............................(percent)	43
Turning radius................................(ft)	27½
Fording depth................................(in.)	26
Angle of approach.................................(deg)	31
Angle of departure................................(deg)	18
Fuel consumption, average conditions........(miles per gal)	9
Cruising range, average conditions..................(miles)	279
Maximum allowable speed.....................(mph)	54
Number of speeds forward..............................	5

ENGINE

Manufacturer......IHC.................Model FAC-269	
Type.............In-line, 4 cycle.....Number of cylinders	6
Displacement.....................................(cu in.)	269.1
Governed speed.................................(rpm)	3,000
Brake horsepower.......................................	88
Ignition type ....Battery	

ADDITIONAL DATA

. . . .

. . . .

. . . .

. . . .

TRUCK, OIL SERVICING, 660-GAL, L-1, 2½-TON, 4 x 4

Technical Order: T.O. 19-25-23   Parts List:

Manufacturers: Vehicle—The Autocar Co.; Equipment—The Heil Co.

RA PD 309030

Classification: Limited standard

Purpose: Used by Army Air Forces to provide mobile oil servicing facilities for airfields.

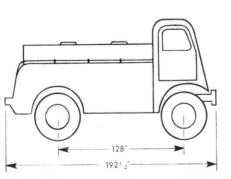

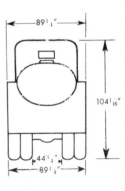

232

TRUCK, OIL SERVICING, 660-GAL, L-1, 2½-TON, 4 x 4

GENERAL DATA

Crew. . . . . :. . .   2
Weight. . . . . .Net. . . . .(lb)   8,770
                                  Payload. . . . .(lb)   5,000
                                  Gross. . . . .(lb)   13,770
Shipping dimensions. . . . . . .(cu ft) 1,929. . . . .(sq ft) 220
Tires. .Ply. . . 10. . . . . Size. . . 9.00 x 20
Tread, center to center (in.).Front   . . . . .Rear
Ground clearance. . . . .(in.)   11⅝
Electrical system. . . . .(volts)   6
Capacities. . . . . .Fuel, 70 octane gasoline. . . .(gal)   40
                                  Cooling system. . . . .(qt)   23
                                  Crankcase (refill). . . . .(qt)   10
Brakes. . . . . .Air

PERFORMANCE

Maximum gradability. . . . .(percent)   29
Turning radius. . . . .(ft)   22
Angle of approach. . . . .(deg)   50
Angle of departure. . . . .(deg)   56
Fuel consumption, average conditions. . . . .(miles per gal)   6¾
Cruising range, average conditions. . . . .(miles)   250
Maximum allowable speed. . . . .(mph)   45
Number of speeds forward. . . . .

ENGINE

Manufacturer. . . . . . .Hercules. . . . . .Model JXD
Type. . . . . .In-line, 4 cycle. . . . .Number of cylinders   6
Displacement. . . . .(cu in.)   320
Governed speed. . . . .(rpm)   2,600
Brake horsepower.   110
Ignition type. . . . . .Battery

ADDITIONAL DATA

. . . .
. . . .
. . . .
. . . .

TRUCK, CARGO, 2½-TON, 6 x 4

Technical Manual: Studebaker,   Parts Lists: SNL G-508 (GMC)
TM 10-1565.   SNL G-630 (Stude.)

Manufacturers: General Motors Truck & Coach Div. of Yellow Truck
& Coach Mfg. Co.; International Harvester Co.; The Studebaker Corp.

RA PD 308972

Vehicle illustrated above: Studebaker

Classification: Substitute standard

Purpose: To transport general cargo.

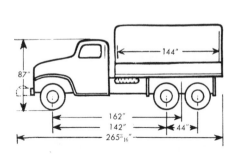
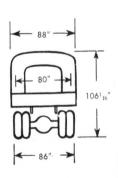

TRUCK, CARGO, 2½-TON, 6 x 4

GENERAL DATA

Crew 2
Weight . . . . Net . . . . (lb) 9,635*
Payload . . . . (lb) 10,000*
Gross . . . . (lb) 19,635*
Shipping dimensions . . . . (cu ft) w/o winch 88 . . . (sq ft) 154
w/winch 93 162
Tires . . . . Ply . . 8 . . . . Size . . . 7.50 x 20
Tread, center to center (in.) . Front 66⅞ . . . . Rear 67¾
Ground clearance . . . . (in.) 10
Pintle height (in.) . . . . Loaded 30⅞ . . . . . Unloaded 32⅝
Electrical system . . . . (volts) 6
Capacities . . . . Fuel, 70 octane gasoline . . . . (gal) 40
Cooling system . . . . (qt) 21
Crankcase (refill) . . . . (qt) 6½
Brakes . . . . (Lockheed) Hydraulic with booster

PERFORMANCE

Maximum gradability . . . . (percent) 30
Turning radius (ft) . . . . Right 34½ . . . . Left 35
Angle of approach (deg) . . . . . with winch 30 . . without winch 40
Angle of departure . . . . (deg) 44
Fuel consumption, average conditions . . . . (miles per gal) 5.9
Cruising range, average conditions . . . . (miles) 230
Maximum allowable speed . . . . (mph) 45
Number of speeds forward 5

ENGINE

Manufacturer . . . . . . Hercules . . . . Model JXD
Type . . . . In-line, 4 cycle . . . . . Number of cylinders 6
Displacement . . . . : . (cu in.) 320
Governed speed . . . . (rpm) 2,620
Brake horsepower 87
Ignition type . . . . Battery

ADDITIONAL DATA

Winch capacity . . . . (lb) 10,000

*Figures given are for vehicles without winch. For vehicles with winch
use the following data:

Weight (lb)   Net 10,245 . . . . Payload 10,000 . . . . . Gross 20,245

TRUCK, SEARCHLIGHT, C.O.E., 2½-TON, 6 x 4

Technical Manual: Parts List: SNL G-628

Manufacturer: General Motors Truck and Coach Div. of Yellow Truck and Coach Mfg. Co.

RA PD 66621

Classification: Limited standard

Purpose: To transport searchlight equipment.

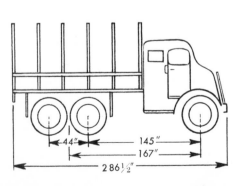
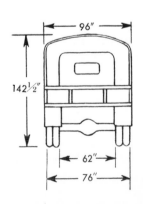

TRUCK, SEARCHLIGHT, C.O.E., 2½-TON, 6 x 4

GENERAL DATA

Crew 2
Weight . . . . .Net . . . .(lb) 10,820
Payload . . . .(lb) 5,000
Gross . . . .(lb) 15,820
Shipping dimensions,
  with top up . . . .(cu ft) 2,304 . . . .(sq ft) 192
Tires . . . . .Ply . . .8 . . . . . . .Size . . .7.00 x 20
Ground clearance . . . .(in.) 9
Electrical system . . . .(volts) 6
Capacities . . . . .Fuel, 70 octane gasoline . . . .(gal) 40
Cooling system . . . .(qt) 24
Crankcase . . . .(qt) 10
Brakes . . . .(Hydrovac) Hydraulic

PERFORMANCE

Maximum gradability . . . .(percent) 45
Turning radius (ft) . . . . .Right 34¾ . . . . .Left 31½
Fording depth . . . .(in.)
Angle of approach . . . .(deg) 40
Angle of departure . . . .(deg) 22
Fuel consumption, average conditions
                      with towed load . . . . . (miles per gal) 9
Cruising range, average conditions
                      with towed load . . . .(miles) 360
Maximum allowable speed . . . .(mph) 45
Number of speeds forward . . . .

ENGINE

Manufacturer . . . . . .GMC . . . . .Model 256
Type . . . . .In-line, 4 cycle . . . . .Number of cylinders
Displacement . . . .(cu in.) 256.8
Governed speed . . . .(rpm) 2,700
Brake horsepower . . . .
Ignition type . . . . .Battery

ADDITIONAL DATA

. . . .
. . . .
. . . .
. . . .

TRUCK, AIR COMPRESSOR, 2½-TON, 6 x 6

Technical Manuals: Parts List: SNL G-508

Manufacturers: Chassis and Cab, General Motors Truck and Coach
    Div. of Yellow Truck and Coach Mfg. Co.; Air Compressor, Le Roi
    Model D 318.

RA PD 308990

Classification: Standard

Purpose: To provide mobile air compression equipment (Corps of
    Engineers).

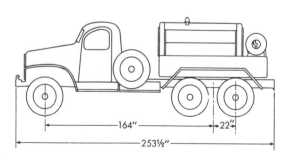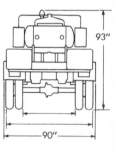

238

TRUCK, AIR COMPRESSOR, 2½-TON, 6 x 6

GENERAL DATA

Crew...		2
Weight............... Gross.................... (lb)		14,300
Shipping dimensions........ (cu ft) 1,304......... (sq ft) 163		
Tires.................... Ply...8....... Size...7.50 x 20		
Ground clearance.................................... (in.)		10
Electrical system.................................. (volts)		6
Capacities.............. Fuel, 70 octane gasoline....(gal)		40
Cooling system............ (qt)		19
Crankcase (refill)..........(qt)		11
Brakes........................... (Hydrovac) Hydraulic		

PERFORMANCE

Maximum gradability............................ (percent)	65
Turning radius (ft)........ Right 34.............Left 35	
Fording depth.. (in.)	
Angle of approach.................................... (deg)	54
Angle of departure................................... (deg)	36
Fuel consumption, average conditions........ (miles per gal)	7.5
Cruising range, average conditions................. (miles)	240
Maximum allowable speed..........................(mph)	45
Number of speeds forward................................	

ENGINE

Manufacturer...... GMC.................... Model 270	
Type............. In-line, 4 cycle..... Number of cylinders	6
Displacement.. (cu in.)	269.5
Governed speed.................................... (rpm)	2,750
Brake horsepower......................................	104
Ignition type.................................... Battery	

ADDITIONAL DATA

Motorized air compressor, Le Roi model 105 GA; powered by Le Roi model D318 (318 cu in.) engine equipped with 50 gallon gasoline tank. These vehicles built with open cab after July, 1943.

APPARATUS, DECONTAMINATING, POWER-DRIVEN, M3A1 (CHASSIS: TRUCK, 2½-TON, 6 x 6)

Technical Manuals: Parts List: SNL G-508

Manufacturer: General Motors Truck and Coach Div. of Yellow Truck and Coach Mfg. Co.

RA PD 308979

Classification: Limited standard

Purpose: Used by Chemical Warfare Service to transport decontamination material and spraying equipment.

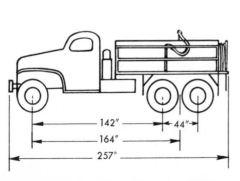
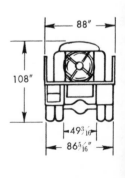

APPARATUS, DECONTAMINATING, POWER DRIVEN, M3A1 (CHASSIS: TRUCK, 2½-TON, 6 x 6)

GENERAL DATA

Crew...			4
Weight...................	Net...................	(lb)	9,910
	Payload.................	(lb)	5,000
	Gross..................	(lb)	14,910
Shipping dimensions........	(cu ft) 1,414........	(sq ft) 157	
Tires...................	Ply...8.......	Size...7.50 x 20	
Ground clearance.................................		(in.)	10
Electrical system................................		(volts)	6
Capacities..............	Fuel, 70 octane gasoline....(gal)		40
	Cooling system............	(qt)	19
	Crankcase (refill)..........	(qt)	11
Brakes..............................	Hydraulic		

PERFORMANCE

Maximum gradability.............................	(percent)	65
Turning radius (ft)........Right 34.............	Left 35	
Fording depth......................................	(in)	
Angle of approach.................................	(deg)	54
Angle of departure................................	(deg)	37
Fuel consumption, average conditions........	(miles per gal)	7.5
Cruising range, average conditions..............	(miles)	240
Maximum allowable speed.......................	(mph)	45
Number of speeds forward..........................		5

ENGINE

Manufacturer......GMC..................	Model 270	
Type............In-line, 4 cycle.....Number of cylinders		6
Displacement.......................................	(cu in.)	269.5
Governed speed....................................	(rpm)	2,750
Brake horsepower..................................		104
Ignition, type................................	Battery	

ADDITIONAL DATA

. . . .

. . . .

. . . .

. . . .

TRUCK, CARGO, L.W.B., 2½-TON, 6 x 6

Technical Manuals:

GMC, TM 9-801.
IHC, TM 10-1505.
Studebaker, TM 10-1385 (C1),
TM 10-1503, TM 10-1565,
TM 10-1387.

Parts Lists: SNL G-508 (GMC)
SNL G-651 (IHC)
SNL G-630 (Stud.)

Manufacturers: General Motors Truck and Coach Division of Yellow Truck and Coach Mfg. Co.; International Harvester Co.; The Studebaker Corp.

RA PD 308983

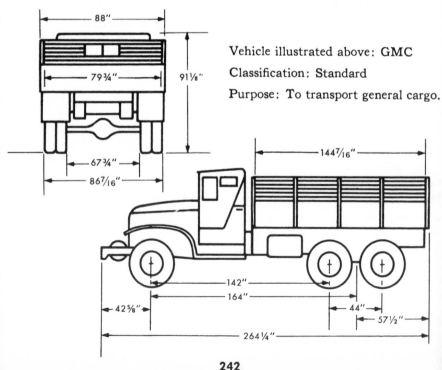

Vehicle illustrated above: GMC

Classification: Standard

Purpose: To transport general cargo.

TRUCK, CARGO, L.W.B., 2½-TON, 6 x 6

GENERAL DATA

Crew, operating. 2
Weight. . . . . .Net. . . . .(lb) 10,050*
. . . . Payload. . . . .(lb) 5,000*
. . . . Gross. . . . .(lb) 15,050*
Shipping dimensions. . . . . . .(cu ft) 1,429. . . . .(sq ft) 156   *
Tires. . . . . .Ply. . .8. . . . . . .Size. . .7.50 x 20
Tread, center to center (in.).Front 62¼. . . . . .Rear 67¾
Ground clearance. . . . .(in.)   10
Pintle height (in.). . . . . .Loaded 30½. . . . . . .Unloaded 32
Electrical system. . . . .(volts)   6
Capacities. . . . . .Fuel, 70 octane gasoline. . . .(gal)   40
. . . . Cooling system. . . . .(qt)   19
. . . . Crankcase (refill). . . . .(qt)   10
Brakes. . . . . .Hydraulic

PERFORMANCE

Maximum gradability. . . . .(percent)   65
Turning radius (ft). . . . . . . .Right 34. . . . . .Left 35
Fording depth. . . . .(in.)
Angle of approach (deg). .with winch 31. . . .without winch 54
Angle of departure. . . . .(deg)   36
Fuel consumption, average conditions. . . . .(miles per gal)   7.5
Cruising range, average conditions. . . . .(miles)   300
Maximum allowable speed. . . . .(mph)   45
Number of speeds forward.   5

ENGINE

Manufacturer. . . . . . .GMC. . . . . .Model 270
Type. . . . . .In-line, 4 cycle. . . . .Number of cylinders   6
Displacement. . . . .(cu in.)   269.5
Governed speed. . . . .(rpm)   2,750
Brake horsepower.   104
Ignition type. . . . . .Battery

ADDITIONAL DATA

Winch capacity. . . . .(lb)   10,000

*Figures given are for vehicles without winch. For vehicles with winch
use the following data:

Weight (lb). . . . .Net 11,000. . . . .Payload 5,000. . . . .Gross 16,000
cu ft 1,511   sq ft 165.

TRUCK, CARGO, L.W.B., 2½-TON, 6 x 6, W/WRECKER SET NO. 7 AND WINCH

Technical Manual: TM 9-801. Parts List: SNL G-508

Manufacturer: General Motors Truck and Coach Div. of Yellow Truck and Coach Mfg. Co.

RA PD 66637

Classification: Standard

Purpose: To provide mobile facilities for maintenance and repair.

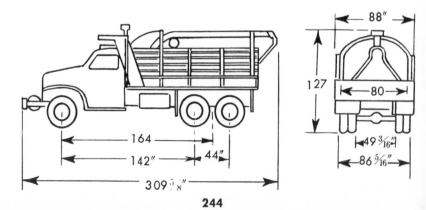

TRUCK, CARGO, L.W.B., 2½-TON, 6 x 6, W/WRECKER SET NO. 7 AND WINCH

GENERAL DATA

Crew..

Weight	Net	(lb)	11,165
	Payload	(lb)	5,000
	Gross	(lb)	16,165

Shipping dimensions........(cu ft) 2,003.........(sq ft) 189
Tires....................Ply...8.......Size...7.50 x 20
Ground clearance......................................(in.) 10
Electrical system.....................................(volts) 6

Capacities	Fuel, 70 octane gasoline....(gal)	40
	Cooling system............(qt)	19
	Crankcase................(qt)	11
	Transmission.............(qt)	14

Brakes.................................Hydraulic

PERFORMANCE

Maximum gradability............................(percent) 65
Turning radius (ft)........Right 34.............Left 35
Fording depth...(in.)
Angle of approach..................................(deg) 31
Angle of departure.................................(deg) 36
Fuel consumption, average conditions........(miles per gal) 7.5
Cruising range, average conditions.................(miles) 240
Maximum allowable speed..........................(mph) 45
Number of speeds forward...............................

ENGINE

Manufacturer......GMC......................Model 270
Type.............In-line, 4 cycle.....Number of cylinders 6
Displacement.......................................(cu in.) 269.5
Governed speed...................................(rpm) 2,750
Brake horsepower..................................... 104
Ignition type.....................................Battery

ADDITIONAL DATA

Winch capacity......................................(lb) 10,000

....
....
....
....

TRUCK, CARGO, S.W.B., 2½-TON, 6 x 6

Technical Manuals:
GMC, TM 9-801.
IHC, TM 10-1505.
Studebaker, TM 10-1385 (C1),
TM 10-1503, TM 10-1565,
TM 10-1387.

Parts Lists: SNL G-508 (GMC)
SNL G-630 (Stud.)
SNL G-651 (IHC)

Manufacturers: General Motors Truck and Coach Div. of Yellow Truck and Coach Mfg. Co.; International Harvester Co.; The Studebaker Corp.

RA PD 308985

Vehicle illustrated above: GMC

Classification: Standard

Purpose: To transport general cargo.

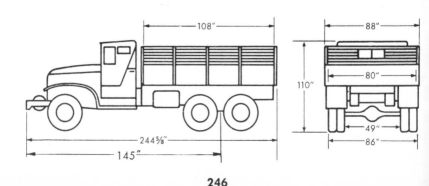

TRUCK, CARGO, S.W.B., 2½-TON, 6 x 6

GENERAL DATA

Crew.. 2
Weight...................Net....................(lb) 10,100*
                 Payload..................(lb) 5,000*
                 Gross....................(lb) 15,100*
Shipping dimensions.......(cu ft) 1,301.........(sq ft) 142   *
Tires....................Ply...8........Size...7.50 x 20
Pintle height (in.)........Loaded 30½......Unloaded 32
Ground clearance.....................................(in.) 9⅞
Tread, center to center (in.) Front 60............Rear 67½
Electrical system.................................(volts) 6
Capacities...............Fuel, 70 octane gasoline....(gal) 40
                 Cooling system............(qt) 19
                 Crankcase (refill)..........(qt) 10
Brakes.....................................Hydraulic

PERFORMANCE

Maximum gradability.............................(percent) 65
Turning radius (ft)........Right 34.............Left 35
Fording depth......................................(in.)
Angle of approach (deg)....with winch 31..without winch 36
Angle of departure................................(deg) 44
Fuel consumption, average conditions........(miles per gal) 7.5
Cruising range, average conditions.................(miles) 300
Maximum allowable speed........................(mph) 45
Number of speeds forward............................. 5

ENGINE

Manufacturer......GMC....................Model 270
Type.............In-line, 4 cycle.....Number of cylinders 6
Displacement.......................................(cu in.) 269.5
Governed speed.....................................(rpm) 2,750
Brake horsepower..................................... 104
Ignition.......................................Battery

ADDITIONAL DATA

Winch capacity....................................(lb) 10,000

*Figures given are for vehicle without winch. For vehicle with winch use
  the following data:

    Weight (lb).....Net 11,000....Payload 5,000.....Gross 16,000
    cu ft 1,365   sq ft 149.

TRUCK, CARGO, C.O.E., 15 FT BODY, 2½-TON, 6 x 6

Technical Manual: TM 9-809.

Parts List: SNL G-508

Manufacturer: General Motors Truck and Coach Div. of Yellow Truck
and Coach Mfg. Co.

RA PD 308951

Classification: Standard

Purpose: To transport general cargo and personnel. This vehicle has a
special 15-foot body and troop seats.

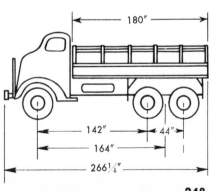

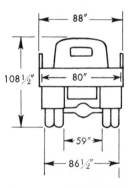

TRUCK, CARGO, C.O.E., 15 FT BODY, 2½-TON, 6 x 6

GENERAL DATA

Crew			2
Weight	Net	(lb)	10,810
	Payload	(lb)	3,600
	Gross	(lb)	14,410
Shipping dimensions	(cu ft) 1,474	(sq ft) 163	
Tires	Ply...8	Size...7.50 x 20	
Tread, center to center (in.)	Front 62¼	Rear 67¾	
Ground clearance		(in.)	9⅞
Electrical system		(volts)	6
Capacities	Fuel, 68 octane gasoline	(gal)	40
	Cooling system	(qt)	19
	Crankcase (refill)	(qt)	11
Brakes		Hydraulic	

PERFORMANCE

Maximum gradability	(percent)	65
Turning radius (ft)	Right 34½	Left 34
Fording depth	(in.)	
Angle of approach	(deg)	45
Angle of departure	(deg)	32½
Fuel consumption, average conditions	(miles per gal)	7.5
Cruising range, average conditions	(miles)	300
Maximum allowable speed	(mph)	45
Number of speeds forward		5

ENGINE

Manufacturer	GMC	Model 270	
Type	In-line, 4 cycle	Number of cylinders	6
Displacement		(cu in.)	269.5
Governed speed		(rpm)	2,750
Brake horsepower			104
Ignition		Battery	

ADDITIONAL DATA

About 25 percent of these vehicles are being equipped with truck mount
M36 for antiaircraft machine gun.

TRUCK, CHEMICAL SERVICE, 2½-TON, 6 x 6, M1

Technical Manuals: Parts List:

Manufacturer: General Motors Truck and Coach Div. of Yellow Truck
and Coach Mfg. Co.

RA PD 308980

Classification: Standard

Purpose: Used by Chemical Warfare Service to transport chemical
handling tools and equipment.

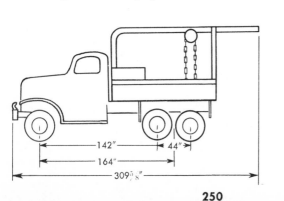

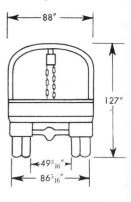

TRUCK, CHEMICAL SERVICE, 2½-TON, 6 x 6, M1

GENERAL DATA

Crew			2
Weight	Net	(lb)	11,100
	Payload	(lb)	5,000
	Gross	(lb)	16,100
Shipping dimensions	(cu ft) 2,011	(sq ft) 190	
Tires	Ply...8	Size...7.50 x 20	
Ground clearance		(in.)	10
Electrical system		(volts)	6
Capacities	Fuel, 70 octane gasoline	(gal)	40
	Cooling system	(qt)	19
	Crankcase (refill)	(qt)	11
Brakes	(Hydrovac) Hydraulic		

PERFORMANCE

Maximum gradability	(percent)	65
Turning radius (ft)	Right 34	Left 35
Fording depth	(in.)	
Angle of approach	(deg)	54
Angle of departure	(deg)	36
Fuel consumption, average conditions	(miles per gal)	7.5
Cruising range, average conditions	(miles)	240
Maximum allowable speed	(mph)	45
Number of speeds forward		5

ENGINE

Manufacturer	GMC	Model 270
Type	In-line, 4 cycle	Number of cylinders	6
Displacement	(cu in.)	269.5
Governed speed	(rpm)	2,750
Brake horsepower		104
Ignition type	Battery	

ADDITIONAL DATA

These vehicles equipped with open cabs after 1 July 1943.

TRUCK, DUMP, L.W.B., 2½-TON, 6 x 6

Technical Manual: TM 10-1261 (C1).   Parts List: SNL G-508

Manufacturer: General Motors Truck and Coach Div. of Yellow Truck and Coach Mfg. Co.

RA PD 309110

Classification: Standard

Purpose: To transport and dump earth, sand, gravel, coal, etc., and to carry general cargo.

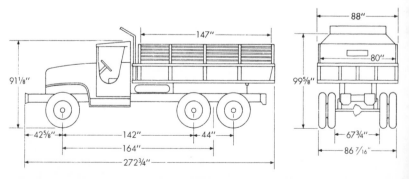

TRUCK, DUMP, L.W.B., 2½-TON, 6 x 6

GENERAL DATA

Crew			2
Weight	Net	(lb)	11,850
	Payload	(lb)	5,000
	Gross	(lb)	16,850
Shipping dimensions	(cu ft)	(sq ft)	
Tires	Ply...8	Size...7.50 x 20	
Ground clearance		(in.)	10
Electrical system		(volts)	6
Capacities	Fuel, 70 octane gasoline	(gal)	40
	Cooling system	(qt)	19
	Crankcase (refill)	(qt)	11
Brakes	(Hydrovac) Hydraulic		

PERFORMANCE

Maximum gradability		(percent)	65
Turning radius (ft)	Right 37½	Left 37	
Fording depth		(in.)	
Angle of approach		(deg)	31
Angle of departure		(deg)	36
Fuel consumption, average conditions		(miles per gal)	
Cruising range, average conditions		(miles)	
Maximum allowable speed		(mph)	45
Number of speeds forward			

ENGINE

Manufacturer	GMC	Model 270	
Type	In-line, 4 cycle	Number of cylinders	6
Displacement		(cu in.)	269.5
Governed speed		(rpm)	2,750
Brake horsepower			104
Ignition type		Battery	

ADDITIONAL DATA

TRUCK, FUEL OR OIL SERVICING, 750 GAL., 2½-TON, 6 x 6, F-3

Technical Orders: T.O. 19-25-47.   Parts List:

Manufacturers: General Motors Truck and Coach Div. of Yellow Truck
and Coach Mfg. Co.; Equipment—The Heil Co.

RA PD 309031

Classification: Standard

Purpose: Used by Army Air Forces for servicing aircraft with oil or
gasoline.

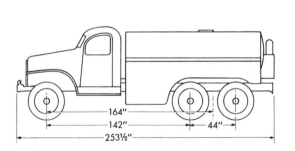
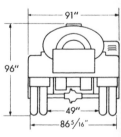

TRUCK, FUEL OR OIL SERVICING, 750 GAL., 2½-TON, 6 x 6, F-3

GENERAL DATA

Crew				2
Weight	Net		(lb)	11,610
	Payload		(lb)	4,500
	Gross		(lb)	16,110
Shipping dimensions	(cu ft) 1,163	(sq ft) 160		
Tires	Ply..8	Size...7.50 x 20		
Tread, center to center (in.)	Front	Rear		
Ground clearance			(in.)	10
Electrical system			(volts)	6
Capacities	Fuel, 70 octane gasoline		(gal)	40
	Cooling system		(qt)	18
	Crankcase (refill)		(qt)	10
Brakes	(Hydrovac) Hydraulic			

PERFORMANCE

Maximum gradability	(percent)	65
Turning radius (ft)........Right 34	Left 35	
Angle of approach	(deg)	
Angle of departure	(deg)	
Fuel consumption, average conditions	(miles per gal)	7.5
Cruising range, average conditions	(miles)	240
Maximum allowable speed	(mph)	45
Number of speeds forward		5

ENGINE

Manufacturer......GMC		Model 270	
Type............In-line, 4 cycle	Number of cylinders		6
Displacement		(cu in.)	269.5
Governed speed		(rpm)	2,750
Brake horsepower			104
Ignition type		Battery	

ADDITIONAL DATA

....
....
....
....
....

TRUCK, MAP REPRODUCTION EQUIPMENT, 2½-TON, 6 x 6

Technical Manuals: Parts List:

Manufacturer: Chassis—General Motors Truck and Coach Div. of Yellow Truck and Coach Mfg. Co.; Bodies—Peter Wendel and Sons, Inc., and McCabe Powers Autobody Co.

RA PD 308994

Classification: Standard

Purpose: Used by Corps of Engineers to transport equipment for map reproduction units.

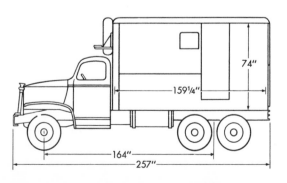
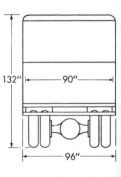

TRUCK, MAP REPRODUCTION EQUIPMENT, 2½-TON, 6 x 6

GENERAL DATA

Crew. . . . .
Weight. . . . . .Gross . . . . (lb) 14,200 to 16,500
Shipping dimensions. . . . . . .(cu ft) 1,892. . . . .(sq ft) 172
Tires. . . . . .Ply . . . . .Size. . . .
Ground clearance. . . . .(in.)   11
Electrical system. . . . .(volts)   6
Capacities. . . . . .Fuel, 68 octane gasoline. . . .(gal)   40
                           Cooling system. . . . .(qt)   19
                           Crankcase (refill). . . . .(qt)   11
Brakes. . . . .

PERFORMANCE

Maximum gradability. . . . .(percent)   65
Turning radius (ft). . . . . . . .Right 34½. . . . . .Left 34
Fording depth. . . . .(in.)   24
Angle of approach. . . . .(deg)   45
Angle of departure. . . . .(deg)   33½
Fuel consumption, average conditions. . . . .(miles per gal)   7.5
Cruising range, average conditions. . . . .(miles)   300
Maximum allowable speed. . . . .(mph)
Number of speeds forward. . . . .

ENGINE

Manufacturer. . . . . . .GMC. . . . . .Model 270
Type. . . . . .In-line, 4 cycle. . . . .Number of cylinders   6
Displacement. . . . .(cu in.)   269.5
Governed speed. . . . .(rpm)   2,750
Brake horsepower.   104
Ignition type. . . . .

ADDITIONAL DATA

The same basic vehicle with different equipment is used as: Laboratory section, Map layout section, Photographic section, Plate grainer section, Plate process section, Camera section, and Press section. Weight varies with equipment.

TRUCK, OIL SERVICING, 660 GAL., 2½-TON, 6 x 6, L-2

Technical Order: T.O. 19-25-34.   Parts List:

Manufacturers: General Motors Truck and Coach Div. of Yellow Truck and Coach Mfg. Co.; Equipment—The Heil Co.

RA PD 309031

Classification: Standard

Purpose: To transport and dispense lubricating oil for Army Air Forces.

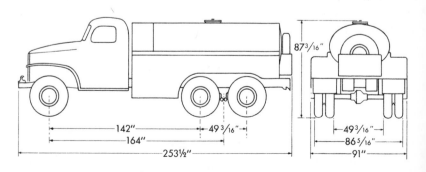

TRUCK, OIL SERVICING, 660 GAL., 2½-TON, 6 x 6, L-2

GENERAL DATA

Crew..		2
Weight..................Net............................(lb)		10,400
	Payload..................(lb)	5,000
	Gross....................(lb)	15,400
Shipping dimensions.......(cu ft) 1,160.........(sq ft) 160		
Tires....................Ply...8.......Size...7.50 x 20		
Tread, center to center (in.).Front ....Rear		
Ground clearance....................................(in.)		10
Electrical system..................................(volts)		6
Capacities..............Fuel, 70 octane gasoline....(gal)		40
	Cooling system............(qt)	18
	Crankcase (refill)..........(qt)	10
Brakes........................(Hydrovac) Hydraulic		

PERFORMANCE

Maximum gradability...........................(percent)	65
Turning radius (ft).........Right 34..............Left 35	
Angle of approach.................................(deg)	54
Angle of departure................................(deg)	36
Fuel consumption, average conditions........(miles per gal)	7.5
Cruising range, average conditions.................(miles)	240
Maximum allowable speed..........................(mph)	45
Number of speeds forward................................	

ENGINE

Manufacturer......GMC.....................Model 270	
Type.............In-line, 4 cycle.....Number of cylinders	6
Displacement.....................................(cu in.)	269.5
Governed speed...................................(rpm)	2,750
Brake horsepower.......................................	104
Ignition type....................................Battery	

ADDITIONAL DATA

....

....

....

....

TRUCK, ORDNANCE MAINTENANCE, 2½-TON, 6 x 6

Technical Manual: TM 9-801. Parts Lists: SNL G-138, SNL G-139,
SNL G-140, SNL G-141, SNL G-142,
SNL G-143, SNL G-144, SNL G-146,
SNL G-149.

Manufacturer: General Motors Truck and Coach Div. of Yellow Truck
and Coach Mfg. Co.

RA PD 309103

Classification: Standard

Purpose:

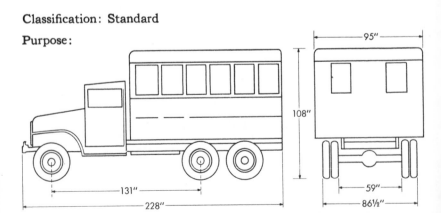

TRUCK, ORDNANCE MAINTENANCE, 2½-TON, 6 x 6

GENERAL DATA

Crew			2
Weight	Net	(lb)	11,930
	Payload	(lb)	1,335
	Gross	(lb)	13,265
Shipping dimensions	(cu ft)	(sq ft)	
Tires	Ply...8	Size...7:50 x 20	
Tread, center to center (in.)	Front 62¼	Rear 67¾	
Ground clearance		(in.)	10
Electrical system		(volts)	6
Capacities	Fuel, 70 octane gasoline	(gal)	40
	Cooling system	(qt)	19
	Crankcase (refill)	(qt)	10
Brakes		Hydraulic	

PERFORMANCE

Maximum gradability	(percent)	65
Turning radius (ft)	Right	Left
Fording depth	(in.)	
Angle of approach	(deg)	56
Angle of departure	(deg)	40
Fuel consumption, average conditions	(miles per gal)	7.5
Cruising range, average conditions	(miles)	240
Maximum allowable speed	(mph)	45
Number of speeds forward		

ENGINE

Manufacturer	GMC	Model 270	
Type	In-line, 4 cycle	Number of cylinders	6
Displacement		(cu in.)	269.5
Governed speed		(rpm)	2,750
Brake horsepower			104
Ignition type		Battery	

ADDITIONAL DATA

Data given is for the Artillery repair truck, M9. The same basic vehicle with different equipment is used as: Truck, artillery repair, M9 and M9A1; Truck, automotive repair, M8 and M8A1; Truck, electrical repair, M18 and M18A1; Truck, instrument bench, M23; Truck, instrument repair, M10 and M10A1; Truck, machine shop, M16 and M16A1; Truck, small arms repair, M7 and M7A1; Truck, spare parts, M14; Truck, tool and bench, M13; Truck, welding, M12 and M12A1.

TRUCK, STOCK RACK, 2½-TON, 6 x 6

Technical Manual: TM 9-801.   Parts List: SNL G-508

Manufacturer: General Motors Truck and Coach Div. of Yellow Truck and Coach Mfg. Co.

Classification: Standard

RA PD 66627

Purpose: To transport bulky but light cargo.

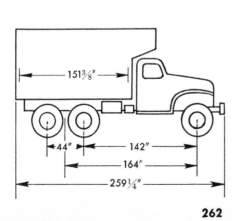

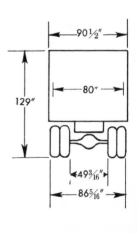

TRUCK, STOCK RACK, 2½-TON, 6 x 6

GENERAL DATA

Crew.. 2
Weight..................Net......................(lb) 13,850
               Payload..................(lb) 5,000
               Gross...................(lb) 18,850
Shipping dimensions.......(cu ft) 1,752........(sq ft) 163
Tires....................Ply...8.......Size...7.50 x 20
Ground clearance....................................(in.) 10
Electrical system..................................(volts) 6
Capacities..............Fuel, 70 octane gasoline....(gal) 40
               Cooling system............(qt) 19
               Crankcase (refill)..........(qt) 11
Brakes...........................(Hydrovac) Hydraulic

PERFORMANCE

Maximum gradability............................(percent) 65
Turning radius (ft) ....Right 37½............Left 37
Fording depth....................................(in.)
Angle of approach................................(deg) 54
Angle of departure...............................(deg) 36
Fuel consumption, average conditions........(miles per gal) 7.5
Cruising range, average conditions.................(miles) 240
Maximum allowable speed........................(mph) 45
Number of speeds forward...............................

ENGINE

Manufacturer......GMC.....................Model 270
Type.............In-line, 4 cycle.....Number of cylinders 6
Displacement....................................(cu in.) 269.5
Governed speed.................................(rpm) 2,750
Brake horsepower....................................... 104
Ignition type....................................Battery

ADDITIONAL DATA

....
....
....
....

TRUCK, TANK, GASOLINE, 750 GAL.
2½-TON, 6 x 6

Technical Manuals: Studebaker, TM 10-1387, TM 10-1565. GMC, TM 9-801.

Parts Lists: SNL G-508 (GMC) SNL G-630 (Stud.)

Manufacturers: General Motors Truck and Coach Div. of Yellow Truck and Coach Mfg. Co.; The Studebaker Corp.

RA PD 308955

Classification: Standard

Purpose: To transport and dispense gasoline.

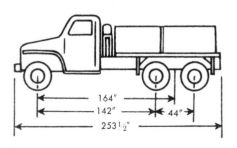

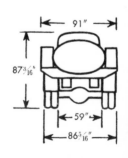

TRUCK, TANK, GASOLINE, 750 GAL.
2½-TON, 6 x 6

GENERAL DATA

Crew..			2
Weight...................Net....................(lb)			10,340
	Payload.................(lb)		4,650
	Gross....................(lb)		14,990
Shipping dimensions.......(cu ft) 1,163.........(sq ft) 160			
Tires...................Ply...8.......Size...7.50 x 20			
Tread, center to center (in.).Front 62¼..........Rear 67¾			
Ground clearance.......................................(in.)			9⅞
Electrical system...................................(volts)			6
Capacities...............Fuel, 68 octane gasoline....(gal)			40
	Cooling system............(qt)		18
	Crankcase (refill)..........(qt)		10
Brakes....................................Hydraulic			

PERFORMANCE

Maximum gradability.............................(percent)	84
Turning radius (ft).........Right 34............Left 35½	
Fording depth.......................................(in.)	
Angle of approach.................................(deg)	54
Angle of departure................................(deg)	36
Fuel consumption, average conditions.........(miles per gal)	7.5
Cruising range, average conditions..................(miles)	300
Maximum allowable speed.......................(mph)	45
Number of speeds forward................................	5

ENGINE

Manufacturer......GMC....................Model 270	
Type.............In-line, 4 cycle.....Number of cylinders	6
Displacement.......................................(cu in.)	269.5
Governed speed....................................(rpm)	2,750
Brake horsepower.......................................	104
Ignition type....................................Battery	

ADDITIONAL DATA

....
....
....
....

TRUCK, TANK, WATER, 700 GAL., 2½-TON, 6 x 6

Technical Manual: TM 9-801.   Parts List: SNL G-508

Manufacturer: General Motors Truck and Coach Div. of Yellow Truck and Coach Mfg. Co.

RA PD 308958

Classification: Standard

Purpose: To transport drinking water.

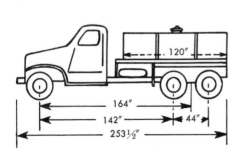

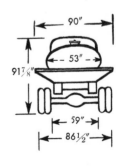

TRUCK, TANK, WATER, 700 GAL., 2½-TON, 6 x 6

GENERAL DATA

Crew..........			2
Weight...........	Net...........	(lb)	10,185
	Payload...........	(lb)	5,000
	Gross...........	(lb)	15,185
Shipping dimensions........(cu ft) 1,032.........(sq ft) 142			
Tires........... Ply...8.......Size...7.50 x 20			
Tread, center to center (in.) Front 62¼ ....Rear 67¾			
Ground clearance...........		(in.)	9⅞
Electrical system...........		(volts)	6
Capacities...........	Fuel, 68 octane gasoline....(gal)		40
	Cooling system...........	(qt)	19
	Crankcase (refill)...........	(qt)	10
Brakes...........		Hydraulic	

PERFORMANCE

Maximum gradability........... (percent)	65
Turning radius (ft)........Right 35.............Left 36	
Fording depth........... (in.)	
Angle of approach........... (deg)	54
Angle of departure........... (deg)	36
Fuel consumption, average conditions........(miles per gal)	7.5
Cruising range, average conditions........... (miles)	300
Maximum allowable speed........... (mph)	
Number of speeds forward...........	5

ENGINE

Manufacturer......GMC........... Model 270	
Type........... In-line, 4 cycle.....Number of cylinders	6
Displacement........... (cu in.)	269.5
Governed speed........... (rpm)	2,750
Brake horsepower...........	104
Ignition type........... Battery	

ADDITIONAL DATA

....

....

....

....

TRUCK, SHOP, MOTORIZED, 2½-TON, 6 x 6

Technical Manuals: Parts List: SNL G-508

Manufacturer: General Motors Truck and Coach Div. of Yellow Truck and Coach Mfg. Co.

RA PD 66623

Classification: Standard

Purpose: Used by Corps of Engineers to provide mobile facilities for maintenance and repairs.

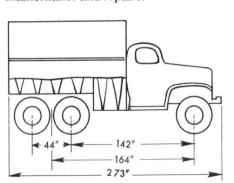

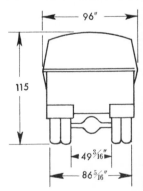

TRUCK, SHOP, MOTORIZED, 2½-TON, 6 x 6

GENERAL DATA

Crew			2
Weight	Net	(lb)	11,130
	Payload	(lb)	5,000
	Gross	(lb)	16,130
Shipping dimensions	(cu ft) 1,748	(sq ft) 182	
Tires	Ply—8	Size—7.50 x 20	
Tread, center to center (in.)	Front	Rear	
Ground clearance		(in.)	10
Electrical system		(volts)	6
Capacities	Fuel, 70 octane gasoline	(gal)	40
	Cooling system	(qt)	19
	Crankcase (refill)	(qt)	11
Brakes		(Hydrovac) Hydraulic	

PERFORMANCE

Maximum gradability		(percent)	65
Turning radius (ft)	Right 34	Left 35	
Fording depth		(in.)	
Angle of approach		(deg)	54
Angle of departure		(deg)	36
Fuel consumption, average conditions		(miles per gal)	7.5
Cruising range, average conditions		(miles)	240
Maximum allowable speed		(mph)	45
Number of speeds forward			

ENGINE

Manufacturer	GMC	Model 270	
Type	In-line, 4 cycle	Number of cylinders	6
Displacement		(cu in.)	269.5
Governed speed		(rpm)	2,750
Brake horsepower			104
Ignition type		Battery	

ADDITIONAL DATA

This chassis with different equipment is used for general purpose, electrical repair, light machine shop, small tool repair, tool and bench, and welding cargo.

Supplied with open cab after July, 1943.

TRUCK, SURGICAL, 2½-TON, 6 x 6

Technical Manual: TM 9-801. Parts List: SNL G-508

Manufacturer: General Motors Truck and Coach Div. of Yellow Truck and Coach Mfg. Co.

RA PD 308937

Classification: Standard

Purpose: Used by Medical Corps to transport and house field surgical supplies and equipment.

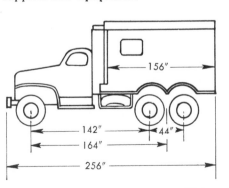

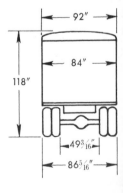

TRUCK, SURGICAL, 2½-TON, 6 x 6

GENERAL DATA

Crew				2
Weight	Net		(lb)	11,280
	Payload		(lb)	5,000
	Gross		(lb)	16,280
Shipping dimensions	(cu ft) 1,603	(sq ft) 160		
Tires	Ply..8	Size..7.50 x 20		
Ground clearance			(in.)	10
Electrical system			(volts)	6
Capacities	Fuel, 70 octane gasoline		(gal)	40
	Cooling system		(qt)	19
	Crankcase (refill)		(qt)	11
Brakes		(Hydrovac) Hydraulic		

PERFORMANCE

Maximum gradability		(percent)	65
Turning radius (ft)	Right 34	Left 35	
Fording depth		(in.)	
Angle of approach		(deg)	36
Angle of departure		(deg)	31
Fuel consumption, average conditions		(miles per gal)	7.5
Cruising range, average conditions		(miles)	240
Maximum allowable speed		(mph)	45
Number of speeds forward			

ENGINE

Manufacturer	GMC	Model 270	
Type	In-line, 4 cycle	Number of cylinders	6
Displacement		(cu in.)	269.5
Governed speed		(rpm)	2,750
Brake horsepower			104
Ignition type		Battery	

ADDITIONAL DATA

....

....

....

....

TRUCK, VAN, 2½-TON, 6 x 6, K-53

Technical Manuals: Parts List:

Manufacturer: General Motors Truck and Coach Div. of Yellow Truck
and Coach Mfg. Co.

Classification: Limited standard   RA PD 308970

Purpose: Used by Signal Corps to transport and house radio equipment.

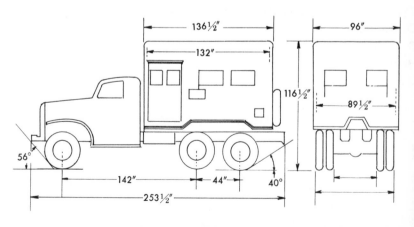

TRUCK, VAN, 2½-TON, 6 x 6, K-53

GENERAL DATA

Crew... 2
Weight................... Net...................... (lb)   10,270
                         Payload.................. (lb)   5,000
                         Gross.................... (lb)   15,270
Shipping dimensions........ (cu ft) 1,664........ (sq ft) 169
Tires.................... Ply...8........ Size...7.50 x 20
Tread, center to center............................ (in.) 67^3_4
Ground clearance................................... (in.)   10
Electrical system................................ (volts)   6
Capacities............... Fuel, 70 octane gasoline....(gal) 40
                         Cooling system............ (qt)   19
                         Crankcase (refill)......... (qt)   11
Brakes...................... (Hydrovac) Hydraulic

PERFORMANCE

Maximum gradability........................... (percent)   65
Turning radius (ft)........ Right 34............. Left 35
Fording depth..................................... (in.)
Angle of approach............................... (deg)   56
Angle of departure.............................. (deg)   40
Fuel consumption, average conditions........ (miles per gal) 7.5
Cruising range, average conditions................ (miles) 240
Maximum allowable speed......................... (mph)   45
Number of speeds forward........................   5

ENGINE

Manufacturer...... GMC.................... Model 270
Type............. In-line, 4 cycle..... Number of cylinders 6
Displacement.................................... (cu in.) 269.5
Governed speed................................... (rpm)   2,750
Brake horsepower...............................   104
Ignition type.................................... Battery

ADDITIONAL DATA

. . . .
. . . .
. . . .
. . . .

TRUCK, VAN, 2½-TON, 6 x 6, K-60

Technical Manuals: Parts Lists:

Manufacturers: Various

RA PD 66617

Vehicle illustrated above: Chassis, GMC; Body, York Hoover

Classification: Standard

Purpose: To transport Signal Corps field equipment.

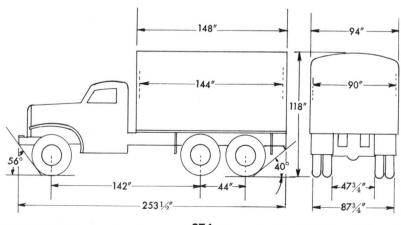

TRUCK, VAN, 2½-TON, 6 x 6, K-60

GENERAL DATA

Crew..			2
Weight....................Net....................(lb)			11,070
	Payload..................(lb)		4,000
	Gross....................(lb)		15,070
Shipping dimensions.......(cu ft) 1,643.........(sq ft) 169			
Tires....................Ply...8.......Size...7.50 x 20			
Tread, center to center............................(in.)			67¾
Ground clearance.....................................(in.)			10
Electrical system....................................(volts)			6
Capacities...............Fuel, 70 octane gasoline....(gal)			40
	Cooling system.............(qt)		19
	Crankcase (refill)..........(qt)		10
Brakes...................................Hydraulic			

PERFORMANCE

Maximum gradability.............................(percent)	65
Turning radius (ft).........Right 35.............Left 34	
Fording depth......................................(in.)	18
Angle of approach..................................(deg)	56
Angle of departure.................................(deg)	40
Fuel consumption, average conditions.........(miles per gal)	7.5
Cruising range, average conditions..................(miles)	240
Maximum allowable speed...........................(mph)	45
Number of speeds forward...............................	5

ENGINE

Manufacturer......GMC....................Model 270	
Type............In-line, 4 cycle......Number of cylinders	6
Displacement.....................................(cu in.)	269.5
Governed speed.....................................(rpm)	2,750
Brake horsepower.......................................	104
Ignition type.................................Battery	

ADDITIONAL DATA

Similar body manufactured by Superior Coach Corp., Wayne Works, Transportation Engineers, Hackney Bros., Oneonta Linn Corp., York Hoover Body Corp.

....

....

TRUCK, WATER PURIFICATION UNIT, MOBILE, 2½-TON, 6 x 6

Technical Manuals: TM 5-2000, TM 5-2032.   Parts List:

Manufacturers: Chassis, General Motors Truck and Coach Div. of Yellow Truck and Coach Mfg. Co.; Water Purification Unit, Wallace Tiernan Co., Inc.

RA PD 66633

Classification: Standard

Purpose: Used by Corps of Engineers to provide mobile facilities for water purification.

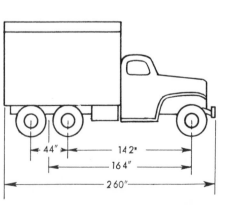

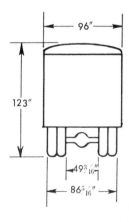

TRUCK, WATER PURIFICATION UNIT, MOBILE, 2½-TON, 6 x 6

GENERAL DATA

Crew		2
Weight................Gross....................(lb)		16,400
Shipping dimensions.......(cu ft) 1,780........(sq ft) 174		
Tires...................Ply...8.........Size...7.50 x 20		
Ground clearance..............................(in.)		10
Electrical system.............................(volts)		6
Capacities..............Fuel, 70 octane gasoline....(gal)		40
Cooling system............(qt)		19
Crankcase (refill)..........(qt)		11
Brakes..Hydraulic		

PERFORMANCE

Maximum gradability.........................(percent)	65
Turning radius (ft)........Right 34.............Left 35	
Fording depth...............................(in.)	
Angle of approach...........................(deg)	54
Angle of departure..........................(deg)	36
Fuel consumption, average conditions........(miles per gal)	7.5
Cruising range, average conditions..............(miles)	240
Maximum allowable speed.......................(mph)	45
Number of speeds forward................................	

ENGINE

Manufacturer......GMC....................Model 270	
Type.............In-line, 4 cycle......Number of cylinders	6
Displacement.................................(cu in.)	269.5
Governed speed..............................(rpm)	2,750
Brake horsepower..	104
Ignition type...................................Battery	

ADDITIONAL DATA

These vehicles equipped with open cabs after July 1943. Equipped with a portable water purification unit, driven by an air-cooled, single cylinder Wisconsin Model AB engine.

TRUCK, CARGO, 4-TON, 4 x 4

Technical Manual: TM 9-815.   Parts List: SNL G-531

Manufacturer: Four Wheel Drive Auto Co. (Model HAR-1)

RA PD 309099

Classification:

Purpose: To transport general cargo.

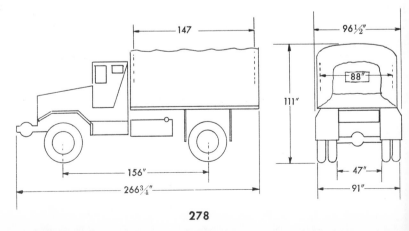

TRUCK, CARGO, 4-TON, 4 x 4

GENERAL DATA

Crew, operating....2......Passenger capacity, including crew	5
Weight.....................Net.....................(lb)	11,425
Payload..................(lb)	8,000
Gross....................(lb)	19,425
Shipping dimensions........(cu ft) ....(sq ft)	
Tires.....................Ply...........Size...9.00 x 20	
Tread, center to center (in.).Front 67½.............Rear 69	
Ground clearance.....................................(in.)	11
Electrical system..............................(volts)	6
Capacities..............Fuel, 68 octane gasoline....(gal)	40
Cooling system...........(qt)	23
Crankcase (refill)..........(qt)	10
Brakes.............................Hydraulic	

PERFORMANCE

Maximum gradability.....................(percent)	40
Turning radius.........................(ft)	38½
Fording depth.........................(in.)	28
Angle of approach.....................(deg)	35
Angle of departure....................(deg)	30
Fuel consumption, average conditions........(miles per gal)	5.5
Cruising range, average conditions..................(miles)	220
Maximum allowable speed........................(mph)	35
Number of speeds forward......................	5

ENGINE

Manufacturer......Waukesha.................Model BZ	
Type.............In-line, 4 cycle......Number of cylinders	6
Displacement........................(cu in.)	320
Governed speed........................(rpm)	2,800
Brake horsepower..............................	88
Ignition type.............................Battery	

ADDITIONAL DATA

TRUCK, SHOVEL-CRANE, W/TRAILER, 4-TON, 4 x 4

Technical Manuals: Parts List:

Manufacturers: Truck—Coleman Motor Co.; Shovel-Crane, Trailer—
Quick-Way Truck Shovel Co.   Model E-55

RA PD 309094

Classification: Limited standard

Purpose: Used by Corps of Engineers to provide mobile facilities for
crane, shovel, dragline, clamshell and pile driver operations.

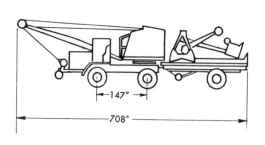

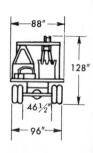

TRUCK, SHOVEL-CRANE, W/TRAILER, 4-TON, 4 x 4

GENERAL DATA

Crew...			2
Weight....................	Net....................	(lb)	13,083
	Payload...................	(lb)	13,327
	Gross....................	(lb)	26,410
	Boxed for export..........	(lb)	34,800

Shipping dimensions........(cu ft) 2,533.........(sq ft) 378
Tires....................Ply...12......Size...10.00 x 20
Tread....................Front 72.............Rear 71
Ground clearance...................................(in.)   11½
Electrical system.................................(volts)   6
Capacities..............Fuel, 70 octane gasoline....(gal)   50
                        Cooling system............(qt)   48
                        Crankcase (refill)..........(qt)   10
Brakes.....................(Bendix-Westinghouse) Air

PERFORMANCE

Maximum gradability...........................(percent)
Turning radius.....................................(ft)   31
Fording depth.....................................(in.)   46
Angle of approach (deg)...With winch 17...Without winch 35
Angle of departure................................(deg)   35
Fuel consumption, average conditions.........(miles per gal) 5
Cruising range, average conditions..................(miles) 250
Maximum allowable speed..........................(mph)   53
Number of speeds forward............................   5

ENGINE

Manufacturer......Buda....................Model 10525
Type............In-line, 4 cycle......Number of cylinders   6
Displacement.....................................(cu in.)   525
Governed speed....................................(rpm)   2,100
Brake horsepower....................................   139
Ignition type...................................Battery

ADDITIONAL DATA

Winch capacity..(lb)   12,000

Flat bed trailer: payload capacity 8,000 pounds; loading height, 53 inch; weight 6,750 pounds; tires—operating 4, size—10.00 x 20, ply—12; brakes —(Bendix-Westinghouse) air; packed for export 1,526 cubic feet; weight 20,650 pounds.

TRUCK, CARGO, L.W.B., 4-TON, 6 x 6

Technical Manuals: TM 10-1297, TM 10-1517,   Parts List: SNL G-509
TM 10-1533, TM 10-1603,
TM 10-1605, TM 10-1607.

Manufacturer: Diamond T Motor Car Co.

RA PD 66641

Classification: Standard

Purpose: To transport general cargo and personnel.

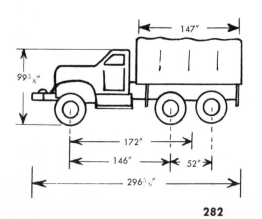
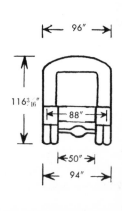

TRUCK, CARGO, L.W.B., 4-TON, 6 x 6

GENERAL DATA

Crew, operating 2 . . . . Passenger capacity, including crew

Weight	Net	(lb)	18,500
	Payload	(lb)	8,000
	Gross	(lb)	26,500

Shipping dimensions . . . . (cu ft) 1,769 . . . . (sq ft) 179

Tires . . . . Ply . . . 10 . . . . . . Size . . . 9.00 x 20

Tread, center to center (in.) . Front 73¾ . . . . Rear 72

Ground clearance . . . . (in.)   11

Pintle height (in.) . . . . Loaded 40 . . . . . . Unloaded 41¼

Electrical system . . . . (volts)   6

Capacities . . . . Fuel, 72 octane gasoline . . . . (gal)   60

Cooling system . . . . (qt)   46

Crankcase (refill) . . . . (qt)   14

Brakes . . . . Air

PERFORMANCE

Maximum gradability . . . . (percent)   65

Turning radius (ft) . . . . Right 38½ . . . . Left 37

Fording depth . . . . (in.)   24

Angle of approach . . . . (deg)   37

Angle of departure . . . . (deg)   39

Fuel consumption, average conditions . . . . (miles per gal)   3

Cruising range, average conditions . . . . (miles)   180

Maximum allowable speed . . . . (mph)   40

Number of speeds forward   5

ENGINE

Manufacturer . . . . . . Hercules . . . . Model RXC

Type . . . . In-line, 4 cycle . . . . . . Number of cylinders   6

Displacement . . . . (cu in.)   529

Governed speed . . . . (rpm)   2,300

Brake horsepower   119

Ignition type . . . . Battery

ADDITIONAL DATA

Winch capacity . . . . (lb)   15,000

About 25 percent of these vehicles are being equipped with truck mount M36 for antiaircraft machine gun.

Will have open cab after July 1943. Body contains troop seats and backs.

TRUCK, CARGO, S.W.B., 4-TON, 6 x 6

Technical Manuals: TM 10-1297, TM 10-1517,　Parts List: SNL G-509
TM 10-1533, TM 10-1603,
TM 10-1605, TM 10-1607.

Manufacturer: Diamond T Motor Car Co.

RA PD 308976

Classification: Standard

Purpose: To transport general cargo personnel.

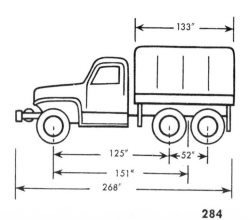

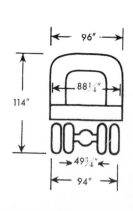

TRUCK, CARGO, S.W.B., 4-TON, 6 x 6

GENERAL DATA

Crew, operating 2	Passenger capacity, including crew		
Weight	Net	(lb)	18,400
	Payload	(lb)	8,000
	Gross	(lb)	26,400
Shipping dimensions	(cu ft) 1,769	(sq ft) 179	
Tires	Ply 10	Size 9.00 x 20	
Tread, center to center (in.)	Front $73\frac{3}{4}$	Rear 72	
Ground clearance		(in.)	11
Pintle height (in.)	Loaded 40	Unloaded $41\frac{1}{4}$	
Electrical system		(volts)	6
Capacities	Fuel, 70 octane gasoline	(gal)	60
	Cooling system	(qt)	46
	Crankcase (refill)	(qt)	16
Brakes		Air	

PERFORMANCE

Maximum gradability	(percent)	65
Turning radius (ft)	Right $38\frac{1}{2}$	Left 37
Fording depth	(in.)	24
Angle of approach	(deg)	37
Angle of departure	(deg)	39
Fuel consumption, average conditions	(miles per gal)	3
Cruising range, average conditions	(miles)	180
Maximum allowable speed	(mph)	40
Number of speeds forward		5

ENGINE

Manufacturer	Hercules	Model RXC
Type	In-line, 4 cycle	Number of cylinders 6
Displacement	(cu in.)	529
Governed speed	(rpm)	2,300
Brake horsepower		119
Ignition type		Battery

ADDITIONAL DATA

Winch capacity .... (lb) 15,000

Body contains troop seats and backs.

About 25 percent of these vehicles are being equipped with truck mount
M36 for antiaircraft machine gun.

TRUCK, CRANE, SWINGING BOOM, W/WINCH, 4-TON, 6 x 6, M1

Technical Manuals: Parts List:

Manufacturer: Diamond T Motor Car Co.

RA PD 66643

Classification: Standard

Purpose: Used by Chemical Warfare Service to lift and transport heavy chemical containers.

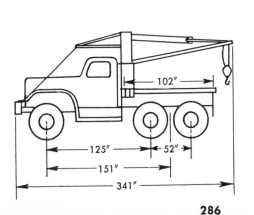

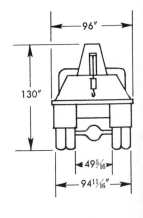

TRUCK, CRANE, SWINGING BOOM, W/WINCH, 4-TON, 6 x 6, M1

GENERAL DATA

Crew			2
Weight	Net	(lb)	18,400
	Payload	(lb)	8,000
	Gross	(lb)	26,400
Shipping dimensions	(cu ft) 1,948	(sq ft) 227	
Tires	Ply...10	Size...9.00 x 20	
Ground clearance		(in.)	11
Electrical system		(volts)	6
Capacities	Fuel, 70 octane gasoline	(gal)	60
	Cooling system	(qt)	46
	Crankcase (refill)	(qt)	16
Brakes		Air	

PERFORMANCE

Maximum gradability	(percent)	65
Turning radius (ft)	Right 36½	Left 35
Fording depth	(in.)	24
Angle of approach	(deg)	37
Angle of departure	(deg)	46
Fuel consumption, average conditions	(miles per gal)	3
Cruising range, average conditions	(miles)	120
Maximum allowable speed	(mph)	40
Number of speeds forward		5

ENGINE

Manufacturer	Hercules	Model RXC	
Type	In-line, 4 cycle	Number of cylinders	6
Displacement		(cu in.)	529
Governed speed		(rpm)	2,300
Brake horsepower			119
Ignition type		Battery	

ADDITIONAL DATA

Winch capacity	(lb)	15,000

TRUCK, DISTRIBUTOR, WATER, 1000 GAL.
4-TON, 6 x 6

Technical Manuals: Parts List:

Manufacturers: Chassis and cab, Diamond T Motor Car Co.; Tank and equipment, Littleford Bros.

RA PD 308996

Classification: Standard

Purpose: Used by Corps of Engineers as water-distributing unit.

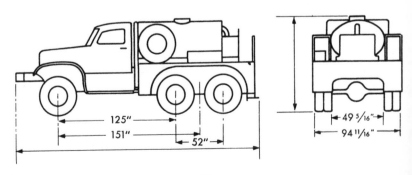

TRUCK, DISTRIBUTOR, WATER, 1000 GAL.
4-TON, 6 x 6

GENERAL DATA

Crew			2
Weight	Net	(lb)	18,750
	Payload	(lb)	8,330
	Gross	(lb)	27,080
Shipping dimensions	(cu ft)	(sq ft)	
Tires	Ply...10	Size...9.00 x 20	
Tread, center to center (in.) Front 73¾		Rear 72	
Ground clearance		(in.)	11
Pintle height (in.)	Loaded 40	Unloaded 41½	
Electrical system		(volts)	6
Capacities	Fuel, 70 octane gasoline	(gal)	60
	Cooling system	(qt)	46
	Crankcase (refill)	(qt)	16
Brakes		Air	

PERFORMANCE

Maximum gradability	(percent)	65
Turning radius (ft) Right 38½	Left 37	
Fording depth	(in.)	24
Angle of approach	(deg)	48
Angle of departure	(deg)	67
Fuel consumption, average conditions	(miles per gal)	3
Cruising range, average conditions	(miles)	175
Maximum allowable speed	(mph)	40
Number of speeds forward		5

ENGINE

Manufacturer......Hercules	Model RXC	
Type............In-line, 4 cycle	Number of cylinders	6
Displacement	(cu in.)	529
Governed speed	(rpm)	2,300
Brake horsepower		119
Ignition type	Battery	

ADDITIONAL DATA

TRUCK, DUMP, 4-TON, 6 x 6

Technical Manual: TM 10-1533.

Parts List: SNL G-509

Manufacturer: Diamond T Motor Car Co.

RA PD 66645

Classification: Standard

Purpose: To haul and dump earth, sand, gravel, etc.

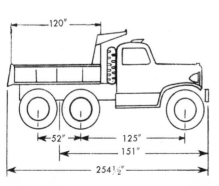

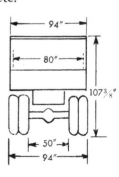

TRUCK, DUMP, 4-TON, 6 x 6

GENERAL DATA

Crew				2
Weight	Net		(lb)	17,500
	Payload		(lb)	8,900
	Gross		(lb)	26,400
Shipping dimensions	(cu ft) 1,475		(sq ft) 167	
Tires	Ply...10	Size...9.00 x 20		
Tread, center to center (in.)	Front 73¾		Rear 72	
Ground clearance			(in.)	11
Electrical system			(volts)	6
Capacities	Fuel, 70 octane gasoline		(gal)	60
	Cooling system		(qt)	46
	Crankcase (refill)		(qt)	16
Brakes			Air	

PERFORMANCE

Maximum gradability	(percent)	65
Turning radius (ft)	Right 36½	Left 35
Fording depth	(in.)	24
Angle of approach	(deg)	48
Angle of departure	(deg)	67
Fuel consumption, average conditions	(miles per gal)	3
Cruising range, average conditions	(miles)	175
Maximum allowable speed	(mph)	40
Number of speeds forward		5

ENGINE

Manufacturer	Hercules	Model RXC	
Type	In-line, 4 cycle	Number of cylinders	6
Displacement		(cu in.)	529
Governed speed		(rpm)	2,300
Brake horsepower			119
Ignition type		Battery	

ADDITIONAL DATA

Will have open cab after September 1943.
Has hydraulic hoist.

TRUCK, MAP REPRODUCTION EQUIPMENT
4-TON, 6 x 6

Technical Manuals: Parts List:

Manufacturers: Chassis and cab, Diamond T Motor Car Co.; Body, McCabe-Powers Autobody Co.

RA PD 308992

Classification: Standard

Purpose: Used by Corps of Engineers to transport equipment for map reproduction units.

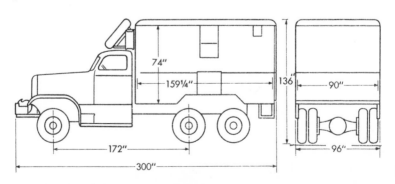

TRUCK, MAP REPRODUCTION EQUIPMENT
4-TON, 6 x 6

GENERAL DATA

Crew...

Weight....................Gross..............(lb) 23,000 to 24,000

Shipping dimensions........(cu ft) 2,260.........(sq ft) 200

Tires....................Ply...10......Size...9.00 x 20

Tread, center to center (in.).Front 73¾.............Rear 72

Ground clearance....................................(in.)   11

Electrical system....................................(volts)   6

Capacities................Fuel, 70 octane gasoline....(gal)   60

Cooling system.............(qt)   46

Crankcase.................(qt)   16

Brakes...Air

PERFORMANCE

Maximum gradability.............................(percent)   65

Turning radius (ft)........Right 38½.............Left 37

Fording depth.....................................(in.)   24

Angle of approach..................................(deg)   48

Angle of departure.................................(deg)   67

Fuel consumption, average conditions.........(miles per gal)   3

Cruising range, average conditions.................(miles)   175

Maximum allowable speed.......................(mph)   40

Number of speeds forward..............................   5

ENGINE

Manufacturer......Hercules................Model RXC

Type.............In-line, 4 cycle......Number of cylinders   6

Displacement.......................................(cu in.)   529

Governed speed....................................(rpm)   2,300

Brake horsepower....................................   119

Ignition type....................................Battery

ADDITIONAL DATA

Equipped with winch.

The same basic vehicle with different equipment is used as:
Camera section, Press section 20 inch x 22½ inch, and Press section
22 inch x 29 inch. Weight varies with equipment.

TRUCK, WRECKER, 4-TON, 6 x 6

Technical Manuals: TM 10-1297,
TM 10-1335, TM 10-1533,
TM 10-1605, TM 10-1607.

Parts List: SNL G-509

Manufacturer: Diamond T Motor Car Co.

RA PD 308957

Classification: Standard

Purpose: To lift and tow disabled vehicles.

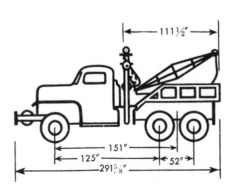

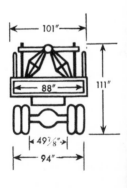

TRUCK, WRECKER, 4-TON, 6 x 6

GENERAL DATA

Crew.. 2
Weight.................Gross....................... 21,700
Shipping dimensions.......(cu ft) 1,917........(sq ft) 195
Tires....................Ply...10......Size...9.00 x 20
Tread, center to center (in.).Front 73¾............Rear 72
Ground clearance.......................................(in.) 11
Electrical system..................................(volts) 12
Capacities..............Fuel, 68 octane gasoline....(gal) 60
                        Cooling system............(qt) 48
                        Crankcase (refill)..........(qt) 16
Brakes......................(Bendix-Westinghouse) Air

PERFORMANCE

Maximum gradability............................(percent) 98
Turning radius (ft)........Right 36½.............Left 36
Fording depth.......................................(in.) 24
Angle of approach..................................(deg) 37
Angle of departure.................................(deg) 46
Fuel consumption, average conditions.........(miles per gal) 3.3
Cruising range, average conditions.................(miles) 182
Maximum allowable speed.........................(mph) 40
Number of speeds forward............................... 5

ENGINE

Manufacturer......Hercules.................Model RXC
Type.............In-line, 4 cycle......Number of cylinders 6
Displacement......................................(cu in.) 521
Governed speed....................................(rpm) 2,300
Brake horsepower..................................... 131
Ignition type......................................Battery

ADDITIONAL DATA

Winch capacity..(lb) 15,000
About 25 percent of these vehicles are being equipped with truck mount
    M36 for antiaircraft machine gun. Winch located at rear of cab.

....

TRUCK, TANK, BITUMINOUS SUPPLY, 800 GAL.
4-TON, 6 x 6

Technical Manuals: Parts List:

Manufacturers: Chassis, Diamond T Motor Car Co.; Equipment, Roscoe
 Mfg. Co.

RA PD 308998

Classification: Standard

Purpose: Used by Corps of Engineers.

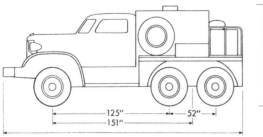

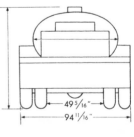

TRUCK, TANK, BITUMINOUS SUPPLY, 800 GAL.
4-TON, 6 x 6

GENERAL DATA

Crew...				2
Weight.....................Net.......................(lb)				19,500
	Payload..................(lb)			6,800
	Gross....................(lb)			26,300
Shipping dimensions........(cu ft) 1,584.........(sq ft)				
Tires....................Ply...10......Size...9.00 x 20				
Tread, center to center (in.). Front 73¾............Rear 72				
Ground clearance.................................(in.)				11
Electrical system.................................(volts)				6
Capacities...............Fuel, 70 octane gasoline....(gal)				60
	Cooling system............(qt)			46
	Crankcase (refill)..........(qt)			16
Brakes...Air				

PERFORMANCE

Maximum gradability...........................(percent)	65
Turning radius (ft)........Right 38½.............Left 37	
Fording depth.......................................(in.)	24
Angle of approach................................(deg)	48
Angle of departure................................(deg)	67
Fuel consumption, average conditions........(miles per gal)	3
Cruising range, average conditions.................(miles)	175
Maximum allowable speed..........................(mph)	40
Number of speeds forward...............................	5

ENGINE

Manufacturer......Hercules.................Model RXC	
Type.............In-line, 4 cycle......Number of cylinders	6
Displacement.......................................(cu in.)	529
Governed speed....................................(rpm)	2,300
Brake horsepower.......................................	119
Ignition type....................................Battery	

ADDITIONAL DATA

....

....

....

....

TRUCK, COMBINATION STAKE AND PLATFORM
5-TON, 4 x 2

Technical Manuals: Parts List:

Manufacturers: Federal Motor Truck Co., General Motors Truck and Coach Div. of Yellow Truck and Coach Mfg. Co., International Harvester Co.

RA PD 309126

Classification: Standard

Purpose: To transport heavy cargo.

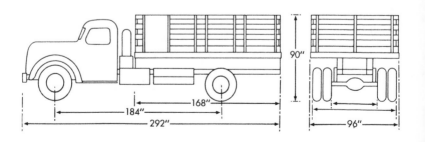

TRUCK, COMBINATION STAKE AND PLATFORM
5-TON, 4 x 2

GENERAL DATA

Crew			2
Weight	Net	(lb)	10,450
	Payload	(lb)	10,000
	Gross	(lb)	20,450
Shipping dimensions	(cu ft) 2,061	(sq ft)	
Tires	Ply...12	Size...10.00 x 20	
Tread, center to center (in.)	Front 70½	Rear 71	
Ground clearance		(in.)	10½
Electrical system		(volts)	6
Capacities	Fuel, 70 octane gasoline	(gal)	37
	Cooling system	(qt)	28
	Crankcase	(qt)	15
Brakes	(Westinghouse) Air		

PERFORMANCE

Maximum gradability	(in low)	(percent)	31
Turning radius		(ft)	21
Fording depth		(in.)	
Angle of approach		(deg)	42
Angle of departure		(deg)	24
Fuel consumption, average conditions		(miles per gal)	4.75
Cruising range, average conditions		(miles)	175
Maximum allowable speed		(mph)	46
Number of speeds forward			

ENGINE

Manufacturer	Hercules	Model WXLC-3	
Type	In-line, 4 cycle	Number of cylinders	6
Displacement		(cu in.)	404
Governed speed		(rpm)	
Brake horsepower			118
Ignition type		Battery	

ADDITIONAL DATA

Truck, cargo, 5-ton, 4 x 2 is similar to this vehicle.

TRUCK, DUMP, 5-TON, 4 x 2

Technical Manuals: IHC, TM 10-1145, TM 10-1337, TM 10-1383, TM 10-1509, TM 10-1555, TM 10-1683.

Parts Lists: SNL G-542 (IHC), SNL G-555 (Federal), SNL G-647 (GMC)

Manufacturers: Autocar Co.; Federal Motor Truck Co.; General Motors Truck and Coach Division of Yellow Truck and Coach Mfg. Co.; International Harvester Co.

RA PD 308981

Vehicle illustrated above: International

Classification: Standard

Purpose: To transport and dump earth, sand, gravel, coal, etc., and to carry general cargo.

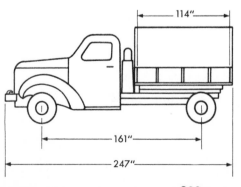

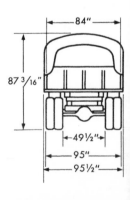

TRUCK, DUMP, 5-TON, 4 x 2

GENERAL DATA

Crew... 2
Weight..................Net...................(lb) 12,950
                   Payload..................(lb) 10,000
                   Gross....................(lb) 22,950
Shipping dimensions........(cu ft)   ....(sq ft)
Tires....................Ply...12......Size...10.00 x 20
Tread, center to center (in.).Front $72\frac{5}{8}$..........Rear $72\frac{3}{16}$
Ground clearance...................................(in.) $10\frac{13}{16}$
Electrical system.....................................(volts) 6
Capacities...............Fuel, 70 octane gasoline....(gal) 40
                Cooling system............(qt) 26
                Crankcase (refill)..........(qt) 10
Brakes...Air

PERFORMANCE

Maximum gradability...........................(percent) 51
Turning radius....................................(ft) 29
Fording depth....................................(in.) $32\frac{1}{2}$
Angle of approach...............................(deg) 34
Angle of departure..............................(deg) 35
Fuel consumption, average conditions........(miles per gal) 5.5
Cruising range, average conditions..................(miles) 220
Maximum allowable speed........................(mph) 38
Number of speeds forward............................. 5

ENGINE

Manufacturer......IHC.................Model RED-450
Type.............In-line, 4 cycle.....Number of cylinders 6
Displacement.....................................(cu in.) 451
Governed speed................................(rpm) 2,700
Brake horsepower..................................... 130
Ignition type.....................................Battery

ADDITIONAL DATA

....
....
....
....

TRUCK, BRIDGE CONSTRUCTION, 6-TON, 6 x 6

Technical Manual: TM 10-1529   Parts List:

Manufacturers: Truck, Brockway Motor Co., Inc.; Crane, The Daybrook Hydraulic Corp. (Steel Treadway Bridge Hydraulic Crane M-II).

RA PD 66652

Classification: Standard

Purpose: Used by Corps of Engineers to transport and erect bridge equipment.

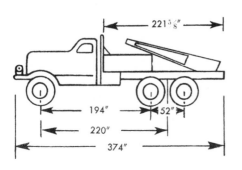

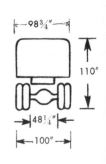

TRUCK, BRIDGE CONSTRUCTION, 6-TON, 6 x 6

GENERAL DATA

Crew			2
Weight	Net	(lb)	26,500
	Payload	(lb)	12,000
	Gross	(lb)	38,500
Shipping dimensions, unboxed (cu ft) 2,437		(sq ft) 266	
Tires	Ply..14	Size...12.00 x 20	
Tread	Front 73⅝	Rear 74⅛	
Ground clearance		(in.)	10¼
Pintle height		(in.)	37
Electrical system		(volts)	12
Capacities	Fuel, 72 octane gasoline	(gal)	80
	Cooling system	(qt)	58
	Crankcase (refill)	(qt)	16
Brakes	(Bendix-Westinghouse) Air		

PERFORMANCE

Maximum gradability	(percent)	37
Turning radius (ft)	Right 49	Left 48
Fording depth	(in.)	
Angle of approach	(deg)	40
Angle of departure	(deg)	28
Fuel consumption, average conditions	(miles per gal)	2.6
Cruising range, average conditions	(miles)	170
Maximum allowable speed	(mph)	37
Number of speeds forward		4

ENGINE

Manufacturer	Hercules	Model HXD	
Type	In-line, 4 cycle	Number of cylinders	6
Displacement		(cu in.)	855
Governed speed		(rpm)	2,150
Brake horsepower			202
Ignition type		Battery	

ADDITIONAL DATA

Winch capacity . . . . (lb)

. . . .

. . . .

. . . .

TRUCK, SHOVEL-CRANE, 6-TON, 6 x 6

Technical Manual: TM 10-1529.   Parts List:

Manufacturers: Truck, Brockway Motor Co., Inc.; Shovel-Crane, Quick-Way Truck Shovel Co.

RA PD 309130

Classification: Standard

Purpose: Used by Corps of Engineers to provide mobile facilities for crane, shovel, dragline, clamshell and pile driver operations.

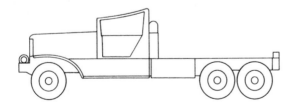 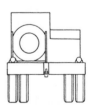

TRUCK, SHOVEL-CRANE, 6-TON, 6 x 6

GENERAL DATA

Crew..		
Weight.....................Net.......................(lb)		
Payload..................(lb)		
Gross.....................(lb)		
Shipping dimensions........(cu ft) ....(sq ft)		
Tires.....................Ply...14......Size...12.00 x 20		
Ground clearance..................................(in.)	11
Electrical system...............................(volts)	12
Capacities...............Fuel, 72 octane gasoline....(gal)	80
Cooling system.............(qt)	58
Crankcase (refill)...........(qt)	16
Brakes........................(Bendix-Westinghouse) Air	

PERFORMANCE

Maximum gradability.............................(percent)	37
Turning radius (ft)........Right 49.....................Left 48	
Fording depth...(in.)	
Angle of approach......................................(deg)	
Angle of departure.....................................(deg)	
Fuel consumption, average conditions.........(miles per gal)	
Cruising range, average conditions..................(miles)	
Maximum allowable speed...........................(mph)	
Number of speeds forward.................................	4

ENGINE

Manufacturer......Hercules.................Model HXD	
Type.............In-line, 4 cycle.....Number of cylinders	6
Displacement......................................(cu in.)	855
Governed speed....................................(rpm)	2,150
Brake horsepower...	202
Ignition type....................................Battery	

ADDITIONAL DATA

Winch capacity.......................................(lb)

No photo of complete unit available.

....

....

TRUCK, PRIME MOVER, 6-TON, 6 x 6

Technical Manuals: Corbitt, TM 10-1109,
TM 10-1159, TM 10-1553.
Mack, TM 10-1477, TM 10-1601.
White, TM 10-1221, TM 10-1467.

Parts Lists:
SNL G-512 (Corbitt)
SNL G-514 (Mack)
SNL G-532 (Mack)
SNL G-547 (Brock.)

Manufacturers: Brockway Motor Co., Inc., Corbitt Co., Mack Mfg. Corp., White Motor Co.

RA PD 308953

Vehicle illustrated above: Corbitt

Classification: Standard

Purpose:

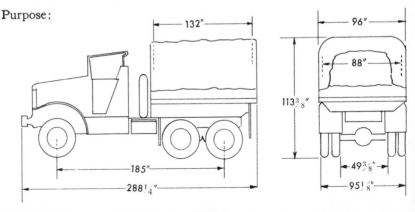

TRUCK, PRIME MOVER, 6-TON, 6 x 6

GENERAL DATA

Crew			2
Weight	Net	(lb)	22,070
	Payload	(lb)	12,070
	Gross	(lb)	34,140
Shipping dimensions	(cu ft) 1,868	(sq ft) 190	
Tires	Ply...12	Size...9.75 x 22	
Tread, center to center (in.) Front 72½		Rear 72¼	
Ground clearance		(in.)	10
Pintle height		(in.)	31
Electrical system		(volts)	6
Capacities	Fuel, 65 octane gasoline	(gal)	75
	Cooling system	(qt)	72
	Crankcase (refill)	(qt)	18
Brakes		(Westinghouse) Air	

PERFORMANCE

Maximum gradability	(percent)	30
Turning radius (ft)	Right 40½	Left 41
Fording depth	(in.)	24
Angle of approach	(deg)	52
Angle of departure	(deg)	43
Fuel consumption, average conditions	(miles per gal)	2
Cruising range, average conditions	(miles)	175
Maximum allowable speed	(mph)	35
Number of speeds forward		4

ENGINE

Manufacturer	Hercules	Model HXC
Type	In-line, 4 cycle	Number of cylinders 6
Displacement	(cu in.)	855
Governed speed	(rpm)	2,150
Brake horsepower		180
Ignition type		Battery

ADDITIONAL DATA

Winch capacity........(located at rear of cab).....(lb) 25,000
About 25 percent of these vehicles are being equipped with truck mount
M36 for antiaircraft machine gun. Applied to Mack and Corbitt only
in this instance.

TRUCK, PRIME MOVER, 7½-TON, 6 x 6

Technical Manual: TM 10-1479   Parts List: SNL G-532

Manufacturer: Mack Mfg. Corp.

RA PD 66662

Classification: Standard

Purpose: To tow heavy artillery (155-mm and 240-mm) and transport cargo.

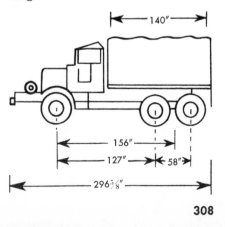

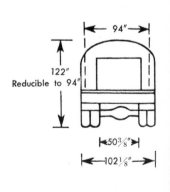

TRUCK, PRIME MOVER, 7½-TON, 6 x 6

GENERAL DATA

Crew, operating......2...Passenger capacity, including crew		4
Weight.................Net......................(lb)		29,620
Payload.................(lb)		15,000
Gross...................(lb)		44,620
Shipping dimensions.......(cu ft) 2,132.........(sq ft) 210		
Tires.................Ply...14.....Size...12.00 x 24		
Tread, center to center (in.).Front 78...........Rear 76¼		
Ground clearance...................................(in.)		13½
Pintle height.....................................(in.)		42⅝
Electrical system.................................(volts)		12
Capacities...............Fuel, 70 octane gasoline....(gal)		160
Cooling system............(qt)		55½
Crankcase (refill)..........(qt)		29
Brakes.............................(Westinghouse) Air		

PERFORMANCE

Maximum gradability...........................(percent)	65
Turning radius (ft).........Right 34.............Left 33	
Fording depth.......................................(in.)	
Angle of approach...................................(deg)	35
Angle of departure.................................(deg)	45
Fuel consumption, average conditions.........(miles per gal)	
Cruising range, average conditions.................(miles)	400
Maximum allowable speed..........................(mph)	31½

ENGINE

Manufacturer......Mack.....................Model EY	
Type.............In-line, 4 cycle......Number of cylinders	6
Displacement.......................................(cu in.)	707
Governed speed...................................(rpm)	2,100
Brake horsepower.......................................	156
Ignition type...................................Battery	

ADDITIONAL DATA

Winch capacity.....................................(lb)	25,000

TRUCK, CARGO, 10-TON, 6 x 4

Technical Manuals: Mack, TM 10-1197,   Parts Lists:
           TM 10-1421, TM 10-1545.   SNL G-642 (White)
           White, TM 10-1467.   SNL G-528 (Mack)

Manufacturers: Mack Mfg. Corp.; White Motor Co.

RA PD 308952

Vehicle illustrated above: Mack

Classification:

Purpose: To transport general cargo.

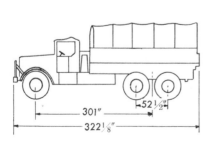

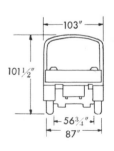

TRUCK, CARGO, 10-TON, 6 x 4

GENERAL DATA

Crew			
Weight	Net	(lb)	20,950
	Payload	(lb)	22,000
	Gross	(lb)	42,950
Shipping dimensions	(cu ft)	(sq ft)	
Tires	Front..Ply.. Size..11.00 x 24		
	Rear...Ply.. Size..14.00 x 20		
Ground clearance		(in.)	13
Tread, center to center (in.).Front 79½		Rear 75¼	
Electrical system		(volts)	24
Capacities	Fuel, 50 cetane, Diesel fuel oil	(gal)	150
	Cooling system	(qt)	19
	Crankcase (refill)	(qt)	
Brakes		Air	

PERFORMANCE

Maximum gradability	(percent)	32
Turning radius (ft)	Right 38 .... Left 39½	
Fording depth	(in.)	
Angle of approach	(deg)	36
Angle of departure	(deg)	38
Fuel consumption, average conditions	(miles per gal)	
Cruising range, average conditions	(miles)	
Maximum allowable speed	(mph)	37
Number of speeds forward		5

ENGINE

Manufacturer	Mack	Model ED
Type	Diesel	Number of cylinders 6
Displacement	(cu in.)	518.64
Governed speed	(rpm)	
Brake horsepower		
Ignition type	Battery	

ADDITIONAL DATA

. . . .

. . . .

. . . .

. . . .

TRUCK, HEAVY WRECKER, 10-TON, 6 x 6, M1

Technical Manuals: Kenworth, TM 9-795,
TM 9-1795A, TM 9-1795B,
TM 9-1795C, TM 9-1795D.

Parts List: SNL G-116

Manufacturers: Kenworth Motor Truck Corp.; Ward-LaFrance Truck
Corp.

RA PD 308956

Vehicle illustrated above: Ward-LaFrance

Classification: Standard

Purpose: To lift and tow disabled heavy vehicles.

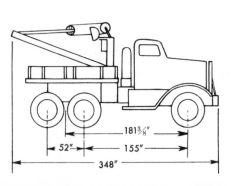

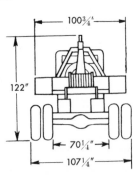

TRUCK, HEAVY WRECKER, 10-TON, 6 x 6, M1

GENERAL DATA

Crew			2
Weight	Net	(lb)	27,330
	Payload	(lb)	8,000
	Gross	(lb)	35,330
Shipping dimensions	(cu ft)	(sq ft)	
Tires	Ply...12	Size...11.00 x 20	
Tread, center to center (in.)	Front 73¼	Rear 88¾	
Ground clearance		(in.)	12¾
Electrical system		(volts)	12
Capacities	Fuel, 68 octane gasoline	(gal)	100
	Cooling system	(qt)	40
	Crankcase (refill)	(qt)	10
Brakes		Air	

PERFORMANCE

Maximum gradability	(percent)	60
Turning radius	(ft)	37½
Fording depth	(in.)	40
Angle of approach	(deg)	55½
Angle of departure	(deg)	55
Fuel consumption, average conditions	(miles per gal)	2.5
Cruising range, average conditions	(miles)	200
Maximum allowable speed	(mph)	45
Number of speeds forward		5

ENGINE

Manufacturer	Continental	Model 22R	
Type	In-line, 4 cycle	Number of cylinders	6
Displacement		(cu in.)	501
Governed speed		(rpm)	2,400
Brake horsepower			133
Ignition type		Battery	

ADDITIONAL DATA

Winch capacity	(lb)	20,000

Series 1, 2 and 3 have battery and magneto ignition.

TRUCK TRACTOR, 1½-TON, 4 x 2

Technical Manuals: Chevrolet, TM 10-1299, TM 10-1305, TM 10-1321, TM 10-1411. Ford, TM 10-1257, TM 10-1433.

Parts Lists: SNL G-617 (Chev.) SNL G-540 (Ford)

Manufacturers: Chevrolet Motor Div. (General Motors Corp.); Ford Motor Co.

RA PD 308929

Vehicle illustrated above: Chevrolet

Classification: Standard

Purpose: To tow semitrailers.

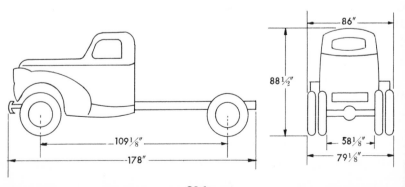

TRUCK TRACTOR, 1½-TON, 4 x 2

GENERAL DATA

Crew			2
Weight	Net	(lb)	5,225
	Payload	(lb)	4,500
	Gross	(lb)	9,725
Shipping dimensions	(cu ft)	(sq ft)	
Tires	Ply...8	Size...7.50 x 20	
Ground clearance		(in.)	9¾
Tread, center to center (in.) Front 56⅟₁₆		Rear 68⅝	
Electrical system		(volts)	6
Capacities	Fuel, 72 octane gasoline	(gal)	25
	Cooling system	(qt)	16
	Crankcase (refill)	(qt)	5
Brakes		Hydraulic	

PERFORMANCE

Maximum gradability	(percent)	36
Turning radius (ft)........Right 20	Left 20½	
Fording depth	(in.)	
Angle of approach	(deg)	41
Angle of departure	(deg)	40
Fuel consumption, average conditions	(miles per gal)	7
Cruising range, average conditions	(miles)	175
Maximum allowable speed	(mph)	
Number of speeds forward		

ENGINE

Manufacturer......Chevrolet.....Model 1942 BLA 1001 up		
Type............In-line, 4 cycle......Number of cylinders		6
Displacement	(cu in.)	235.5
Governed speed	(rpm)	
Brake horsepower		83
Ignition type	Battery	

ADDITIONAL DATA

TRUCK TRACTOR, 1½-TON, 4 x 4

Technical Manuals: TM 10-1127,   Parts List: SNL G-50(
    TM 10-1203, TM 10-1431.

Manufacturer: Chevrolet Motor Div. (General Motors Corporation).

RA PD 309095

Classification: Standard

Purpose: To tow semitrailers.

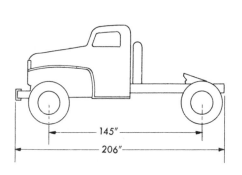

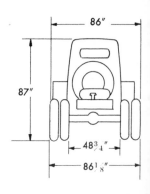

316

TRUCK TRACTOR, 1½-TON, 4 x 4

GENERAL DATA

Crew...			1
Weight..................	Net.....................	(lb)	6,140
	Payload..................	(lb)	4,500
	Gross...................	(lb)	10,640
Shipping dimensions........(cu ft)	.........(sq ft)		
Tires...............Ply...8.......Size...7.50 x 20			
Tread, center to center (in.).Front 60½..........Rear 67½			
Ground clearance...................................(in.)			9⅞
Electrical system...................................(volts)			6
Capacities...............Fuel, 72 octane gasoline....(gal)			30
	Cooling system............(qt)		17
	Crankcase (refill)..........(qt)		5
Brakes...............................Hydraulic			

PERFORMANCE

Maximum gradability............................(percent)	65
Turning radius.....................................(ft)	29½
Fording depth.......................................(in.)	32
Angle of approach.................................(deg)	45
Angle of departure................................(deg)	30
Fuel consumption, average conditions........(miles per gal)	9
Cruising range, average conditions.................(miles)	270
Maximum allowable speed.......................(mph)	48
Number of speeds forward...............................	4

ENGINE

Manufacturer......Chevrolet......Model 1942 BV 1001 up	
Type..............In-line, 4 cycle......Number of cylinders	6
Displacement.....................................(cu in.)	235.5
Governed speed...................................(rpm)	3,100
Brake horsepower.......................................	83
Ignition type....................................Battery	

ADDITIONAL DATA

Equipped with trailer electric brake hand control (Warner).

....
....
....

TRUCK TRACTOR, 2½-TON, 4 x 2

Technical Manual: TM 10-1261 (C1).   Parts List: SNL G-627

Manufacturer: General Motors Truck & Coach Div. of Yellow Coach & Truck Mfg. Co.

RA PD 309100

Classification: Limited standard

Purpose: To tow semitrailers.

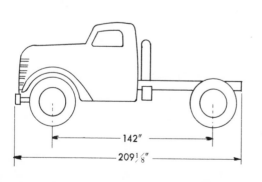

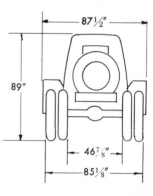

TRUCK TRACTOR, 2½-TON, 4 x 2

GENERAL DATA

Crew. 2
Weight. . . . . .Net. . . . .(lb) 6,890
                       Payload. . . . .(lb) 7,000
                       Gross. . . . .(lb) 13,890
Shipping dimensions. . . . .(cu ft)   . . . .(sq ft)
Tires. .Ply. . .10. . . . . .Size. . .8.25 x 20
Tread, center to center (in.).Front   . . . . .Rear
Ground clearance. . . . .(in.)
Electrical system. . . . .(volts) 6
Capacities. . . . . .Fuel,   octane gasoline. . . .(gal) 29
                       Cooling system. . . . .(qt) 18
                       Crankcase (refill). . . . .(qt) 6½
Brakes. . . . .(Timken-Westinghouse) Air

PERFORMANCE

Maximum gradability. . . . .(percent)
Turning radius. . . . .(ft) 30
Fording depth. . . . .(in.)
Angle of approach. . . . .(deg)
Angle of departure. . . . .(deg)
Fuel consumption, average conditions. . . . .(miles per gal) 10
Cruising range, average conditions. . . . .(miles) 290
Maximum allowable speed. . . . .(mph)
Number of speeds forward. . . . .

ENGINE

Manufacturer. . . . . . .GMC. .Model 308
Type. . . . . .In-line, 4 cycle. . . . .Number of cylinders 6
Displacement. . . . .(cu in.) 308.23
Governed speed. . . . .(rpm)
Brake horsepower. . . . .
Ignition type. . . . . .Battery

ADDITIONAL DATA

. . . .
. . . .
. . . .
. . . .

TRUCK TRACTOR, C.O.E., 2½-TON, 4 x 4

Technical Manuals: TM 10-1390,
TM 10-1396.

Parts List: SNL G-626

Manufacturer: The Autocar Co.

RA PD 66668

Classification: Limited standard

Purpose: To tow semitrailers.

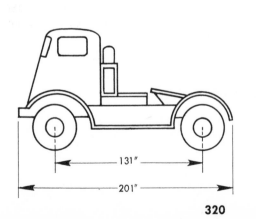

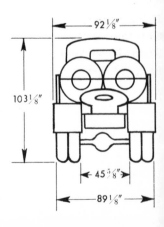

320

TRUCK TRACTOR, C.O.E., 2½-TON, 4 x 4

GENERAL DATA

Crew			2
Weight	Net	(lb)	10,000
	Payload	(lb)	5,000
	Gross	(lb)	15,000
Shipping dimensions	(cu ft) 1,146	(sq ft) 131	
Tires	Ply	Size...9.00 x 20	
Ground clearance		(in.)	11⅝
Electrical system		(volts)	6
Capacities	Fuel, 70 octane gasoline	(gal)	40
	Cooling system	(qt)	23
	Crankcase	(qt)	10
	Transmission	(qt)	12
Brakes		Air	

PERFORMANCE

Maximum gradability	(percent)	45
Turning radius	(ft)	22
Fording depth	(in.)	
Angle of approach	(deg)	50
Angle of departure	(deg)	38
Fuel consumption, average conditions, with towed load	(miles per gal)	4
Cruising range, average conditions	(miles)	160
Maximum allowable speed	(mph)	45
Number of speeds forward		

ENGINE

Manufacturer	Autocar	Model 358	
Type	In-line, 4 cycle	Number of cylinders	6
Displacement		(cu in.)	358
Governed speed		(rpm)	2,600
Brake horsepower			
Ignition type		Battery	

ADDITIONAL DATA

....

....

....

....

TRUCK TRACTOR, 2½-TON, 6 x 4

Technical Manuals: TM 10-1385,
TM 10-1565.

Parts List: SNL G-63(

Manufacturer: The Studebaker Corp.

RA PD 309097

Classification: Substitute standard

Purpose: To tow semitrailers.

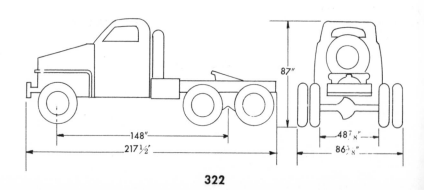

TRUCK TRACTOR, 2½-TON, 6 x 4

GENERAL DATA

Crew...		2
Weight..................Net.....................(lb)		8,190
Payload..................(lb)		15,650
Gross....................(lb)		23,840
Shipping dimensions........(cu ft) ....(sq ft)		
Tires.....................Ply...8.......Size...7.50 x 20		
Tread, center to center (in.).Front 66⅞..........Rear 67¾		
Ground clearance....................................(in.)		10
Electrical system...................................(volts)		6
Capacities...............Fuel, 70 octane gasoline....(gal)		40
Cooling system............(qt)		21
Crankcase (refill)..........(qt)		8
Brakes......................(Lockheed) Hydraulic		

PERFORMANCE

Maximum gradability.............................(percent)	17
Turning radius...(ft)	32
Fording depth...(in.)	
Angle of approach....................................(deg)	52
Angle of departure...................................(deg)	45
Fuel consumption, average conditions.........(miles per gal)	8
Cruising range, average conditions.................(miles)	320
Maximum allowable speed.........................(mph)	45
Number of speeds forward................................	

ENGINE

Manufacturer......Hercules.................Model JXD	
Type.............In-line, 4 cycle.....Number of cylinders	6
Displacement...................................(cu in.)	320
Governed speed....................................(rpm)	
Brake horsepower..	
Ignition type.......................................Battery	

ADDITIONAL DATA

. . . .

. . . .

. . . .

. . . .

TRUCK TRACTOR, 4-5 TON, 4 x 4

Technical Manuals: Autocar, TM 10-1117,   Parts Lists:
           TM 10-1567, TM 10-1569.   SNL G-513 (Federal)
    Federal, TM 10-1107, TM 10-1407,   SNL G-510 (Autocar)
           TM 10-1459.

Manufacturers: The Autocar Co.; Federal Motor Truck Co.

Vehicle illustrated above: Autocar   RA PD 308954

Classification: Standard

Purpose: To tow semitrailers.

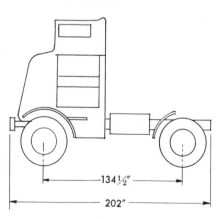

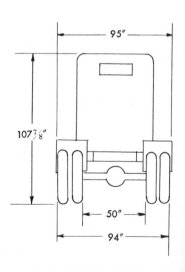

TRUCK TRACTOR, 4-5 TON, 4 x 4

GENERAL DATA

Crew..			2
Weight.................	Net.....................	(lb)	12,200
	Payload.................	(lb)	9,000
	Gross..................	(lb)	21,200
Shipping dimensions.......	(cu ft)	........(sq ft)	
Tires....................	Ply...10......	Size...9.00 x 20	
Ground clearance..		(in.)	11⅞
Tread, center to center (in.).	Front 73¾............	Rear 72	
Pintle height...		(in.)	35¾
Electrical system.......................................		(volts)	6
Capacities..............	Fuel, 64 octane gasoline....	(gal)	60
	Cooling system...........	(qt)	38
	Crankcase (refill).........	(qt)	14½
Brakes......................	(Bendix-Westinghouse) Air		

PERFORMANCE

Maximum gradability............................	(percent)	74
Turning radius..................................	(ft)	30
Fording depth..................................	(in.)	24½
Angle of approach..............................	(deg)	54
Angle of departure.............................	(deg)	50
Fuel consumption, average conditions.........	(miles per gal)	3.2
Cruising range, average conditions.............	(miles)	200
Maximum allowable speed......................	(mph)	41
Number of speeds forward......................		5

ENGINE

Manufacturer......	Hercules.................	Model **RXC**	
Type.............	In-line, 4 cycle.....	Number of cylinders	6
Displacement......................................		(cu in.)	529
Governed speed....................................		(rpm)	2,300
Brake horsepower.................................			131
Ignition type......................................		Battery	

ADDITIONAL DATA

. . . .

. . . .

. . . .

. . . .

TRUCK TRACTOR, PONTON, C.O.E., 5-6 TON, 4 x 4

Technical Manuals: Autocar, TM 10-1119.   Parts Lists:
                         Mack, TM 10-1705.   SNL G-511 (Autocar)
                                           SNL G-639 (Mack)

Manufacturers: The Autocar Co., Model U-8144-T; Mack Mfg. Corp., Model NJU-1.

RA PD 308973

Vehicle illustrated above: Autocar

Classification: Standard

Purpose: To tow semitrailer with ponton bridge equipment.

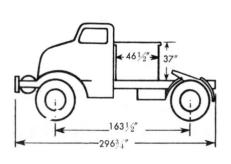

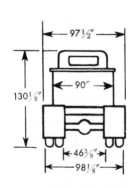

TRUCK TRACTOR, PONTON, C. O. E., 5-6 TON, 4 x 4

GENERAL DATA

Crew			2
Weight	Net	(lb)	16,600
	Payload	(lb)	10,700
	Gross	(lb)	27,300
Shipping dimensions	(cu ft) 1,536	(sq ft) 166	
Tires	Ply...14	Size...12.00 x 20	
Tread, center to center (in.)	Front 71¾	Rear 72¼	
Ground clearance		(in.)	10¹³⁄₁₆
Electrical system		(volts)	6
Capacities	Fuel, 70 octane gasoline	(gal)	90
	Cooling system	(qt)	38
	Crankcase (refill)	(qt)	14
Brakes	(Bendix-Westinghouse) Air		

PERFORMANCE

Maximum gradability	(percent)	30
Turning radius	(ft)	35
Fording depth	(in.)	24
Angle of approach	(deg)	33
Angle of departure	(deg)	54
Fuel consumption, average conditions	(miles per gal)	5.3
Cruising range, average conditions	(miles)	470
Maximum allowable speed	(mph)	46
Number of speeds forward		

ENGINE

Manufacturer	Hercules	Model RXC
Type	In-line, 4 cycle	Number of cylinders 6
Displacement	(cu in.)	529
Governed speed	(rpm)	2,400
Brake horsepower		131
Ignition type	Battery	

ADDITIONAL DATA

Winch capacity	(lb)	15,000

The data given above is for vehicle with winch.

Vehicles made by **Mack** have slightly different dimensions and weights.

TRUCK TRACTOR, FUEL SERVICING, F-1,
7½-TON, 6 x 6

Technical Order: T.O. 19-25-19   Parts List:

Manufacturers: Biederman Motors Co.; Federal Motor Truck Co.; Reo Motor Car Co.

RA PD 66684

Vehicle illustrated above: Reo

Classification: Standard

Purpose: Used by Army Air Forces to tow fuel servicing semitrailer, F-1.

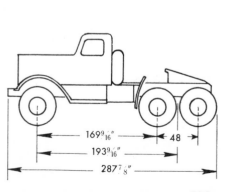

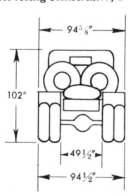

TRUCK TRACTOR, FUEL SERVICING, F-1, 7½-TON, 6 x 6

GENERAL DATA

Crew... 2
Weight................Net.....................(lb) 18,960
                     Payload..................(lb) 15,000
                     Gross....................(lb) 33,960
Shipping dimensions.......(cu ft) 1,603.........(sq ft) 189
Tires....................Ply...12.....Size...10.00 x 22
Tread, center to center (in.).Front ....Rear
Ground clearance..................................(in.) 11¾
Electrical system.................................(volts) 12
Capacities................Fuel, 70 octane gasoline....(gal) 84
                         Cooling system............(qt) 53
                         Crankcase (refill)..........(qt) 16
Brakes...Air

PERFORMANCE

Maximum gradability...........................(percent) 59
Turning radius.....................................(ft) 34
Fording depth.....................................(in.)
Angle of approach................................(deg) 54
Angle of departure...............................(deg) 66
Fuel consumption, average conditions........(miles per gal) 4.12
Cruising range, average conditions.................(miles) 225
Maximum allowable speed..........................(mph) 41
Number of speeds forward.............................

ENGINE

Manufacturer......Hercules.................Model HXD
Type.............In-line, 4 cycle.....Number of cylinders 6
Displacement......................................(cu in.) 855
Governed speed....................................(rpm) 2,100
Brake horsepower.......................................
Ignition type...................................Battery

ADDITIONAL DATA

....

....

....

....

TRUCK TRACTOR, WRECKING, 7½-TON, 6 x 6, C-2

Technical Orders: T.O. 19-20-9; T.O. 19-20-10   Parts List:

Manufacturer: Federal Motor Truck Co.

RA PD 66680

Classification: Standard

Purpose: Used by Army Air Forces to salvage crashed planes and perform general towing.

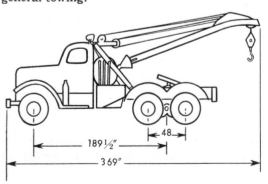

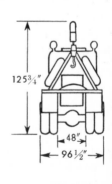

TRUCK TRACTOR, WRECKING, 7½-TON, 6 x 6, C-2

GENERAL DATA

Crew			4
Weight	Net	(lb)	27,500
	Payload..(wgt. on 5th wheel) (lb)		13,000
	Gross	(lb)	40,500
Shipping dimensions	(cu ft) 2,072	(sq ft) 197	
Tires	Ply...12	Size...11.00 x 20	
Ground clearance		(in.)	12⅛
Electrical system		(volts)	12
Capacities	Fuel, 70 octane gasoline	(gal)	110
	Cooling system	(qt)	60
	Crankcase (refill)	(qt)	16
Brakes		Air	

PERFORMANCE

Maximum gradability	(percent)	58
Turning radius (ft)	Right 44	Left 40
Fording depth	(in.)	23
Angle of approach	(deg)	52
Angle of departure	(deg)	44
Fuel consumption, average conditions	(miles per gal)	3
Cruising range, average conditions	(miles)	150
Maximum allowable speed	(mph)	30
Number of speeds forward		

ENGINE

Manufacturer	Hercules	Model HXD
Type	In-line, 4 cycle	Number of cylinders 6
Displacement		(cu in.) 855
Governed speed		(rpm) 1,700
Brake horsepower		
Ignition type		Battery

ADDITIONAL DATA

Winch capacity	(lb)	15,000

Equipped with a 10-ton capacity boom crane, rear-mounted underslung winch, 110-volt DC electric power plant, 3,000 watts capacity, and floodlamps.

TRUCK TRACTOR, 8-TON, 6 x 4

Technical Manual: TM 10-1551   Parts List: SNL G-556

Manufacturers: Corbitt Co.; General Motors Truck & Coach Div. of
    Yellow Truck & Coach Mfg. Co.

RA PD 308947

Vehicle illustrated above: Corbitt

Classification: Limited standard

Purpose: To tow semitrailers.

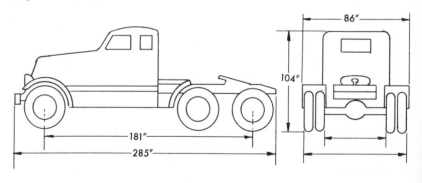

TRUCK TRACTOR, 8-TON, 6 x 4

GENERAL DATA

Crew.. 2
Weight.................Net.....................(lb) 14,300
                   Payload..................(lb) 16,000
                   Gross....................(lb) 30,300
Shipping dimensions.......(cu ft)   ....(sq ft)
Tires....................Ply...10.......Size...9.00 x 20
Tread, center to center (in.).Front ....Rear
Ground clearance................................(in.)
Electrical system...............................(volts) 12
Capacities..............Fuel,   octane gasoline....(gal) 75
                  Cooling system...........(qt) 35
                  Crankcase (refill)..........(qt) 10
Brakes..............................(Westinghouse) Air

PERFORMANCE

Maximum gradability............................(percent)
Turning radius......................................(ft) 42½
Fording depth......................................(in.)
Angle of approach.................................(deg)
Angle of departure................................(deg)
Fuel consumption, average conditions.........(miles per gal) 2.6
Cruising range, average conditions.................(miles) 195
Maximum allowable speed.........................(mph)
Number of speeds forward.............................

ENGINE

Manufacturer......Continental...............Model 22R
Type.............In-line, 4 cycle.....Number of cylinders 6
Displacement......................................(cu in.)
Governed speed....................................(rpm)
Brake horsepower....................................
Ignition type....................................Battery

ADDITIONAL DATA

....
....
....
....

TRACTOR, CRANE, 2-TON, M3

Technical Manuals: Parts Lists: SNL G- 69 (CAT.)
SNL G-132 (IHC)

Manufacturers: International Harvester Co.; Crane: Hughes-Keenan
Co., Model MC-1R; Caterpillar Tractor Co., Model D6; Crane:
Cardwell Crane Co., Model B.

Vehicle illustrated : International TD14

Classification: Standard

Purpose: Used by Army Air Forces
to perform light towing and lifting
operations.

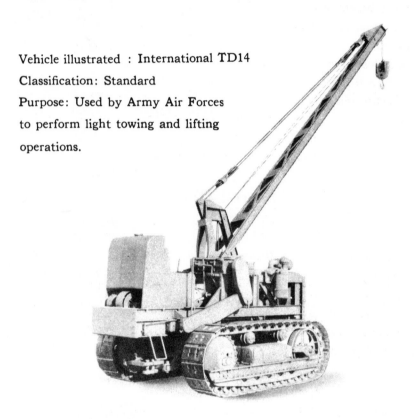

RA PD 309107

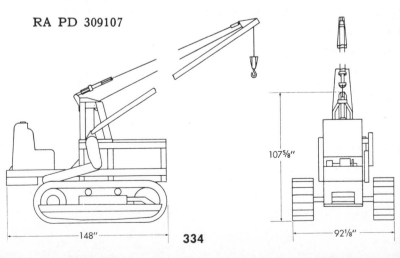

334

TRACTOR, CRANE, 2-TON, M3

GENERAL DATA

Crew. 1
Weight. . . . . .Net. . . . .(lb) 21,540
Shipping dimensions. . . . . .(cu ft) . . . .(sq ft)
Tread, center to center. . . . .(in.) 74
Track width. . . . .(in.) 16
Ground clearance. . . . .(in.) 9⅞
Ground pressure. . . . .(lbs per sq in.) 8.71
Electrical system. . . . . .None
Capacities. . . . . .Fuel, commercial Diesel fuel oil. . . . . .(gal) 46½
                         Cooling system. . . . .(qt) 80
                         Crankcase (refill). . . . .(qt)
Brakes. . . . . .Mechanical

PERFORMANCE

Maximum gradability. . . . .(percent)
Turning radius. . . . . .Without boom. . . . .(ft) 8¾
Fording depth. . . . .(in.)
Fuel consumption, average conditions. . . . .(miles per gal)
Cruising range, average conditions. . . . .(miles) 110
Maximum allowable speed. . . . .(mph) 5.8
Number of speeds forward. 6

ENGINE

Manufacturer. . . . . .IHC. . . . . .Model TD14
Type. . . . . .In-line, 4 cycle, Diesel . . . No. of cylinders 4
Displacement. . . . .(cu in.) 460.7
Governed speed. . . . .(rpm)
Brake horsepower. 68.5
Ignition type. . . . . .Compression

ADDITIONAL DATA

Maximum lifting capacity 4,000 pounds at 12-foot radius. Boom traverse, 260°. Hoisting speed 45 feet per minute.

Caterpillar Model D6 with Cardwell Crane Model B differs considerably from International Model TD-14 in weights, etc.

TRACTOR, CRANE, 6-TON, M4

Technical Manuals: Parts List: SNL G-126

Manufacturers: Caterpillar Tractor Co.; Crane: Cardwell Crane Co.

RA PD 66495

Classification: Standard

Purpose: Used by Army Air Forces to lift aircraft engines into engine
mounts.

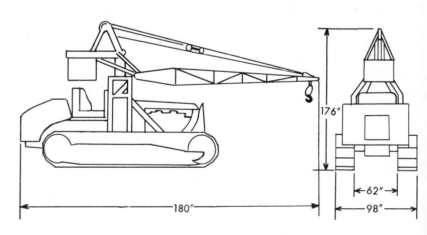

TRACTOR, CRANE, 6-TON, M4

GENERAL DATA

Crew 1
Weight . . . . Gross . . . . (lb) 41,846
Shipping dimensions . . . . . . (cu ft) 1,520 . . . . (sq ft) 104
Track width . . . . (in.) 18
Ground clearance . . . . (in.) 15½
Ground pressure . . . . (lbs per sq in.) 10.5
Electrical system . . . . (volts) 6
Capacities . . . . Fuel, 50 cetane Diesel fuel oil . . . . (gal) 65
Cooling system . . . . (qt) 72
Crankcase (refill) . . . . (qt) 22
Brakes . . . . Mechanical

PERFORMANCE

Maximum gradability . . . . (percent) 40
Turning radius . . . . (ft) 11
Fording depth . . . . (in.) 35
Angle of approach . . . . (deg) 40
Angle of departure . . . . (deg) 30
Fuel consumption, average conditions
   (w/o towed load) . . . . (miles per gal) 1.5
Cruising range, average conditions . . . . (miles) 100
Maximum allowable speed . . . . (mph) 6
Number of speeds forward . . . .

ENGINE

Manufacturer . . . . . Caterpillar . . . . Model D7
Type . . . . In-line, 4 cycle, Diesel . . . . No. of cylinders 4
Displacement . . . . (cu in.) 831
Governed speed . . . . (rpm) 1,000
Brake horsepower 80
Ignition type . . . . Compression

ADDITIONAL DATA

Maximum lifting capacity 17,900 pounds at 10-foot radius. Boom traverse
300°. Hoisting speed 51 feet per minute.

. . . .
. . . .
. . . .

TRACTOR, CRANE, 2-TON, M5

Technical Manuals: Parts List: SNL G-99

Manufacturers: International Harvester Co. T9; Crane: Trackson Co., Model CT-9.

Classification: Standard   RA PD 309106

Purpose: Used by Aviation Ordnance companies.

338

TRACTOR, CRANE, 2-TON, M5

GENERAL DATA

Crew			1
Weight	Net	(lb)	18,725
Shipping dimensions	(cu ft)	(sq ft)	
Tread, center to center		(in.)	60
Track width		(in.)	15
Ground clearance		(in.)	10
Ground pressure		(lbs per sq in.)	8.68
Electrical system		(volts)	6
Capacities	Fuel, 70 octane gasoline	(gal)	31
	Cooling system	(qt)	48
	Crankcase (refill)	(qt)	11
Brakes		Mechanical	

PERFORMANCE

Maximum gradability	(percent)	
Turning radius	(ft)	8
Fording depth	(in.)	
Fuel consumption, average conditions	(miles per gal)	
Cruising range, average conditions	(miles)	55
Maximum allowable speed	(mph)	
Number of speeds forward		5

ENGINE

Manufacturer	IHC	Model T9	
Type	In-line, 4 cycle	Number of cylinders	4
Displacement		(cu in.)	353
Governed speed		(rpm)	
Brake horsepower			52
Ignition type		Magneto	

ADDITIONAL DATA

Maximum lifting capacity 4,000 pounds at 8-foot radius. Boom traverse 260°. Hoisting speed 71 feet per minute.

TRACTOR, LIGHT

Technical Manuals: Parts Lists: SNL G-151 (CAT.)
                                                   SNL G- 99 (IHC)

Manufacturers: Caterpillar Tractor Co., Model D4; International
    Harvester Co., Model TD9

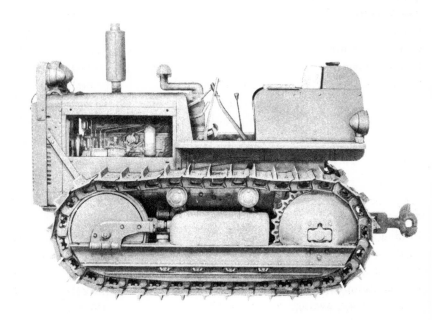

RA PD 66477

Vehicle illustrated above: International TD9

Classification: Standard

Purpose: To tow artillery over light terrain.

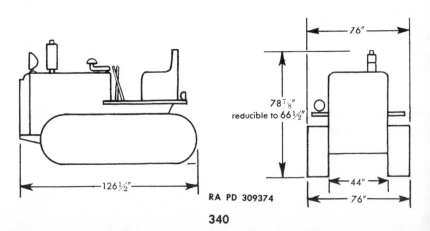

RA PD 309374

TRACTOR, LIGHT

GENERAL DATA

Crew. 1
Weight. . . . . .Gross. (lb) 11,325
Shipping dimensions. . . . . .(cu ft) 439. . . . . (sq ft) 67
Track width. . . . .(in.) 16
Ground clearance. . . . .(in.) $9\frac{5}{8}$
Ground pressure. . . . .(lbs per sq in.) 5.58
Electrical system. . . . .(volts) 6
Capacities. . . . . . . .Fuel, 50 cetane Diesel fuel oil. . . . . . .(gal) 31
                        Cooling system. . . . .(qt) 52
                        Crankcase (refill). . . . .(qt) 11
Brakes. . . . . .Mechanical

PERFORMANCE

Maximum gradability. . . . .(percent) 58
Turning radius. . . . .(ft) $7\frac{1}{4}$
Fording depth. . . . .(in.) 31
Angle of approach. . . . .(deg) 45
Angle of departure. . . . .(deg) 14
Fuel consumption, average conditions. . . . .(miles per gal) 3.3
Cruising range, average conditions. . . . .(miles) 51
Maximum allowable speed. . . . .(mph) 5.3

ENGINE

Manufacturer. . .IHC. . . . . .Model TD9
Type. . . . . .In-line, 4 cycle, Diesel. . . . . .No. of cylinders 4
Displacement. . . . .(cu in.) 334.5
Governed speed. . . . .(rpm) 1,400
Brake horsepower. . . . .
Ignition type. . . . . .Compression and magneto

ADDITIONAL DATA

Gasoline and magneto used for starting.
Gasoline tank capacity $\frac{2}{3}$ gal.

. . . .
. . . .
. . . .

TRACTOR, MEDIUM, M1

Technical Manuals: Allis-Chalmers—TM 9-783B, TM 9-1783A, TM 9-1783B, TM 9-1783C.

Parts Lists:
SNL G-132 (IHC)
SNL G-125 (A-C)
SNL G- 69 (Cat.)

Manufacturers: Allis-Chalmers Co., Model HD7W; Caterpillar Tractor Co., Model D6; Cleveland Tractor Co.; International Harvester Co. Model TD14

RA PD 66481

Vehicle illustrated above: International, Model TD14

Classification: Standard

Purpose: To tow artillery or equipment over rough terrain.

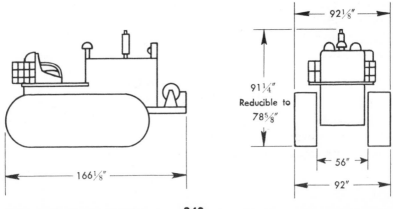

342

TRACTOR, MEDIUM, M1

GENERAL DATA

Crew			1
Weight	Gross	(lb)	21,600
Shipping dimensions	(cu ft)	(sq ft) 106	
Track width		(in.)	18
Ground clearance		(in.)	$9\frac{3}{8}$
Ground pressure		(lbs per sq in.)	7.63
Electrical system		(volts)	6
Capacities	Fuel, 50 cetane Diesel fuel oil	(gal)	90
	Cooling system	(qt)	80
	Crankcase (refill)	(qt)	16
Brakes		Mechanical	

PERFORMANCE

Maximum gradability	(percent)	36
Turning radius	(ft)	$9\frac{1}{3}$
Fording depth	(in.)	38
Angle of approach	(deg)	29
Angle of departure	(deg)	$10\frac{1}{2}$
Fuel consumption, average conditions	(miles per gal)	2.75
Cruising range, average conditions	(miles)	180
Maximum allowable speed	(mph)	$8\frac{1}{2}$
Number of speeds forward		

ENGINE

Manufacturer	IHC	Model TD14	
Type	In-line, 4 cycle, Diesel	No. of cylinders	4
Displacement		(cu in.)	
Governed speed		(rpm)	1,350
Brake horsepower			
Ignition type		Compression and magneto	

ADDITIONAL DATA

Winch capacity	(lb)	25,000

Gasoline and magneto used for starting.
Gasoline tank capacity $1\frac{1}{2}$ gal.

TRACTOR, HIGH SPEED, 7-TON, M2

Technical Manuals: Parts List: SNL G-96

Manufacturer: Cletrac Tractor Co. (The Cleveland Tractor Co.)

RA PD 309092

Classification: Standard

Purpose: Used by Army Air Forces to tow equipment over rough terrain.

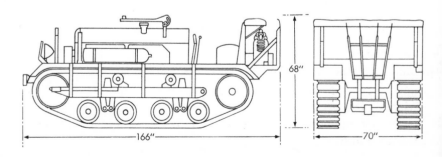

TRACTOR, HIGH SPEED, 7-TON, M2

GENERAL DATA

Crew		3
Weight . . . . Net . . . . (lb)		14,700
Shipping dimensions . . . . . . (cu ft) 495 . . . . (sq ft) 79		
Track width . . . . (in.)		14
Tread, center to center . . . . (in.)		52
Ground clearance . . . . (in.)		19
Ground pressure . . . . (lbs per sq in.)		7.9
Electrical system . . . . (volts)		12
Capacities . . . . Fuel, 70 octane gasoline . . . . . . (gal)		33
Cooling system . . . . (qt)		37
Crankcase (refill) . . . . (qt)		11
Brakes . . . . Mechanical		

PERFORMANCE

Maximum gradability . . . . (percent)	60
Turning radius . . . . (ft)	10½
Fording depth . . . . (in.)	32
Maximum vertical obstacle vehicle will climb . . . . (in.)	20
Fuel consumption, average conditions . . . . (miles per gal)	3
Cruising range, average conditions . . . . (miles)	100
Maximum allowable speed . . . . (mph)	22
Number of speeds forward	4

ENGINE

Manufacturer . . . . . Hercules WXLC3	
Type . . . . In-line, 4 cycle . . . . . . Number of cylinders	6
Displacement . . . . (cu in.)	404
Governed speed . . . . (rpm) 2500 and 3280	
Brake horsepower	150
Ignition type . . . . Battery	

ADDITIONAL DATA

Winch capacity . . . . (lb) 10,000

Has auxiliary generator, 3KW, 110 volts, DC current, driven by V-belt from tractor engine. Has air compressor driven by tractor engine, 16.7 cubic feet per minute, three stage, 2,000 pounds per square inch. Compressor equipped with pressure outlets reducible to 100 pounds per square inch.

TRACTOR, HIGH SPEED, 18-TON, M 4

Technical Manuals: TM 9-785.   Parts List: SNL G-150

Manufacturer: Allis-Chalmers Co.

Armament: One Gun, machine, cal. .50, HB, M2 (flexible).

Ammunition: 54 rounds, 3-in., when towing 3-in. AA gun; 54 rounds, 90-mm, when towing 90-mm AA gun; 30 rounds, 155-mm, when towing 155-mm gun; 20 rounds, 8-in., when towing 8-in. howitzer; 12 rounds, 240-mm, when towing 240-mm howitzer; 500 rounds, cal. .50.

RA PD 66483

Classification: Standard

Purpose: To tow heavy artillery over rough terrain.

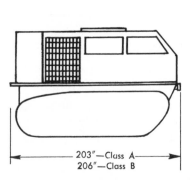

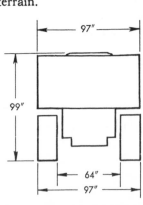

TRACTOR, HIGH SPEED, 18-TON, M4

GENERAL DATA

Crew		11
Weight (without crew or ammunition box—estimated)	(lb)	28,000
Weight (with crew and ammunition box—estimated)	(lb)	31,400
Shipping dimensions ...... (cu ft) 1,138 .... (sq ft)		
Track width	(in.)	16⁹⁄₁₆
Ground clearance	(in.)	20
Ground pressure, when towing 90-mm gun	(lb per sq in.)	7.6
when towing 155-mm gun	(lb per sq in.)	8.75
Electrical system	(volts)	12
Capacities .... Fuel, 70 octane gasoline	(gal)	125
Cooling system	(qt)	72
Crankcase (refill)	(qt)	20
Brakes	Mechanical	

PERFORMANCE

Maximum gradability	(percent)	45
Turning radius	(ft)	18½
Fording depth	(in.)	41
Angle of approach	(deg)	30
Angle of departure	(deg)	30
Fuel consumption, average conditions w/towed load	(miles per gal)	2
Cruising range, average conditions	(miles)	180
Maximum allowable speed	(mph)	35
Number of speeds forward		

ENGINE

Manufacturer ..... Waukesha .... Model 145GZ		
Type .... In-line, 4 cycle ..... Number of cylinders		6
Displacement	(cu in.)	815
Governed speed	(rpm)	2,100
Brake horsepower		
Ignition type	Battery	

ADDITIONAL DATA

Winch capacity	(lb)	30,000

TRACTOR, HIGH SPEED, 13-TON, M5

Technical Manuals: TM 9-786.   Parts List: SNL G-16?

Manufacturer: International Harvester Co.

Ammunition: Carries 56 rounds, 105-mm; or 24 rounds, 155-mm; or 38 rounds, 4.5 in.

RA PD 309101

Classification: Standard

Purpose: To tow artillery over rough terrain.

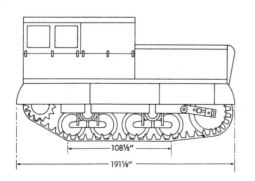

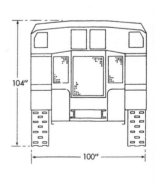

TRACTOR, HIGH SPEED, 13-TON, M 5

GENERAL DATA

Crew			9
Weight	Payload	(lb)	5,000
	Gross (with crew)	(lb)	28,000
Shipping dimensions	(cu ft)	(sq ft)	
Track width		(in.)	$11\frac{5}{8}$
Ground clearance		(in.)	$19\frac{3}{4}$
Ground pressure	(idler on ground)	(lb per sq in.)	11.1
Electrical system		(volts)	12
Capacities	Fuel, 70 octane gasoline	(gal)	100
	Cooling system	(qt)	
	Crankcase (refill)	(qt)	
Brakes			

PERFORMANCE

Maximum gradability	(percent)	
Turning radius	(ft)	18
Fording depth	(in.)	
Maximum vertical obstacle vehicle will climb	(in.)	
Angle of approach	(deg)	
Angle of departure	(deg)	
Fuel consumption, average conditions	(miles per gal)	
Cruising range, average conditions	(miles)	
Maximum allowable speed	(mph)	35
Number of speeds forward		4

ENGINE

Manufacturer	Continental	Model R6572	
Type	In-line, 4 cycle	Number of cylinders	6
Displacement		(cu in.)	572
Governed speed		(rpm)	2,900
Brake horsepower			235

ADDITIONAL DATA

TRACTOR, HEAVY, M1

Technical Manual: TM 9-1773

Parts List:

SNL G-98 (Allis-Chalmers)
SNL G-101 (IHC)
SNL G-126 (Caterpillar)

Manufacturers: Allis-Chalmers Co., Model HD10W; Caterpillar Tractor Co., Model D7; International Harvester Co., Model TD18

RA PD 66487

Vehicle illustrated above: Caterpillar Model D7

Classification: Standard

Purpose: To tow 155-mm gun.

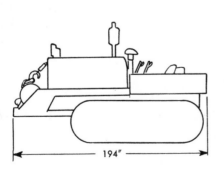

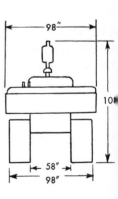

TRACTOR, HEAVY, M1

GENERAL DATA

Crew		4
Weight............Gross.....................(lb)		30,100
Shipping dimensions.....(cu ft) 1,188..........(sq ft) 132		
Track width...(in.)		20
Ground clearance...................................(in.)		15½
Ground pressure.........................(lb per sq in.)		8.05
Electrical system..................................(volts)		6
Capacities.............Fuel, 50 cetane Diesel fuel oil..(gal)		
Cooling system..............(qt)		72
Crankcase (refill)...........(qt)		22
Brakes.....................................Mechanical		

PERFORMANCE

Maximum gradability.......................(percent)		62
Turning radius......................................(ft)		11¼
Fording depth.....................................(in.)		35
Angle of approach................................(deg)		24
Angle of departure...............................(deg)		30
Fuel consumption, average conditions		
(w/towed load).........................(miles per gal)		1.4
(w/o towed load)........................(miles per gal)		2.8
Cruising range, average conditions...................(miles)		175
Maximum allowable speed.......................(mph)		11
Number of speeds forward................................		

ENGINE

Manufacturer...Caterpillar.....................Model D7		
Type..........In-line, 4 cycle, Diesel..Number of cylinders		4
Displacement......................................(cu in.)		831
Governed speed.....................................(rpm)		1,050
Brake horsepower......................................		80
Ignition type.................................Compression		

ADDITIONAL DATA

Winch capacity..........(with Hyster D7).............(lb)		40,000

. . . .

. . . .

TRACTOR, HIGH SPEED, 38-TON, M6

Technical Manuals: Parts List: SNL G-184

Manufacturer: Allis-Chalmers Mfg. Co.

RA PD 309112

Classification: Standard

Purpose: To tow heavy artillery over rough terrain.

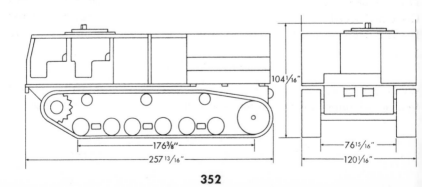

TRACTOR, HIGH SPEED, 38-TON, M6

GENERAL DATA

Crew, operating ...1.....Passenger capacity, including crew | 10
Weight.............. Net........................(lb) | 60,000
Payload.....................(lb) | 15,000
Gross.....................(lb) | 75,000
Shipping dimensions......(cu ft) 1,935...........(sq ft) 215
Track width...(in.) | 21$\frac{9}{16}$
Ground clearance....................................(in.) | 21$\frac{1}{2}$
Ground pressure, track......................(lb per sq in.) | 8
Electrical system....................................(volts) | 12
Capacities..............Fuel, 70 octane gasoline......(gal) | 300
Cooling system (each).........(qt) | 72
Crankcase (each) (refill).......(qt) | 20
Transmission................(qt) | 84
Final drive (each)...........(qt) | 28
Brakes......................................Mechanical

PERFORMANCE

Maximum gradability...........................(percent) | 40
Turning radius..(ft) | 14$\frac{1}{2}$
Fording depth..(in.) | 54
Angle of approach..................................(deg) | 35
Angle of departure.................................(deg) | 35
Fuel consumption, average conditions........(miles per gal) | .5
Cruising range, average conditions................(miles) | 150
Maximum allowable speed........................(mph) | 20.5

	1st	2nd or high gear
Cruising speeds..	6	20.5

ENGINES (two)

Manufacturer.....Waukesha...............Model 145GZ
Type.............In-line, 4 cycle......Number of cylinders | 6
Displacement, each...............................(cu in.) | 815
Governed speed....................................(rpm) | 2,100
Brake horsepower, each................................ | 215

ADDITIONAL DATA

Winch capacity.......................................(lb) | 60,000
Vehicle is equipped with torque converter.

....

....

AMBULANCE, ½-TON, 4 x 4

Technical Manuals: TM 10-1179, TM 10-1153, Parts List: SNL G-505
TM 10-1123 (C1), TM 10-1209,
TM 10-1201 (C1), TM 10-1443.

Manufacturer: Dodge Brothers Corp. (Div. of Chrysler Corp.)

RA PD 66313

Classification: Limited standard

Purpose: To transport sick and wounded personnel.

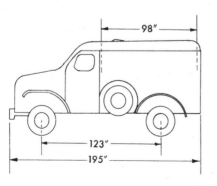

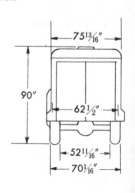

AMBULANCE, ½-TON, 4 x 4

GENERAL DATA

Crew.. 2
Weight................. Net........................(lb) 5640
                   Payload...................(lb) 1000
                   Gross.....................(lb) 6640
Shipping dimensions.......(cu ft) 770...........(sq ft) 103
Tires....................Ply...6........Size...7.50 x 16
Tread, center to center (in.).Front 59⅜...........Rear 61⅜
Ground clearance....................................(in.) 9
Electrical system.................................(volts) 6
Capacities...............Fuel, 70 octane gasoline.....(gal) 25
                   Cooling system.............(qt) 17
                   Crankcase (refill)...........(qt) 5
Brakes..Hydraulic

PERFORMANCE

Maximum gradability...........................(percent) 58
Turning radius......................................(ft) 27
Fording depth......................................(in.) 32
Angle of approach.................................(deg) 62
Angle of departure................................(deg) 30
Fuel consumption, average conditions..........(miles per gal) 12
Cruising range, average conditions..................(miles) 300
Maximum allowable speed..........................(mph) 55
Number of speeds forward............................... 4

ENGINE

Manufacturer......Dodge.........Models T207, T211, T215
Type.............In-line, 4 cycle......Number of cylinders 6
Displacement....................................(cu in.) 230.2
Governed speed...................................(rpm) 3100
Brake horsepower.......................................
Ignition type.....................................Battery

ADDITIONAL DATA

....
....
....
....

AMBULANCE, ¾-TON, 4 x 4

Technical Manuals: TM 10-1531.   Parts List: SNL G-50?

Manufacturer: Dodge Brothers Corp. (Div. of Chrysler Corp.)

RA PD 66315

Classification: Standard

Purpose: To transport sick and wounded personnel.

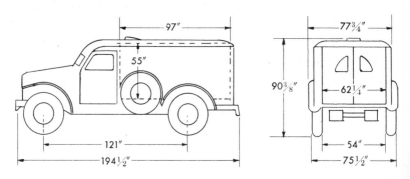

AMBULANCE, ¾-TON, 4 x 4

GENERAL DATA

Crew			2
Weight	Net	(lb)	5,920
	Payload	(lb)	1,800
	Gross	(lb)	7,720
Shipping dimensions	(cu ft) 790	(sq ft) 105	
Tires	Ply . . . 8	Size . . . 9.00 x 16	
Tread, center to center		(in.)	64¾
Ground clearance		(in.)	10⅝
Electrical system		(volts)	6
Capacities	Fuel, 72 octane gasoline	(gal)	30
	Cooling system	(qt)	8
	Crankcase (refill)	(qt)	5
Brakes		Hydraulic	

PERFORMANCE

Maximum gradability	(percent)	54
Turning radius (ft)	Right 24	Left 26
Fording depth	(in.)	34
Angle of approach	(deg)	53
Angle of departure	(deg)	24
Fuel consumption, average conditions	(miles per gal)	8
Cruising range, average conditions	(miles)	240
Maximum allowable speed	(mph)	54
Number of speeds forward		4

ENGINE

Manufacturer	Dodge	Model T214
Type	In-line, 4 cycle	Number of cylinders 6
Displacement	(cu in.)	230.2
Governed speed	(rpm)	3,200
Brake horsepower		76
Ignition type		Battery

ADDITIONAL DATA

. . . .

. . . .

AMBULANCE, METROPOLITAN, ¾-TON, 4 x 2

Technical Manuals:

Parts Lists: SNL G-549 (Packard)
SNL G-548 (Cadillac)

Manufacturers: Packard Motor Car Co.; Body by Henney

Cadillac Motor Car Div. (General Motors Corp.); Body by Superior

RA PD 308964

Vehicle illustrated above: Packard Motor Car Co.

Classification: Standard

Purpose: To transport sick and wounded personnel.

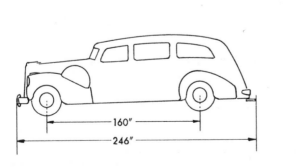
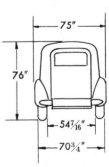

AMBULANCE, METROPOLITAN, ¾-TON, 4 x 2

GENERAL DATA

Crew, operating.....2......Passenger capacity, including crew   12

Weight.................Net.......................(lb)   5,125

Payload...................(lb)   1,500

Gross.....................(lb)   6,625

Tires....................Ply...6.......Size...7.50 x 16

Ground clearance....................................(in.)

Electrical system..................................(volts)   6

Capacities..............Fuel, 68 octane gasoline.....(gal)   20

Cooling system.............(qt)   17

Crankcase (refill)...........(qt)   6

Brakes...................4-wheel.............Hydraulic

PERFORMANCE

Turning radius (ft)........Right 26..............Left 27

Fuel consumption, average conditions.........(miles per gal)   12

Cruising range, average conditions..................(miles)   240

Maximum allowable speed..........................(mph)   50

Number of speeds forward.............................   3

ENGINE

Manufacturer......Packard.................Model 2001-A

Type.............In-line, 4 cycle......Number of cylinders   8

Displacement......................................(cu in.)   282

Governed speed....................................(rpm)   2,830

Brake horsepower...

Ignition type....................................Battery

ADDITIONAL DATA

. . . .
. . . .
. . . .
. . . .

AMBULANCE, FIELD, 1½-TON, 4 x 2

Technical Manuals: TM 10-1365, TM 10-1403. Parts List: SNL G-617

Manufacturer: Chevrolet Motor Division (General Motors Corp.)

RA PD 308965

Classification: Limited standard

Purpose: To transport sick and wounded personnel.

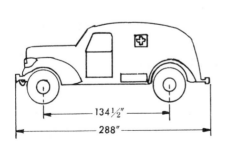

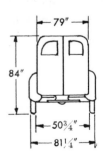

AMBULANCE, FIELD, 1½-TON, 4 x 2

GENERAL DATA

Crew, operating.....2......Passenger capacity, including crew   10

Weight.................Net.....................(lb)   5,485

Payload...................(lb)   2,400

Gross....................(lb)   7,885

Shipping dimensions........(cu ft)   ....(sq ft)

Tires...................Ply...6.......Size...6.50 x 20

Tread, center to center (in.). Front 59¹⁵⁄₁₆............Rear 66

Ground clearance......................................(in.)   8⅞

Electrical system...............................(volts)   6

Capacities...............Fuel, 68 octane gasoline.....(gal)   18

Cooling system.............(qt)   16

Crankcase (refill)...........(qt)   6

Brakes.................4 wheel.............Hydraulic

PERFORMANCE

Turning radius (ft).......Right 25.................Left 26

Fuel consumption, average conditions.........(miles per gal)   8

Cruising range, average conditions................(miles)   150

Maximum allowable speed........................(mph)   45

Number of speeds forward.................................   4

ENGINE

Manufacturer......Chevrolet............Model BQ-1001 up

Type.............In-line, 4 cycle......Number of cylinders   6

Displacement.......................................(cu in.)   216.5

Governed speed.................................(rpm)   2,860

Brake horsepower...

Ignition type......................................Battery

ADDITIONAL DATA

....

....

....

....

BUS, SEDAN, CONVERTED, 15-PASSENGER, 4 x 2

Technical Manuals: Parts List: SNL G-520

Manufacturers—Chassis: Chevrolet Motor Division (General Motors Corp.)—Body by various manufacturers.

RA PD 308962

Classification: Substitute standard

Purpose: To transport personnel.

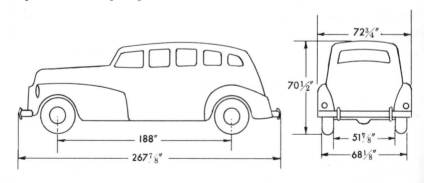

BUS, SEDAN, CONVERTED, 15-PASSENGER, 4 x 2

GENERAL DATA

Crew, operating.....1......Passenger capacity, including crew   16
Weight...................Net.....................(lb)   4,950
                      Payload..................(lb)   2,250
                      Gross....................(lb)   7,200
Shipping dimensions.......(cu ft)   ....(sq ft)
Tires....................Ply...6........Size...7.50 x 16
Tread, center to center (in.).Front 57⅝.............Rear 60
Ground clearance......................................(in.)   8¾
Electrical system....................................(volts)   6
Capacities...............Fuel, 70 octane gasoline.....(gal)   16
                      Cooling system.............(qt)   15
                      Crankcase (refill)...........(qt)   5
Brakes.................4-wheel.............Hydraulic

PERFORMANCE

Turning radius (ft).........Right 21½............Left 20½
Angle of approach....................................(deg)
Angle of departure...................................(deg)
Fuel consumption, average conditions.........(miles per gal)   15
Cruising range, average conditions..................(miles)   240
Maximum allowable speed.........................(mph)   35
Number of speeds forward.............................   3

ENGINE

Manufacturer....Chevrolet....................Model 1942
Type...........In-line, 4 cycle.......Number of cylinders   6
Displacement......................................(cu in.)   216.5
Governed speed......................................   1667
Brake horsepower....................................   90
Ignition type....................................Battery

ADDITIONAL DATA

. . . .
. . . .
. . . .
. . . .

BUS, PASSENGER, 25-PASSENGER

Technical Manuals: TM 10-1389   Parts List:

Manufacturers: Available Truck Co.; Ford Motor Company.

RA PD 308960

Vehicle illustrated above: Available Truck Co.

Classification: Standard

Purpose: To transport personnel.

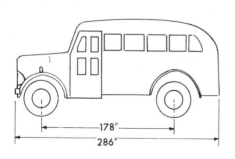

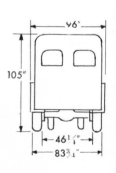

BUS, PASSENGER, 25-PASSENGER

GENERAL DATA

Crew, operating.....1......Passenger capacity, including crew 26

Weight.................Net......................(lb) 9,100

Payload...................(lb) 4,000

Gross....................(lb) 13,100

Shipping dimensions........(cu ft) ....(sq ft)

Tires....................Ply...8........Size...7.50 x 20

Tread, center to center (in.).Front 69..............Rear 65

Ground clearance.....................................(in.) 10 1/16

Electrical system....................................(volts) 6

Capacities...............Fuel, 68 octane gasoline.....(gal) 34

Cooling system.............(qt) 18

Crankcase (refill)...........(qt) 8

Brakes..................4-wheel.....Hydraulic (Lockheed)

PERFORMANCE

Turning radius (ft)..........Right 30...............Left 31

Angle of approach................................(deg)

Angle of departure...............................(deg)

Fuel consumption, average conditions..........(miles per gal) 6

Cruising range, average conditions..................(miles) 204

Maximum allowable speed........................(mph) 35

Number of speeds forward.............................. 4

ENGINE

Manufacturer......Waukesha................Model 6-BM

Type.............In-line, 4 cycle......Number of cylinders 6

Displacement.....................................(cu in.) 263

Governed speed....................................(rpm) 2,310

Brake horsepower.....................................

Ignition type......................................Battery

ADDITIONAL DATA

....

....

....

....

BUS, COMMERCIAL TYPE, 20-29 PASSENGER, 1½-TON, 4 x 2

Technical Manuals:

Manufacturers: Various

Parts List: SNL G-540

RA PD 308910

Vehicle illustrated above: Ford

Classification: Substitute standard

Purpose: To transport personnel.

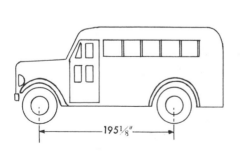

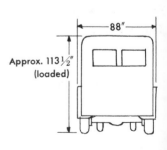

BUS, COMMERCIAL TYPE, 20-29 PASSENGER, 1½-TON, 4 x 2

GENERAL DATA

Crew, operating.....1......Passenger capacity, including crew   30

Weight................Net....................(lb) 8,250

Payload...................(lb) 4,500

Gross....................(lb) 12,750

Shipping dimensions.......(cu ft) ....(sq ft)

Tires...................Ply...8 or 10...Size...7.50 x 20

Tread, center to center (in.).Front 58⅝.............Rear 66

Ground clearance...................................(in.) 9¾

Electrical system....................................(volts) 6

Capacities..............Fuel, 68 octane gasoline.....(gal) 18

Cooling system.............(qt) 14

Crankcase (refill)...........(qt) 5

Brakes................4-wheel.............Hydraulic

PERFORMANCE

Turning radius (ft)........Right 28...............Left 30

Angle of approach...................................(deg)

Angle of departure..................................(deg)

Fuel consumption, average conditions.........(miles per gal) 9

Cruising range, average conditions..................(miles) 160

Maximum allowable speed..........................(mph) 35

Number of speeds forward.............................. 4

ENGINE

Manufacturer......Various..............Model—Will vary

Type............Various.............Number of cylinders 6 & 8

Displacement.......................................(cu in.) 232-239

Brake horsepower......................................

Ignition type....................................Battery

ADDITIONAL DATA

All data given are approximate and will vary with
different manufacturers.

....

....

....

BUS, 40-PASSENGER, 2½-TON, 4 x 2

Technical Manual: TM 10-1389.   Parts List:

Manufacturers: Available Truck Co.; Diamond T Motor Car Co.; Federal Motor Truck Co.

RA PD 308961

Vehicle illustrated above: Available Truck Co.

Classification: Limited standard

Purpose: To transport personnel.

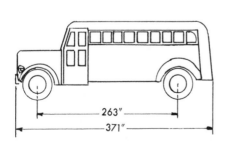

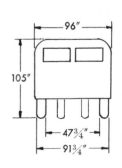

BUS, 40-PASSENGER, 2½-TON, 4 x 2

GENERAL DATA

Crew, operating.....1.....Passenger capacity, including crew 41
Weight...............Net...................(lb) 13,260
           Payload.................(lb) 6,000
           Gross...................(lb) 19,260
Shipping dimensions.......(cu ft) ....(sq ft)
Tires...............Ply...10......Size...9.00 x 20
Tread, center to center (in.).Front 69............Rear 69¾
Ground clearance....................................(in.) 10¹⁵⁄₁₆
Electrical system....................................(volts) 6
Capacities.............Fuel, 68 octane gasoline.....(gal) 34
           Cooling system.............(qt) 24
           Crankcase (refill)...........(qt) 8
Brakes...................Timken-Westinghouse.......Air

PERFORMANCE

Turning radius (ft)........Right 40...............Left 41
Angle of approach....................................(deg)
Angle of departure....................................(deg)
Fuel consumption, average conditions.........(miles per gal) 6
Cruising range, average conditions....................(miles) 204
Maximum allowable speed..........................(mph) 35
Number of speeds forward................................ 5

ENGINE

Manufacturer......Waukesha................Model 6-BZ
Type.............In-line, 4 cycle......Number of cylinders 6
Displacement...(cu in.) 320
Governed speed..(rpm) 2,900
Brake horsepower.......................................
Ignition type.......................................Battery

ADDITIONAL DATA

. . . .

. . . .

. . . .

. . . .

BUS, SEMITRAILER, CONVERTED, 40-45 PASSENGER

Technical Manuals: Parts List:

Manufacturers: Various

RA PD 308963

Classification: Substitute standard

Purpose: To transport personnel.

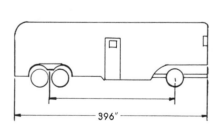

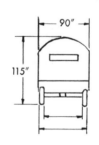

BUS, SEMITRAILER, CONVERTED, 40-45 PASSENGER

GENERAL DATA

Body type...Bus*

Trailer Weight............Net..............Approx. (lb) 12,000

Payload capacity.............................45 passengers

Tread†...

Tires...................Operating...................... 4

               Size**...

Brakes.......................................Air or vacuum

Towing tractor..Truck tractor, 1½-ton—2-ton commercial type

Ground clearance, under bed.........Varies, unit is very low

ADDITIONAL DATA

*These units were purchased as used new-car haulaway trailers, reconditioned and converted by cutting away part of the original superstructure and building a bus body on the remaining chassis.

†Treads vary.

**Tires were those on the vehicles at the time of purchase and varied in size from 7.00 x 20 to 8.25 x 20. Approximately 25 different contractors made these bus conversions.

CAR, LIGHT SEDAN, 5-PASSENGER, 4 x 2

Technical Manuals: Chevrolet—
      TM 10-1303, TM 10-1133.
      Ford—TM 10-1375.
Plymouth—TM 10-1149, TM 10-1151.

Parts Lists:
  SNL G-520 (Chev.)
  SNL G-521 (Plym.)
  SNL G-522 (Ford)

Manufacturers: Chevrolet Motor Division (General Motors Corp.); Ford Motor Co.; Plymouth Division, Chrysler Motor Corporation.

RA PD 66355

Vehicle illustrated above: Chevrolet

Classification: Standard

Purpose: To transport personnel.

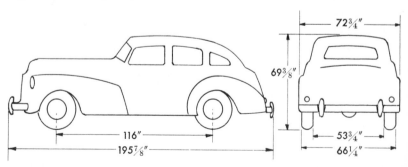

CAR, LIGHT SEDAN, 5-PASSENGER, 4 x 2

GENERAL DATA

Crew, operating.....2......Passenger capacity, including crew — 5
Weight................Net....................(lb) — 3,275
                      Payload..................(lb) — 800
                      Gross...................(lb) — 4,075
Shipping dimensions.......(cu ft) 575.............(sq ft) 99
Tires...................Ply...4.......Size...6.00 x 16
Tread, center to center (in.).Front $57\frac{21}{32}$............Rear 60
Ground clearance...................................(in.) — $7\frac{5}{8}$
Electrical system...................................(volts) — 6
Capacities...............Fuel, 72 octane gasoline.....(gal) — 16
                        Cooling system.............(qt) — 14
                        Crankcase (refill)...........(qt) — 6
Brakes.......................................Hydraulic

PERFORMANCE

Maximum gradability............................(percent) — 38
Turning radius (ft).........Right $20\frac{1}{2}$...........Left $19\frac{1}{2}$
Angle of approach...................................(deg) — 25
Angle of departure..................................(deg) — 15
Fuel consumption, average conditions..........(miles per gal) — 14
Cruising range, average conditions..................(miles) — 224
Maximum allowable speed..........................(mph)
Number of speeds forward.............................. — 3

ENGINE

Manufacturer......Chevrolet........Model 1942—BA-1001
Type..............In-line, 4 cycle.....Number of cylinders — 6
Displacement....................................(cu in.) — 216.5
Governed speed...........................Not governed
Brake horsepower.....................................
Ignition type...................................Battery

ADDITIONAL DATA

. . . .
. . . .
. . . .
. . . .

CAR, MEDIUM SEDAN, 5-PASSENGER, 4 x 2

Technical Manuals: Parts List: SNL G-644

Manufacturers: Buick Motors Division (General Motors Corp.); Packard
  Motor Car Co.

RA PD 66361

Vehicle illustrated above: Packard

Classification: Standard

Purpose: To provide transportation for staff officers.

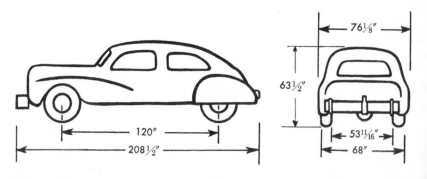

CAR, MEDIUM SEDAN, 5-PASSENGER, 4 x 2

GENERAL DATA

Crew, operating.....2.....Passenger capacity, including crew 5
Weight..................Net.......................(lb) 3,700
                        Payload..................(lb) 700
                        Gross....................(lb) 4,400
Shipping dimensions.......(cu ft) 583............(sq ft) 110
Tires....................Ply...4.......Size...6.50 x 15
Tread, center to center (in.). Front ....Rear
Ground clearance.....................................(in.) $6^{11}/_{16}$
Electrical system....................................(volts) 6
Capacities..............Fuel, 70 octane gasoline.....(gal) 17
                        Cooling system.............(qt) 17
                        Crankcase (refill)..........(qt) $5\frac{1}{2}$
Brakes..Hydraulic

PERFORMANCE

Maximum gradability............................(percent) 25
Turning radius......................................(ft) 21
Fording depth......................................(in.) $18\frac{3}{4}$
Angle of approach..................................(deg) 15
Angle of departure.................................(deg) 16
Fuel consumption, average conditions,
  with overdrive...........................(miles per gal) 20.9
Fuel consumption, average conditions, without
  overdrive................................(miles per gal) 18.4
Cruising range, average conditions, with overdrive.......(miles) 355
Cruising range, average conditions, without overdrive...(miles) 312
Maximum allowable speed..........................(mph) 90-95
Number of speeds forward................................. 3

ENGINE

Manufacturer......Packard....................Model 2001
Type.............In-line, 4 cycle......Number of cylinders 8
Displacement.....................................(cu in.) 282
Brake horsepower...
Ignition type....................................Battery

ADDITIONAL DATA

....
....
....

MOTORCYCLE, SOLO

Technical Manuals: Harley-Davidson—   Parts Lists:
TM 10-1177, TM 10-1359, TM 10-1361,   SNL G-524 (Ind.)
       TM 10-1175, TM 10-1331.   SNL G-523 (H.-D.)
         Indian—TM 10-1279.

Manufacturers: Harley-Davidson Motor Co., Model WLA;
      Indian Motocycle Co., Model 640-B

RA PD 66343

Vehicle shown above: Harley-Davidson, Model WLA

Classification: Standard

Purpose: To provide transportation for personnel engaged in reconnaissance, messenger service and police operations.

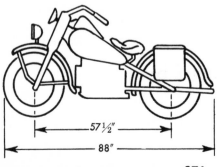
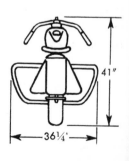

376

MOTORCYCLE, SOLO

GENERAL DATA

			Indian 640B	H.-D. WLA
Weight	Net	(lb)	537	535
	Payload	(lb)	200	200
	Gross	(lb)	737	735
Shipping dimensions		(sq ft)	20	16
		(cu ft)	78	54
Tires	Size		4.00 x 18	4.00 x 18
	Ply		4	4
Ground clearance		(in.)	5	4
Electrical system		(volts)	6	6
Capacities	Fuel, 70 octane gasoline	(gal)	3½	3⅓
	Crankcase (refill)	(qt)	3	4½
	Transmission	(pt)	1	¾
	Cooling system	Air cooled		

PERFORMANCE

Maximum gradability		(percent)	60	60
Turning radius	Left	(ft)	7¼	7½
	Right	(ft)	7¼	7¼
Fording depth		(in.)	11	18
Fuel consumption, average conditions	(miles per gal)		42	37
Cruising range, average conditions	(miles)		147	120
Maximum speed—not less than	(mph)		60	60
Number of speeds forward			3	3

ENGINE

Manufacturer . . Indian . . . . Model 640B
Harley-Davidson . . . . . . Model WLA

Type . . . . 42° "VEE", 4 cycle . No. of cylinders		2	2
Displacement	(cu in.)	45.44	45.12
Bore	(in.)	2⅞	2¾
Stroke	(in.)	3½	3¹³⁄₁₆

Ignition type . . . . Battery

ADDITIONAL DATA

. . . .
. . . .
. . . .

MOTORCYCLE, W/SIDE CAR

Technical Manuals: Harley-Davidson—
TM 10-1175, TM 10-1177, TM 10-1331,
TM 10-1359, TM 10-1361.
Indian—TM 10-1283.

Parts Lists:
SNL G-524 (Ind.)
SNL G-523 (H.-D.)

Manufacturers: Harley-Davidson Motor Co. Model ELA
Indian Motocycle Co. Model 340

RA PD 66353

Vehicle illustrated above: Indian, Model 340.

Classification: Standard

Purpose: To provide transportation for personnel engaged in reconnaissance, messenger service and police operations.

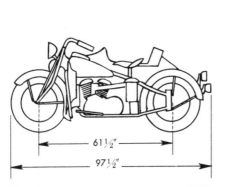

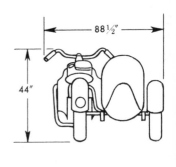

MOTORCYCLE, W/SIDE CAR

GENERAL DATA

			Indian 340	H. D. ELA
Weight	Net	(lb)	845	850
	Payload	(lb)	400	400
	Gross	(lb)	1,245	1,250
Shipping dimensions		(sq ft)	60	45
		(cu ft)	219	157
Tires	Size		4.50 x 18	4.50 x 18
	Ply		4	4
Ground clearance		(in.)	5¼	4⅛
Electrical system		(volts)	6	6
Capacities	Fuel, 70 octane gasoline	(gal)	3½	4
	Crankcase (refill)	(qt)	3	4
	Transmission	(pt)	1	1½
	Cooling system	Air cooled		

PERFORMANCE

Maximum gradability	(percent)		40	40
Turning radius	Left	(ft)	9	7½
	Right	(ft)	9	7½
Fording depth	(in.)		15	15
Cruising range, average conditions	(miles)		105	112
Maximum speed—not less than	(mph)		55	55
Number of speeds forward			3	3
Fuel consumption, average conditions	(miles per gal)		30	28

ENGINE

Manufacturer	Indian	Model 340		
	Harley-Davidson	Model ELA		
Type	42° "VEE", 4 cycle	No. of cylinders	2	2
Displacement	(cu in.)		73.625	60.32
Bore	(in.)		3¼	3⁵⁄₁₆
Stroke	(in.)		4⁷⁄₁₆	3½
Ignition type	Battery			

ADDITIONAL DATA

. . . .

. . . .

. . . .

. . . .

SCOOTER, MOTOR, W/PACKAGE CARRIER

Technical Manuals: TM 10-1399, T.O. 19-1-70. Parts List: SNL G-551

Manufacturer: Cushman Motor Co. (Model 39)

RA PD 66690

Classification: Standard

Purpose: To provide transportation for stock chasing, light delivery and messenger service.

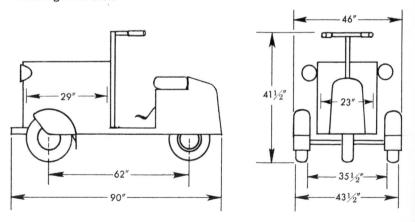

SCOOTER, MOTOR, W/PACKAGE CARRIER

GENERAL DATA

Crew... 1

Weight.................. Net (not more than)........(lb) 420

Payload (with driver).......(lb) 425

Gross (not more than).......(lb) 845

Shipping dimensions........(cu ft) 102...........(sq ft) 30

Tires....................Ply...4.........Size...4.00 x 8

Ground clearance....................................(in.) 4½

Electrical system..................................(volts) 6

Capacities...............Fuel, 70 octane gasoline.....(gal) 1⅛

Cooling system........Air cooled

Crankcase (refill)............(qt) 1½

Transmission..............(pt) 1½

Brakes......................................Mechanical

PERFORMANCE

Maximum gradability......(with load)............(percent) 15

Turning radius.......................................(ft) 17

Fuel consumption, average conditions, without load (miles per gal) 60

Cruising range, average conditions..................(miles) 60

Maximum speed....................................(mph) 25

ENGINE

Manufacturer......Cushman.................Model 10M70

Type.............4 cycle............Number of cylinders 1

Displacement.....................................(cu in.) 14.89

Bore..(in.) 2⅝

Stroke..(in.) 2¾

Brake horsepower....................................... 4

ADDITIONAL DATA

. . . .

. . . .

. . . .

. . . .

TRAILER, CARGO, AMPHIBIAN, ¼-TON

Technical Manuals: American Bantam,   Parts List: SNL G-605
   TM 10-1281. Willys-Overland, TM 10-1230.

Manufacturers: American Bantam Car Co.; Willys-Overland Motors,
   Inc.

Vehicle illustrated above: Willys-Overland   RA PD 66501

Classification: Standard

Purpose: To transport general cargo on land or through water.

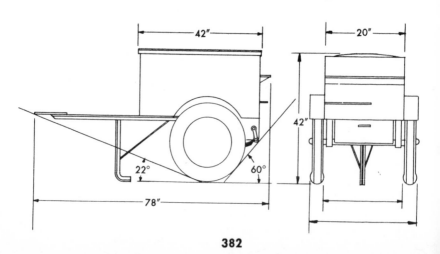

TRAILER, CARGO, AMPHIBIAN, ¼-TON

GENERAL DATA

Body type..Cargo

Weight.................Net.........................(lb)   550

                         Payload...................(lb)   500

                         Gross......................(lb)   1050

Loading height..(in.)   22

Ground clearance......................................(in.)   12½

Tread..(in.)   49

Tires.................Operating.......................   2

                        Ply.............................   6

                        Size ....6.00 x 16

Brakes..............................Hand parking only

Towing tractor..............Truck, ¼-ton and ¾-ton, 4 x 4

Shipping dimensions........(cu ft) 141.............(sq ft) 42

ADDITIONAL DATA

Trailer will float with 500 pound load, with 6 inches freeboard.

....
....
....
....

TRAILER, TELEPHONE CABLE SPLICER, ¼-TON, K38

Technical Manuals: Parts List:

Manufacturer: York Hoover Body Corp.

RA PD 308941

Classification: Standard

Purpose: Used by Signal Corps to store and transport cable splicers tool
equipment (TE-56).

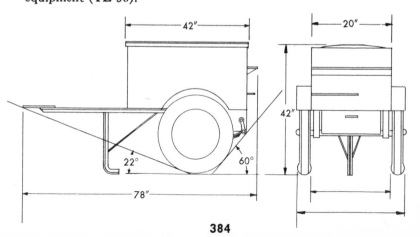

GENERAL DATA

Body type..			
Weight..................	Net......................	(lb)	410
	Payload..................	(lb)	500
	Gross....................	(lb)	910
Loading height.......................................		(in.)	
Ground clearance....................................		(in.)	13
Tread...		(in.)	33
Tires....................	Operating....................		2
	Ply.......................		4
	Size.......................		4.00 x 18
Brakes...			
Towing tractor.......................................			
Shipping dimensions....... (cu ft) 68............ (sq ft) 21			

ADDITIONAL DATA

....

....

....

....

TRAILER, AIRDROME UTILITY, ½-TON, TYPE F-1

Technical Manuals: Parts List:

Manufacturer: Ohio Tubular Products Co.

RA PD 309057

Classification: Standard

Purpose: Used by Army Air Forces for general utility purposes.

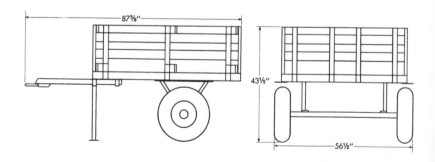

TRAILER, AIRDROME UTILITY, ½-TON, TYPE F-1

GENERAL DATA

Body type...Cargo

Weight.....................Net......................(lb)   300

Payload..................(lb) 1,000

Gross....................(lb) 1,300

Loading height.....................................(in.)   27

Ground clearance..................................(in.)

Tread...(in.)   49

Tires...................Operating....................   2

Ply.......................   6

Size....................... 6.00 x 8

Brakes..None

Towing tractor.......................Truck, ¼-ton, 4 x 4

Shipping dimensions........(cu ft) 25............(sq ft)

Weight, packed for export...........................(lb)   500

ADDITIONAL DATA

....
....
....
....

TRAILER, VAN, PUBLIC ADDRESS, ½-TON

Technical Manuals: Streich, TM 10-1216,   Parts List: SNL G-605
TM 10-1358.

Manufacturers: Bartlett Mfg. Co.; A. J. Miller (Auto Cruiser Trailer Co.);
Streich & Brothers Co.

Vehicle illustrated above: Streich   RA PD 66503

Classification: Limited standard

Purpose: To transport public address equipment, particularly for the
use of Chaplains in conducting field services.

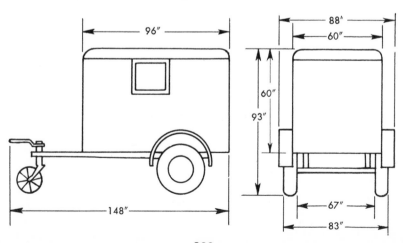

TRAILER, VAN, PUBLIC ADDRESS, ½-TON

GENERAL DATA

Body type..Van

Weight.................Net.......................(lb) 2150

Payload..................(lb) 1000

Gross...................(lb) 3150

Loading height....................................(in.) 22

Ground clearance..................................(in.) 13

Tread..(in.) 75

Tires..................Operating.................... 2

Ply....................... 8

Size........................ 7.50 x 20

Brakes............................Hand parking only

Towing tractor...................................

Shipping dimensions.......(cu ft) 485...........(sq ft) 63

ADDITIONAL DATA

....

....

....

....

TRAILER, CARGO, 1-TON

Technical Manual: TM 9-883

Parts List: SNL G-518

Manufacturers: Various.

RA PD 66505

Vehicle illustrated above: Ben Hur Mfg. Co.

Classification: Standard

Purpose: To transport general cargo.

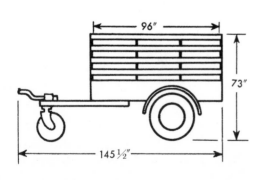
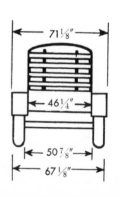

TRAILER, CARGO, 1-TON

GENERAL DATA

Body type . . . . Cargo

Weight	Net (steel body)	(lb)	1,470
	Net (wood body)	(lb)	1,282
	Payload	(lb)	2,000
	Gross (steel body)	(lb)	3,470
	Gross (wood body)	(lb)	3,282

Loading height, empty . . . . (in.)   32

Ground clearance . . . . (in.)   16½

Tread . . . . (in.)   59

Tires	Operating	2
	Ply	8
	Size	7.50 x 20

Brakes . . . . Hand parking only

Towing tractor . . . . Various

Shipping dimensions . . . . (cu ft) 438 . . . . (sq ft) 72

ADDITIONAL DATA

Similar vehicles manufactured by American Bantam Car Co.; Ben Hur Mfg. Co.; Century Boat Works; Checker Cab Mfg. Co.; Dorsey Brothers; Gerstenlager Co.; Henney Motor Co.; Hercules Body Co.; Highland Body Co.; J. W. Hobbs Corp.; Mifflinburg Body Co.; W. C. Nabors Co.; Nash-Kelvinator Corp. (Nash Motors Div.); Omaha Standard Body Corp.; Pike Trailer Co.; Queen City Mfg. Co.; Redman Trailer Co.; Steel Products Co. Inc.; Strick Co.; (The) Transportation Equipment Co.; Truck Engineering Corp.; Willys-Overland Motors Co.; Winter-Weiss Co.

TRAILER, 1-TON, MOBILE COMMUNICATION, K-19

Technical Manuals: Parts List: SNL G-517

Manufacturers: Fleetwheels, Inc.; A. J. Miller (Auto Cruiser Co.).

RA PD 66509

Vehicle illustrated above: Miller

Classification: Limited standard

Purpose: Used by Signal Corps to provide a mobile communication center.

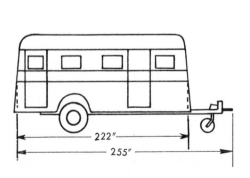

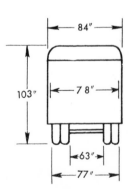

TRAILER, 1-TON, MOBILE COMMUNICATION, K-19

GENERAL DATA

Body type.................................Van, window
Weight..................Net.....................(lb)   5,385
                       Payload.................(lb)   2,000
                       Gross...................(lb)   7,385
Loading height....................................(in.)
Ground clearance..................................(in.)   15½
Tread...(in.)   72
Tires...................Operating....................   2
                       Ply.........................   8
                       Size........................   7.00 x 20
Brakes..Electric
Towing tractor..............................Truck K-18
Shipping dimensions........(cu ft)1, 276..........(sq ft) 148

ADDITIONAL DATA

....
....
....
....

TRAILER, CARGO, 1-TON, K-52 AND K-63

Technical Manuals: Parts List:

Manufacturers: Various.

RA PD 66505

Vehicle illustrated above: Ben-Hur Mfg. Co.

Classification: Standard

Purpose: To transport general cargo for Signal Corps.

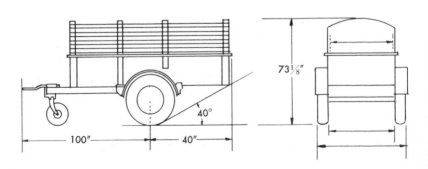

TRAILER, CARGO, 1-TON, K-52 AND K-63

GENERAL DATA

Body type		Cargo	
Weight	Net (wood body)	(lb)	1,282
	Payload	(lb)	2,000
	Gross	(lb)	3,232
Loading height, empty		(in.)	32
Ground clearance		(in.)	16½
Tread		(in.)	59
Tires	Operating		2
	Ply		8
	Size		7.50 x 20
Brakes	Hand parking only		
Towing tractor	Various		
Shipping dimensions	(cu ft) 438	(sq ft) 72	

ADDITIONAL DATA

Similar vehicles manufactured by: American Bantam Car Co.; Checker Cab Mfg. Co.; Gerstenslager Co.; Nash-Kelvinator Corp. (Nash Motors Div.) and Willys-Overland Motors, Inc.

Model K52 and K63 are the same and similar to Ordnance 1-ton cargo trailer.

TRAILER, 2-HORSE, VAN, 1-TON

Technical Manuals: Parts List: SNL G-606

Manufacturers: Bartlett Mfg. Co.; A. J. Miller (Auto Cruiser Trailer Co.); Porto Products Co.; Schult.

RA PD 66511

Vehicle illustrated above: Schult

Classification:

Purpose: To transport horses.

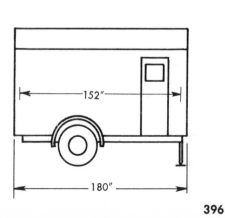

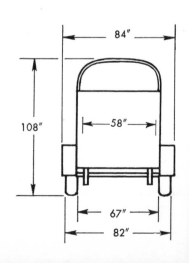

TRAILER, 2-HORSE, VAN, 1-TON

GENERAL DATA

Body type . . . . .Van

Weight . . . . .Net . . . . (lb) 2,300

        Payload . . . . (lb) 2,400

        Gross . . . . (lb) 4,700

Loading height . . . . (in.) 21

Ground clearance . . . . (in.) 13½

Tires . . . . .Operating 2

        Ply 6

        Size . . . . 7.50 x 16

Brakes . . . . .Electric

Towing tractor . . . .Various

Shipping dimensions . . . .(cu ft) 1,032 . . . . (sq ft) 105

ADDITIONAL DATA

. . . .

. . . .

. . . .

. . . .

TRAILER, PIGEON LOFT, 1-TON, PG45

Technical Manuals: Parts List:

Manufacturer: A. J. Miller (Auto Cruiser Trailer Co.).

RA PD 309105

Classification: Limited standard

Purpose: Used by Signal Corps to transport pigeons.

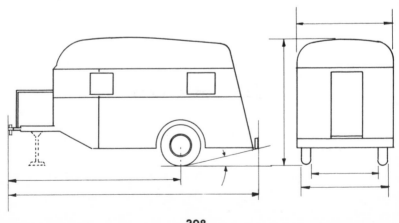

TRAILER, PIGEON LOFT, 1-TON, PG45

GENERAL DATA

Body type...

Weight.................Net.......................(lb)   4,010

                      Payload..................(lb)   1,000

                      Gross....................(lb)   5,010

Loading height......................................(in.)

Ground clearance....................................(in.)

Tires..................Operating......................   2

                      Spare........................   1

                      Ply..........................   8

                      Size........................ 7.50 x 20

Brakes...

Towing tractor.......................................

Shipping dimensions.......(cu ft)   ....(sq ft)

ADDITIONAL DATA

. . . .

. . . .

. . . .

. . . .

TRAILER, WATER TANK, 250-GAL., 1-TON

Technical Manual: TM 9-883   Parts List: SNL G-527

Manufacturers: Ben-Hur Mfg. Co.; Checker Cab Mfg. Co.; Springfield
     Auto Works

RA PD 66515

Vehicle illustrated above: Ben-Hur Model **K-WT**.

Classification: Standard

Purpose: To transport, store and dispense drinking water.

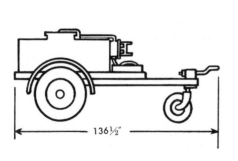
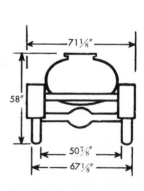

TRAILER, WATER TANK, 250-GAL., 1-TON

GENERAL DATA

Body type..Tank

Weight.....................Net.......................(lb) 1,400

Payload........250 gallons..(lb) 2,000

Gross.....................(lb) 3,400

Ground clearance......................................(in.) 16¼

Tread..(in.) 59

Tires...................Operating..................... 2

Ply.......................... 8

Size........................ 7.50 x 20

Brakes.............................Hand parking only

Towing tractor..................................Various

Shipping dimensions........(cu ft) 324...........(sq ft) 67

ADDITIONAL DATA

....
....
....
....

TRAILER, HOUSE TYPE, 1½-TON
(6-TON GROSS) K-35 AND K-65

Technical Manuals: Parts List:

Manufacturer: Checker Cab Mfg. Co.

RA PD 66513

Classification: K-35 substitute standard, K-65 standard

Purpose: To transport and house Signal Corps equipment.

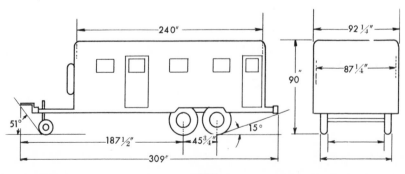

TRAILER, HOUSE TYPE, 1½-TON
(6-TON GROSS) K-35 AND K-65

GENERAL DATA

Body type...Van

Weight...................Net.....................(lb)   7,800

Payload.................(lb)   3,000

Gross...................(lb)   10,800

Ground clearance...................................(in.)   17

Tread..(in.)   75

Tires...................Operating....................   4

Ply...........................   8

Size........................   7.50 x 20

Brakes...................................Electric

Towing tractor...

Shipping dimensions........(cu ft) 1,880.........(sq ft)

ADDITIONAL DATA

K-35 and K-65 are identical.

. . . .
. . . .
. . . .
. . . .

TRAILER, 2-TON (5-TON GROSS), K-76 AND K-77

Technical Manuals: Parts List:

Manufacturer: Fruehauf Trailer Co.

RA PD 308938

Classification: Standard

Purpose: To transport radio equipment for Signal Corps.

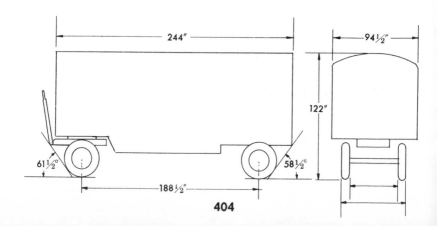

404

TRAILER, 2-TON (5-TON GROSS), K-76 AND K-77

GENERAL DATA

Body type	Special platform, bows and tarpaulin		
Weight	Net	(lb)	5,600
	Payload	(lb)	4,000
	Gross	(lb)	9,600
Loading height		(in.)	33
Ground clearance		(in.)	15½
Tread		(in.)	60
Tires	Operating		4
	Ply		8
	Size		7.50 x 20
Brakes	Electric		
Towing tractor	Truck, 2½-ton		
Shipping dimensions	(cu ft) 1713	(sq ft)	
Weight packed for export	(Loaded)	(lb)	10,910

ADDITIONAL DATA

K-76 and K-77 are identical.

. . . .
. . . .
. . . .
. . . .

TRAILER, W/SMOKE GENERATOR, 2-TON, M7 (ORDNANCE)

Technical Manual: Parts List:

Manufacturer: J. G. Brill Co.

RA PD 66517

Classification: Standard

Purpose: Used by Chemical Warfare Service to provide mobile smoke generating equipment.

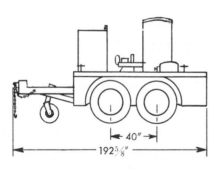

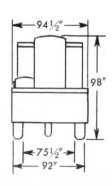

TRAILER, W/SMOKE GENERATOR, 2-TON, M7 (ORDNANCE)

GENERAL DATA

Body type...

Weight..................Net......................(lb)   5,750

                       Payload..................(lb)   4,000

                       Gross....................(lb)   9,750

Ground clearance....................................(in.)

Tires..................Operating....................   4

                       Ply..........................   8

                       Size........................ 7.50 x 20

Brakes...Electric

Towing tractor.......................................

Shipping dimensions.......(cu ft) 1,024.........(sq ft) 128

ADDITIONAL DATA

Same trailer with different equipment is used as generating unit M7. (SNL F-226, TM 9-618.)

....

....

TRAILER, TANDEM AXLE, SEARCHLIGHT, 2-TON

Technical Manual: TM 5-7044.   Parts List:

Manufacturer: Fruehauf Trailer Co., Model 1131 Special

RA PD 309018

Classification: Standard

Purpose: Used by Corps of Engineers to transport searchlight equipment.

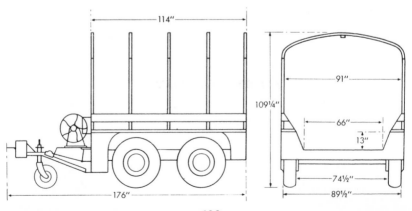

TRAILER, TANDEM AXLE, SEARCHLIGHT, 2-TON

GENERAL DATA

Body type..................................Special cargo
Weight.................Net......................(lb)   5,180
                      Payload...................(lb)   4,000
                      Gross....................(lb)   9,180
Loading height.....................................(in.)   13
Ground clearance..................................(in.)
Tread...(in.)
Tires.................Operating.....................   4
                   Ply...........................   8
                   Size..........................   7.50 x 20
Brakes...Electric
Towing tractor....................Truck, 2½-ton, 6 x 6
Shipping dimensions.......(cu ft)   ....(sq ft)

ADDITIONAL DATA

....
....
....
....

TRAILER, TELEPHONE CONSTRUCTION AND POLE HAULING, 2-TON, K-36

Technical Manuals: Parts List:

Manufacturers: American Coach and Body Co.; Highway Trailer Co.

Classification: Standard   RA PD 308936

Purpose: Used by Signal Corps to transport poles for telephone lines.

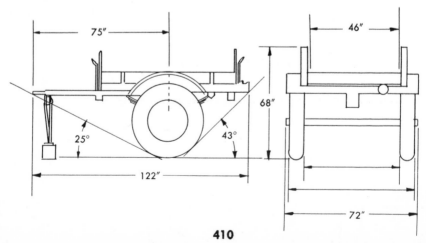

TRAILER, TELEPHONE CONSTRUCTION AND POLE HAULING, 2-TON, K-36

GENERAL DATA

Body type...

Weight.................Net......................(lb)			1,815
	Payload..................(lb)		5,000
	Gross....................(lb)		6,815

Loading height.......................................(in.)

Ground clearance....................................(in.)   16

Tread..(in.)   58

Tires..................Operating.....................   2

Ply.........................   8

Size........................   7.50 x 20

Brakes..............................Hand parking only

Towing tractor..

Shipping dimensions........(cu ft)..............(sq ft) 54

ADDITIONAL DATA

Dimensions given are for trailer only, without allowing for overhang of poles.

. . . .

. . . .

. . . .

. . . .

TRAILER, AIRDROME UTILITY, 2½-TON, TYPE F-2

Technical Orders: Parts List:

Manufacturer: Superior Auto Co., Inc.

RA PD 309056

Classification:

Purpose: Used by Army Air Forces for general utility purposes.

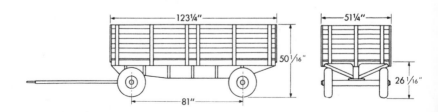

TRAILER, AIRDROME UTILITY, 2½-TON, TYPE F-2

GENERAL DATA

Body type..Cargo

Weight..................Net......................(lb)   1,000

                            Payload..................(lb)   5,000

                            Gross.....................(lb)   6,000

Loading height.....................................(in.)   26

Ground clearance...

Tread...

Tires...................Operating....................   4

                            Ply...........................   8

                            Size.......................   6.00 x 9

Brakes...None

Towing tractor......Airdrome tractors and truck, 6-ton, 4 x 4

Shipping dimensions.......(cu ft) 80...........(sq ft)

Weight, packed for export............................(lb)   1,500

ADDITIONAL DATA

....

....

....

....

TRAILER, UTILITY, POLE TYPE, 2½-TON

Technical Manual: TM 5-9074.   Parts List:

Manufacturer: Deere & Company (Dain Mfg. Div.)

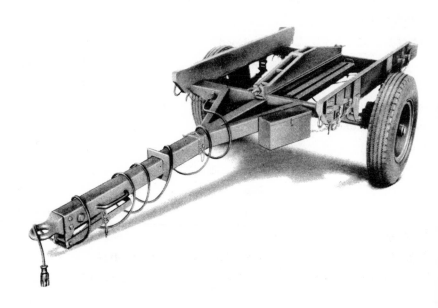

RA PD 309014

Classification: Standard

Purpose: Used by Corps of Engineers to transport special equipment as shown in additional data.

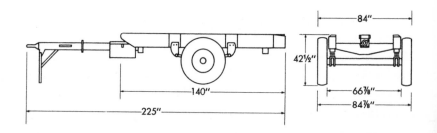

TRAILER, UTILITY, POLE TYPE, 2½-TON

GENERAL DATA

Body type........*Basic trailer; includes load binding beams
   and chains...................................

Weight..................Net....................(lb)   2,460

                          Payload..................(lb)   5,000

                          Gross....................(lb)   7,460

Loading height.....................................(in.)   42½

Ground clearance..................................(in.)

Tread...(in.)

Tires..................Operating.....................   2

                          Ply.......................   10

                          Size......................   9.00 x 20

Brakes...None

Towing tractor.........Truck, 2½-ton, 6 x 6 or 4-ton, 6 x 6

Shipping dimensions........(cu ft)   ....(sq ft)

ADDITIONAL DATA

*The same basic vehicle, outfitted with different equipment, is used as the following vehicles: Type 1—Infantry support raft equipment or pneumatic bridge equipment trailer; Type 2—trestle bat load, 10-ton ponton bridge trailer (basic trailer plus extra load brackets); Type 3—triangulation tower trailer (basic trailer plus extra body); Type 4—utility power boat trailer (basic trailer plus extra bolsters); Type 5—storm boat trailer (basic trailer plus extra bolsters).

Technical Manuals: Parts List:

Manufacturer: Saginaw Stamping & Tool Co.

RA PD 66519

Vehicle illustrated above: Chemical service trailer **M1**.

Classification: Standard

Purpose: Used by Chemical Warfare Service to transport chemical containers and handling equipment.

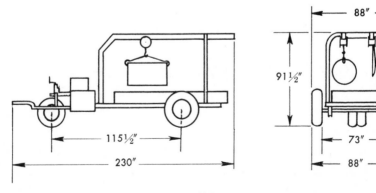

TRAILER, CHEMICAL SERVICE, 4-TON, M1
TRAILER, CHEMICAL HANDLING, 4-TON, M2

GENERAL DATA

Body type...

Weight.................Net.......................(lb)   2,755

                               Payload...................(lb)   5,000

                               Gross....................(lb)   7,755

Loading height..

Ground clearance......................................

Tread...................Front   Rear

Tires...................Operating....................   4

                               Ply, Front 6............Rear 8

                               Size............Front 6.50 x 10

                                               Rear 7.50 x 18

Brakes.......................................Electric

Towing tractor..

Shipping dimensions.......(cu ft)1, 064.........(sq ft) 133

ADDITIONAL DATA

The basic trailer (bomb trailer M5), is used without superstructure as
   chemical handling trailer M2.

....
....
....
....

TRAILER, TELEPHONE CONSTRUCTION AND COMBINATION CABLE HAULER, 5-TON, K-37

Technical Manuals: Parts List:

Manufacturer: Highway Trailer Co.

RA PD 66523

Classification: Standard

Purpose: To transport cable reel and to haul poles for Signal Corps operations.

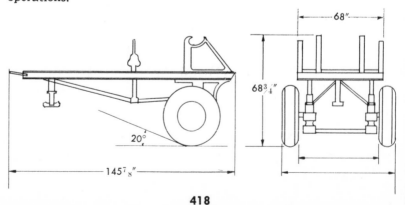

TRAILER, TELEPHONE CONSTRUCTION AND COMBINATION CABLE HAULER, 5-TON, K-37

GENERAL DATA

Body type..
Weight...................Net.......................(lb)   2,900
                   Payload..................(lb)   10,000
                   Gross....................(lb)   12,900
Loading height.....................................(in.)
Ground clearance..................................(in.)   9
Tread..(in.)   74
Tires....................Operating....................   2
                   Ply..........................   10
                   Size.........................   9.00 x 20
Brakes.......................................Electric
Towing tractor...
Shipping dimensions.......(cu ft) 472............(sq ft) 82

ADDITIONAL DATA

....
....
....
....

TRAILER, VAN, 5-TON, K-34

Technical Manuals: Parts List:

Manufacturers: A. J. Miller (Auto Cruiser Trailer Co.); Superior Trailer
Mfg. Corp.

RA PD 308975

Classification: Standard

Purpose: Used by Signal Corps to house power unit and rectifier for
various using arms.

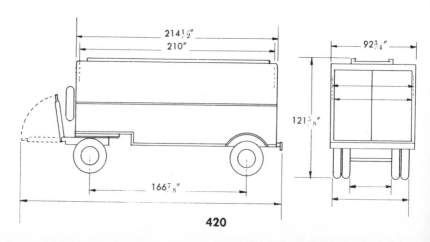

TRAILER, VAN, 5-TON, K-34

GENERAL DATA

Body type......................................Van

Weight..................Net.....................(lb)   8,600

                    Payload...................(lb) 10,000

                    Gross....................(lb) 18,600

Loading height.....................................(in.)   33

Ground clearance..................................(in.)

Tread..(in.) $66\frac{1}{2}$

Tires....................Operating.....................8

                    Spare........................1

                    Ply

                    Size.......................7.50 x 20

Brakes...................................Air 4-wheel

Towing tractor..............................Various

Shipping dimensions........(cu ft) 1,493........(sq ft) 152

Weight packed for export...(Loaded).................(lb) 18,000

ADDITIONAL DATA

....

....

....

....

TRAILER, ATHEY, TRACK LAYING, 6-TON, BT898-1

Technical Manuals: TM 9-790A, Parts List: SNL G-123
TM 9-1790A.

Manufacturer: Athey Truss Wheel Co.

RA PD 66527

Classification: Standard

Purpose: To transport general cargo over soft or rough terrain.

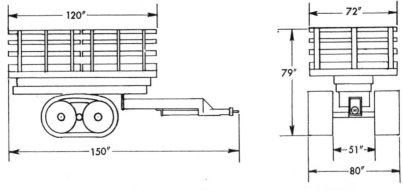

TRAILER, ATHEY, TRACK LAYING, 6-TON, BT898-1

GENERAL DATA

Body type . . . . Platform, stake, with or without canopy

Weight . . . . Net . . . . (approx.) (lb)   6,300

                             Payload . . . . (lb)   12,000

                             Gross . . . . (lb)   18,300

Loading height . . . . (in.)   47

Ground clearance . . . . (in.)

Turning radius . . . . (ft)   11

Track . . . . Width . . . . (in.)   14½

                             Supporting area . . . . (sq ft)   9

Brakes . . . . None

Towing tractor . . . .

Shipping dimensions . . . . (cu ft) 175 . . . . (sq ft)

Weight packed for export . . . . (approx.) (lb)   6,650

ADDITIONAL DATA

. . . .
. . . .
. . . .
. . . .

TRAILER, ATHEY, TRACK LAYING, 6-TON, BT898-4

Technical Manuals: TM 9-790A,   Parts List: SNL G-123
TM 9-1790A.

Manufacturer: Athey Truss Wheel Co.

RA PD 55797

Classification: Standard

Purpose: To transport general cargo over soft or rough terrain.

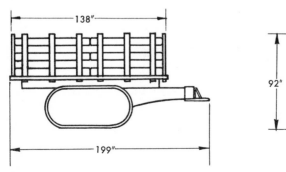
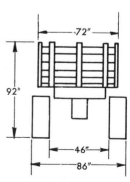

TRAILER, ATHEY, TRACK LAYING, 6-TON, BT898-4

GENERAL DATA

Body type......................Steel platform and stakes
Weight................Net.....................(lb)   8,540
                      Payload..................(lb)   12,000
                      Gross....................(lb)   20,540
Loading height.......................................(in.)   52
Ground clearance.....................................(in.)
Turning radius.......................................(ft)   12
Track................Width....................(in.)   20
                     Supporting area.........(sq ft)   16
Brakes...None
Towing tractor.......................................
Shipping dimensions........(cu ft) 200.........(sq ft)
Weight, packed for export...................(approx.) (lb)   9,000

ADDITIONAL DATA

....
....
....
....

TRAILER, FULL, FLAT BED, 8-TON

Technical Manual: TM 5-5910. Parts List:

Manufacturer: Fruehauf Trailer Co. (Model CPT-8 Special)

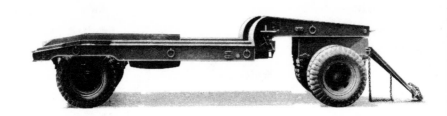

RA PD 309016

Classification: Standard

Purpose: Used by Corps of Engineers.

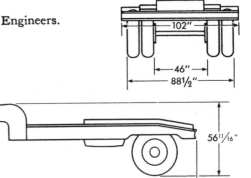

TRAILER, FULL, FLAT BED, 8-TON

GENERAL DATA

Body type.................................Full, flat bed
Weight..................Net....................(lb)   9,990
                   Payload.................(lb)   16,000
                   Gross....................(lb)   25,990
Loading height, empty ....(in.)   39
Ground clearance..................................(in.)   10
Ground pressure..........................(lb per sq in.)   51½
Tread...(in.)
Tires...................Operating.....................   8
                   Spare.......................   1
                   Ply........................   10
                   Size.......................   9.00 x 20
Brakes...................Hand parking.....(Service) Air
Towing tractor.................Truck, 2½- or 4-ton, 6 x 6
Shipping dimensions........(cu ft) 825, boxed 665..(sq ft) 170
Weight, packed for export............................(lb)   10,200

ADDITIONAL DATA

. . . .
. . . .
. . . .
. . . .

TRAILER, FULL, FLAT BED, 16-TON

Technical Manuals: See additional data.　　　Parts List:

Manufacturers: Fruehauf Trailer Co., La Crosse Trailer and Equipment Co., Steel Products Co.

RA PD 309002

Vehicle illustrated above: Fruehauf

Classification: Standard

Purpose: Used by Corps of Engineers.

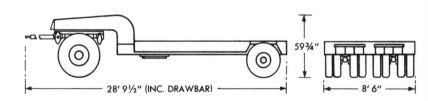

TRAILER, FULL, FLAT BED, 16-TON

GENERAL DATA

Body type................................Full flat bed

			Minimum	Maximum
Weight...................Net...........(lb)			7,400	15,330
	Payload........(lb)		32,000	40,000
	Gross...........(lb)		39,400	55,330

Loading height.......................................(in.) 33

Ground clearance....................................(in.) 11

Ground pressure (lb per sq in.)....Front 65........Rear 75

Tread...(in.)

Tires...................Operating.................... 12

Spare....................... 1

Ply—Front 10.........Rear 12

Size ....Front 9.00 x 20

Rear 8.25 x 15

Brakes...Air

Towing tractor.......................Truck, 6-ton, 6 x 6

Shipping dimensions........(cu ft) 967..........(sq ft) 193

ADDITIONAL DATA

Trailers supplied by various manufacturers vary in weight. The figures given are the maximum and minimum values.

La Crosse Models: DF 6-16-A   TM 5-9040

DF 6-16-B   TM 5-9042

DF 6-16-C   TM 5-9044

DF 6-20   TM 5-9054

Steel Products Co.,
  Model XBBM   TM 5-9004

Fruehauf Trailer Co.,
  Model CPT-16 Special   TM 5-9026

TRAILER, FULL, FLAT BED, 20-TON

Technical Manuals: Parts List:

Manufacturers: La Crosse Trailer and Equipment Co.; Rogers Bros. Co.

RA PD 309134

Vehicle illustrated above: Rogers Bros. Model H-20-L-S-14

Classification: Standard

Purpose: Used by Corps of Engineers.

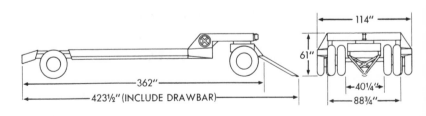

TRAILER, FULL, FLAT BED, 20-TON

GENERAL DATA

Body type . . . . Full, flat bed

Weight . . . . Net . . . . (lb) 15,676

Payload . . . . (lb) 40,000

Gross . . . . (lb) 55,676

Packed for export . . . . (lb) 18,905

Loading height, empty . . . . (in.) 40½

Ground clearance . . . . (in.) 17

Tires . . . . Operating 12

Spare 1

Ply . . . . Front 14; Rear 10

Size . . . . Front 12.00 x 20

Rear 9.00 x 20

Brakes . . . . Air

Towing tractor . . . . Truck, 6-ton, 6 x 6

Shipping dimensions . . . . . . (cu ft) 1080 . . . . (sq ft)

ADDITIONAL DATA

. . . .

. . . .

. . . .

. . . .

TRAILER, ATHEY, TRACK LAYING, 20-TON

Technical Manuals: TM 9-790B,
TM 9-1790A.

Parts List: SNL G-123

Manufacturer: Athey Truss Wheel Co.

RA PD 66531

Classification:

Purpose: To transport general cargo over soft or rough terrain.

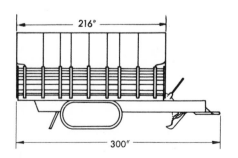

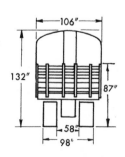

TRAILER, ATHEY, TRACK LAYING, 20-TON

GENERAL DATA

Body type............................Stake with canopy
Weight..................Net......................(lb)   14,700
                    Payload..................(lb)   40,000
                    Gross....................(lb)   54,700
Loading height...(in.)   53
Ground clearance.................................(in.)
Track....................Width....................(in.)   20
                    Supporting area..........(sq ft)   16
Brakes.......................................None
Towing tractor...
Shipping dimensions........(cu ft) 460.........(sq ft)
Weight, packed for export............................(lb)   15,200

ADDITIONAL DATA

....
....
....
....

TRAILER, ANTENNA MOUNT, 4-TON, K-22 AND K-64

Technical Manuals: Parts List:

Manufacturers: Couse Laboratories, Kingham Trailer Co.

RA PD 308934

Vehicle illustrated above: Kingham Trailer Co., Model K-22

Classif.cation: Standard

Purpose: Used by Signal Corps.

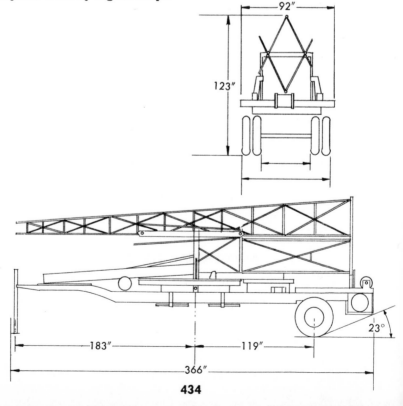

TRAILER, ANTENNA MOUNT, 4-TON, K-22 AND K-64

GENERAL DATA

Body type			Turntable with winch	
Weight	Net		(lb)	15,700
	Payload		(lb)	8,000
	Gross		(lb)	23,700
Loading height			(in.)	53
Ground clearance			(in.)	14
Tread			(in.)	68
Tires	Operating			4
	Ply			8
	Size			7.00 x 20
Brakes			Air	
Towing tractor			Truck tractor, 5-ton, 4 x 4	
Shipping dimensions	(cu ft) 2,377		(sq ft)	
Weight, packed for export			(lb)	17,270

ADDITIONAL DATA

K-22 and K-64 are the same and are used by Signal Corps.

. . . .

. . . .

. . . .

. . . .

TRAILER, ANTENNA MOUNT, 4-TON, K-28

Technical Manuals: Parts List:

Manufacturer: Fruehauf Trailer Co.

Classification: Standard

Purpose: Used by Signal Corps.

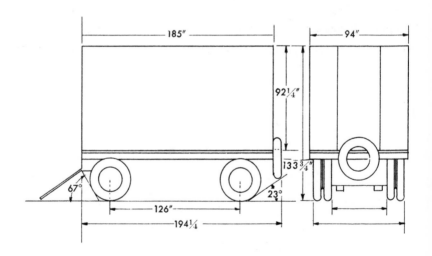

TRAILER, ANTENNA MOUNT, 4-TON, K-28

GENERAL DATA

Body type		Platform only	
Weight	Net	(approx.) (lb)	6,000
	Payload	(approx.) (lb)	10,000
	Gross	(approx.) (lb)	16,000
Loading height		(in.)	$41\frac{2}{5}$
Ground clearance		(in.)	$14\frac{5}{8}$
Tread		(in.)	70
Tires	Operating		8
	Spare		1
	Ply		8
	Size		7.50 x 20
Brakes		Air	
Towing tractor		Truck, K-56	
Shipping dimensions	(cu ft) 1,477	(sq ft)	
Weight, packed for export	(Loaded)	(lb)	12,975

ADDITIONAL DATA

No photo available at date of publication.

....
....
....

TRAILER, ANTENNA MOUNT, 10-TON GROSS, K-75

Technical Manuals: Parts List:

Manufacturers: Kingham Trailer Co., Body by: The Heil Co.

RA PD 308974

Classification: Standard

Purpose: Used by Signal Corps.

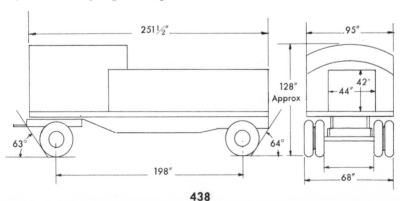

TRAILER, ANTENNA MOUNT, 10-TON GROSS, K-75

GENERAL DATA

Body type.....................Special steel compartments
Weight.................Net.......................(lb)	
	Payload..................(lb)	
	Gross....................(lb)	26,000
Loading height.......................................(in.)	
Ground clearance...................................(in.)	17½
Tread..(in.)	60
Tires..................Operating....................	8
	Spare........................	1
	Ply..........................	10
	Size.........................	9.00 x 20
Brakes...Air
Towing tractor.......................................
Shipping dimensions........(cu ft) 1,904........(sq ft)
Weight, packed for export...(Loaded).................(lb)	28,600

ADDITIONAL DATA

....
....
....
....

TRAILER, LABORATORY, PHOTOGRAPHIC, TYPE A-1A

Technical Manuals: Parts List:

Manufacturer:

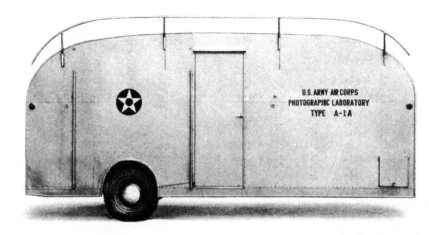

RA PD 309071

Classification: Limited standard

Purpose: Used by Army Air Forces for processing negatives and prints in the field.

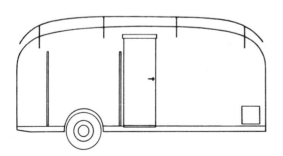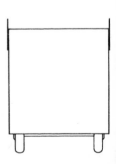

TRAILER, LABORATORY, PHOTOGRAPHIC, TYPE A-1A

GENERAL DATA

Body type...Van

Weight..................Net......................(lb)   6,300

                       Payload...................(lb)   1,500

                       Gross....................(lb)   7,800

Loading height......................................(in.)   21

Ground clearance.................................(in.)

Tread...(in.)

Tires...................Operating....................   2

                       Ply..........................   10

                       Size........................ 8.25 x 18

Brakes........................(6-volt dry cell) Electric

Towing tractor.....................Truck, 2½-ton, 6 x 6

Shipping dimensions........(cu ft)   ....(sq ft)

Weight, packed for export...........................(lb)   6,300

ADDITIONAL DATA

....

....

....

....

TRAILER, LABORATORY, PHOTOGRAPHIC, TYPE A-2

Technical Manuals: Parts List:

Manufacturer: Oneida Ltd.

RA PD 309069

Classification: Limited standard

Purpose: Used by Army Air Forces for the processing of negatives and prints in the field.

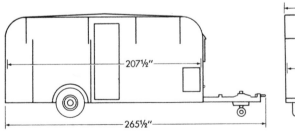

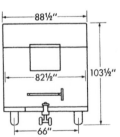

TRAILER, LABORATORY, PHOTOGRAPHIC, TYPE A-2

GENERAL DATA

Body type		Van	
Weight	Net	(lb)	5,205
	Payload	(lb)	1,450
	Gross	(lb)	6,475
Loading height		(in.)	21
Ground clearance		(in.)	14
Tread		(in.)	
Tires	Operating		2
	Ply		10
	Size		8.25 x 18
Brakes		Electric	
Towing tractor		Truck, 2½-ton, 6 x 6	
Shipping dimensions	(cu ft) 1,419	(sq ft) 164	
Weight, packed for export		(lb)	6,475

ADDITIONAL DATA

Van trailer, aluminum body with steel platform, draw bar and lunette ring. Rear wheels are independently suspended type. Front wheels are of the stabilizing type, mounted on a retractable, telescoping jack.

. . . .
. . . .
. . . .

TRAILER, FIRE PUMPER, 500 G.P.M., CLASS 1000

Technical Manuals: Parts List:

Manufacturer: Hale

RA PD 309008

Classification: Standard

Purpose: Used by Corps of Engineers to transport fire-fighting and pumping equipment.

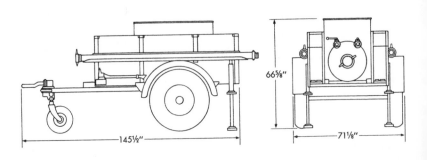

TRAILER, FIRE PUMPER, 500 G.P.M., CLASS 1000

GENERAL DATA

Body type...			
Weight................... Net....................... (lb)			2,000
	Payload................. (lb)		2,000
	Gross..................... (lb)		4,000
Loading height....................................... (in.)			
Ground clearance.................................... (in.)			9
Tread... (in.)			58
Tires................... Operating.....................			2
	Ply...........................		8
	Size.........................		6.50 x 16
Brakes............................... Mechanical			
Towing tractor.......................................			
Shipping dimensions........ (cu ft) 240........... (sq ft) 50			

ADDITIONAL DATA

Pump driven by a 6-cylinder, 4-cycle engine, 236.6 cubic inch displacement, brake horsepower—104.

Fuel tank capacity of 18 gallons.

Crew—5.

....

....

....

TRAILER, FIRE CRASH, HIGH PRESSURE, CLASS 1010

Technical Manuals: Parts List:

Manufacturer: John Bean

RA PD 309006

Classification: Standard

Purpose: Used by Corps of Engineers to transport fire-fighting and crash
equipment at air fields.

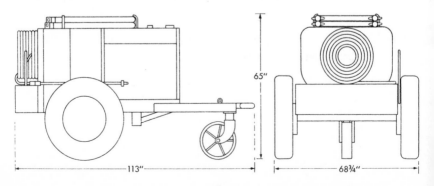

GENERAL DATA

Body type			
Weight	Net	(lb)	2,835
	Payload	(lb)	1,535
	Gross	(lb)	4,370
Ground clearance		(in.)	8½
Tread		(in.)	62
Tires	Operating		2
	Ply		8
	Size		7.50 x 20
Brakes		Mechanical	
Towing tractor			
Shipping dimensions	(cu ft) 292	(sq ft) 54	

ADDITIONAL DATA

Crew		6
Engine	4 cylinder	4 cycle
Displacement		(cu in.) 124
Brake horsepower		31

TRAILER, BOMB, M5

Technical Manual: TM 9-760.   Parts List: SNL G-74.

Manufacturers: American Seating Co., Saginaw Stamping and Tool Co., Oneida Ltd., Trailer Company of America.

RA PD 309124

Classification: Standard

Purpose: Used by Army Air Forces to transport bombs with low loading and ease of handling.

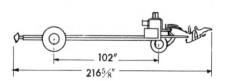

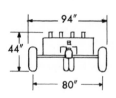

TRAILER, BOMB, M5

GENERAL DATA

Body type.....................................Platform

Weight..................Net........................(lb)   2,200

                        Payload...................(lb)   5,000

                        Gross.....................(lb)   7,200

Loading height, loaded.............................(in.) $21\frac{1}{2}$

Ground clearance..................................(in.) $9\frac{1}{2}$

Tread...(in.)

Tires.....................Operating...................4

                        Ply (front) 6...........(rear) 8

                        Size (front)...........6.50 x 10

                        (rear)...........7.50 x 18

Brakes..Electric

Towing tractor.....................Bomb service truck M6

Shipping dimensions........(cu ft)   ....(sq ft)

ADDITIONAL DATA

Front of hitch yoke has reversible lunette to attach to rear pintle of another trailer, or to a prime mover, so that it can be towed in trains at speeds up to 45 miles per hour on highways.

. . . .
. . . .
. . . .
. . . .

TRAILER, ARMORED, M-8

Technical Manual: TM 9-791.   Parts List: SNL G-157

Manufacturer: John Deere Plow Works

RA PD 66507

Classification: Standard

Purpose: To transport fuel and ammunition.

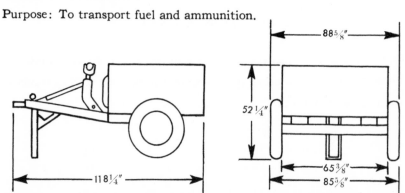

TRAILER, ARMORED, M-8

GENERAL DATA

Body type.................................Armored cargo

Weight..................Net.....................(lb)   2,640

                    Payload.................(lb)   2,200

                    Gross (w/o pintle).........(lb)   4,840

                    Gross (w/ pintle)..........(lb)   5,058

Loading height....................................(in.)

Ground clearance...................................(in.)   16½

Tread...(in.)   75

Tires...................Operating.....................   2

                    Ply..........................   10

                    Size........................   9.00 x 20

Brakes.............................Hand parking only

Towing tractor.................................Tanks

Electrical system...............................(volts)   6

Shipping dimensions........(cu ft) 316...........(sq ft) 73

ADDITIONAL DATA

. . . .

. . . .

. . . .

. . . .

TRAILER, FUEL SERVICING, 600-GAL., TYPE A-1

Technical Order: TO 19-25-38.   Parts List:

Manufacturer: Standard Steel Works

RA PD 309036

Classification: Standard

Purpose: Used by Army Air Forces to transport aircraft engine fuel and to service aircraft.

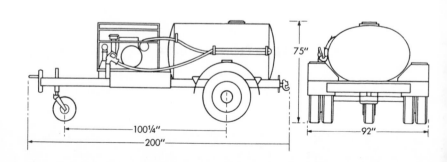

TRAILER, FUEL SERVICING, 600-GAL., TYPE A-1

GENERAL DATA

Body type....................................Tank
Weight..................Net.....................(lb)   3,700
                  Payload.................(lb)   3,600
                  Gross...................(lb)   7,300
Loading height...................................(in.)   75
Ground clearance..
Tires..................Operating.....................   4
                  Ply........................   10
                  Size........................ 7.50 x 20
Brakes....................................Electric
Shipping dimensions........(cu ft) 622...........(sq ft)

ADDITIONAL DATA

Towed by type L-2 oil servicing truck or type F-3 fuel servicing truck. Under favorable conditions as many as four of these trailers can be towed in train formation by one prime mover. Any standard Army truck of 1½-ton or greater capacity can be used. May also be towed by M-2 medium tractor (track-laying). Equipped with power pump.

. . . .
. . . .
. . . .
. . . .

TRAILER, FUEL SERVICING, 220-GAL., TYPE A-2-A

Technical Orders:

Parts List:

Manufacturer:

RA PD 309040

Classification: Standard

Purpose: Used by Army Air Forces to transport aircraft engine fuel and to service aircraft.

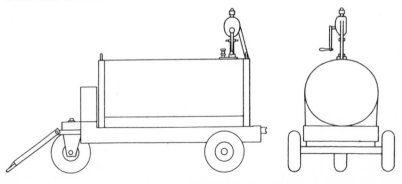

TRAILER, FUEL SERVICING, 220-GAL., TYPE A-2-A

GENERAL DATA

Body type . . . . Tank

Weight . . . . Net . . . . (lb)   400

Payload . . . . (lb)   1,500

Gross . . . . (lb)   1,900

Loading height . . . . (in.)   22

Ground clearance . . . . (in.)

Tread . . . . (in.)

Tires . . . . Operating   3

Ply   4

Size . . . .   6.00 x 6

Brakes . . . .   None

Towing tractor . . . . Airdrome tractor or truck, ¼-ton, 4 x 4

Shipping dimensions . . . . (cu ft) 158 . . . . (sq ft)

Weight, packed for export . . . . (lb)   850

ADDITIONAL DATA

. . . .

. . . .

. . . .

. . . .

TRAILER, FUEL SERVICING, 600-GAL., TYPE A-3

Technical Orders: Parts List:

Manufacturer: Standard Steel Works

RA PD 309038

Classification: Standard

Purpose: Used by Army Air Forces to transport and pump fuel for aircraft refueling.

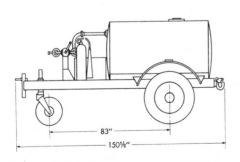
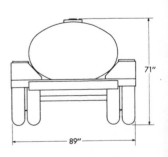

TRAILER, FUEL SERVICING, 600-GAL., TYPE A-3

GENERAL DATA

Body type		Tank	
Weight	Net	(lb)	3,000
	Payload	(lb)	4,000
	Gross	(lb)	7,000
Loading height		(in.)	76
Ground clearance			
Tread		(in.)	
Tires	Operating		4
	Ply		
	Size		7.50 x 20
Brakes		Electric	
Towing tractor			
Shipping dimensions	(cu ft) 622	(sq ft)	

ADDITIONAL DATA

Equipped with hand pump.

. . . .
. . . .
. . . .
. . . .

LIFT TRUCK, M 22

Technical Manual: TM 9-762

Parts List: SNL G-161

Manufacturer: Weaver Mfg. Co.

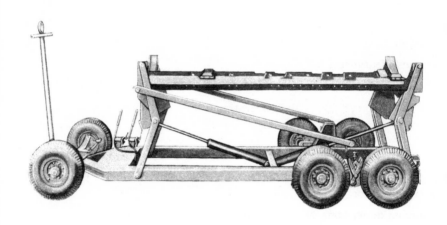

RA PD 66702

Classification: Standard

Purpose: To lift and transport aerial bombs and torpedoes weighing up to 4,000 pounds.

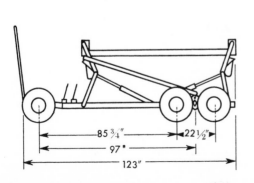 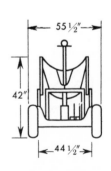

LIFT TRUCK, M22

GENERAL DATA

Body type...			
Weight.................Net....................(lb)			1,453
	Payload..................(lb)		4,188
	Gross....................(lb)		5,641
Loading height.......................................(in.)			
Ground clearance....................................(in.)			4
Tread...(in.)			
Tires..................Operating....................			
	Ply.........................		6
	Size.........................		18 x 5.50
Brakes.................................Parking only			
Towing tractor.......................................			
Shipping dimensions........(cu ft) 71.............(sq ft) 47			

ADDITIONAL DATA

Capacity of hydraulic lift, 14 quarts. This trailer may be towed by a truck, or used as a hand-truck.

....

....

....

SEMITRAILER, VAN, 1½-TON, K-55

Technical Manuals: Parts List:

Manufacturers: A. J. Miller (Auto Cruiser Trailer Co.), Oneonta Linn
  Corp.

RA PD 66391

Vehicle illustrated above: Miller

Classification: Substitute standard

Purpose: Used by Signal Corps to transport Signal Corps equipment.

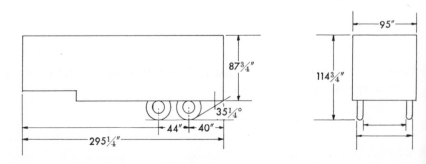

SEMITRAILER, VAN, 1½-TON, K-55

GENERAL DATA

Body type. . . . . Van

Weight. . . . . Net. (lb)   8,200

Payload. . . . . (lb)   4,500

Gross. (lb)   12,700

Loading height. . . . . (in.)   35

Ground clearance. . . . . (in.)   15½

Tread. . . . . (in.)   75

Tires. . . . . Operating.   4

Ply.   8

Size. . . . .   7.50 x 20

Brakes. . . . . Electric

Towing tractor. . . . .

Shipping dimensions. . . . . (cu ft) 1,885. . . . . (sq ft) 202

ADDITIONAL DATA

. . . .

. . . .

. . . .

. . . .

SEMITRAILERS, MAP REPRODUCTION EQUIPMENT, VAN, 2½-TON

Technical Manuals: Parts List:

Manufacturers:

RA PD 66393

Classification: Limited standard

Purpose: Used by Corps of Engineers to transport map reproducing
equipment.

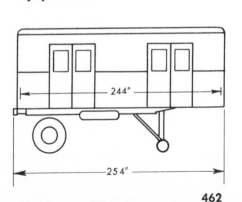

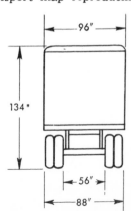

SEMITRAILERS, MAP REPRODUCTION EQUIPMENT, VAN, 2½-TON

GENERAL DATA

Body type..................................Van
Weight..................Gross..............(lb) 13,500 to 14,500
Ground clearance...........................(in.)   12
Fording depth..............................(in.)   30
Tread......................................(in.)
Tires...................Operating.............
                        Ply.....................
                        Size....................
Brakes...
Towing tractor.................................
Shipping dimensions........(cu ft) 2000...(sq ft) 176

ADDITIONAL DATA

The same basic vehicle outfitted with different equipment is used as: camera section, 24- x 24-inch, and press section, 17- x 19-inch.

Gross weight on outfitted vehicles varies from 13,500 to 14,500 pounds, because of different loads.

SEMITRAILER, VAN, 3-TON (6-TON GROSS)

Technical Manuals: Carolina, TM 10-1302;
Highway, TM 10-1363;
Kingham, TM 10-1252;
Steel Products, TM 10-1688;
Strick, TM 10-1360;
Truck Eng., TM 10-1675.

Parts List:

Manufacturers: Various

RA PD 308968

Classification: Standard

Purpose: To transport general cargo.

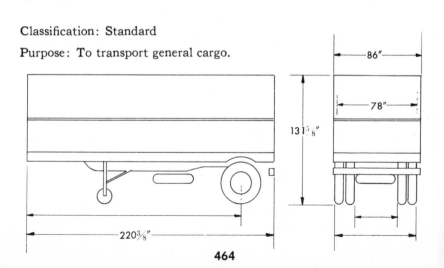

464

SEMITRAILER, VAN, 3-TON (6-TON GROSS)

GENERAL DATA

Body type..........................	Van—wood or steel		
Weight.................	Net, wood................	(lb)	5,750
	Net, steel.................	(lb)	5,800
	Payload..................	(lb)	6,000
	Gross, wood..............	(lb)	11,750
	Gross, steel..............	(lb)	11,800
Loading height..................................		(in.)	49
Ground clearance................................		(in.)	15½
Tread..		(in.)	66
Tires..................	Operating..................		4
	Spares.......................		1
	Ply.........................		8
	Size........................		7.50 x 20
Brakes..		Electric	
Towing tractor...............	Truck tractor, 1½-ton, 4 x 2		
	Truck tractor, 1½ ton, 4 x 4		
Shipping dimensions........	(cu ft)	.........(sq ft)	

ADDITIONAL DATA

Similar vehicles manufactured by: Black Diamond Trailer Co.; Carolina Trailer Co.; Checker Cab Mfg. Co.; Highway Trailer Co.; Kingham Trailer Co.; A. J. Miller (Auto Cruiser Trailer Co.); Steel Products Co., Inc.; Strick Co.; Truck Engineering Corp.

. . . .

. . . .

SEMITRAILER, STAKE AND PLATFORM
3½-TON (6-TON GROSS)

Technical Manuals: Black Diamond, TM 9-886A;   Parts List:
Dorsey, TM 10-1343; Highway, TM 10-1363;
Hobbs, TM 10-1353; Kingham, TM 10-1252;
Strick, TM 10-1360; Utility, TM 10-1300;
Truck Eng., TM 10-1675; Winter-Weiss,
TM 10-1170.

Manufacturers: Various

RA PD 66395

Vehicle illustrated above: Checker Cab Mfg. Co., Model CC-4.

Classification: Standard

Purpose: To transport general cargo.

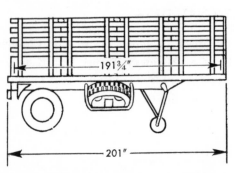

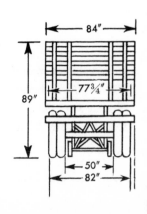

SEMITRAILER, STAKE AND PLATFORM
3½-TON (6-TON GROSS)

GENERAL DATA

Body type................Combination stake and platform

Weight...................Net.....................(lb)   4,582

Payload..................(lb)   7,000

Gross....................(lb)   11,582

Loading height.....................................(in.)   49¼

Ground clearance..................................(in.)   15½

Tread...(in.)   66

Tires....................Operating....................   4

Spares......................   1

Ply.........................   8

Size........................ 7.50 x 20

Brakes.......................................Electric

Towing tractor................Truck tractor, 1½-ton, 4x2

Truck tractor, 1½-ton, 4x4

Shipping dimensions........(cu ft) 459..........(sq ft) 117

ADDITIONAL DATA

Similar vehicles manufactured by: Black Diamond Trailer Co., Dorsey Bros., Highway Trailer Co., Hobbs Mfg. Co., Kingham Trailer Co., Strick Co., Utility Trailer Mfg. Co., Truck Engineering Corp., Winter-Weiss Co.

....

....

....

....

SEMITRAILER, 6-TON GROSS, K-67

Technical Manuals: Parts List:

Manufacturer: Fruehauf Trailer Co.

RA PD 308939

Classification: Standard

Purpose: To transport radio equipment for Signal Corps.

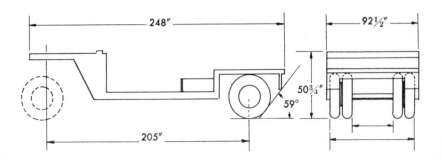

SEMITRAILER, 6-TON GROSS, K-67

GENERAL DATA

Body type..................................Platform only

Weight................Net.............(approx.) (lb)   6,500

                    Payload..................(lb)   6,000

                    Gross............(approx.) (lb) 12,500

Loading height......................................(in.)

Ground clearance....................................(in.)

Tread...(in.)

Tires...................Operating.................... 4

                  Ply.......................... 8

                  Size........................ 7.50 x 20

Brakes...Electric

Towing tractor.....................Truck, 1½-ton, 4x4

Shipping dimensions........(cu ft) 1740.........(sq ft)

Weight packed for export...(Loaded).................(lb) 13,158

ADDITIONAL DATA

....

....

....

....

SEMITRAILER, 7-TON GROSS, K-72

Technical Manuals: Parts List:

Manufacturer: A. J. Miller (Auto Cruiser Trailer Co.).

RA PD 308940

Classification: Standard

Purpose: Used by Signal Corps.

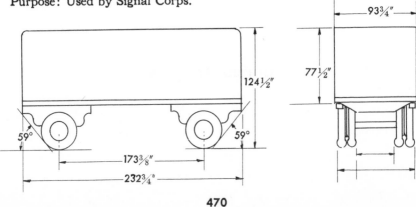

SEMITRAILER, 7-TON GROSS, K-72

GENERAL DATA

Body type...Van

Weight.................Net.......................(lb)   7,500

Payload..................(lb)   4,000

Gross....................(lb)   11,500

Loading height.......................................(in.)   45

Ground clearance....................................(in.) $15\frac{1}{2}$

Tread..(in.) $66\frac{3}{4}$

Tires.................Operating........................   8

Ply.........................   8

Size........................   7.50 x 20

Brakes...Electric

Towing tractor.....................Truck, $2\frac{1}{2}$-ton, 6 x 6

Shipping dimensions........(cu ft) 1,935.........(sq ft)

Weight packed for export...(Loaded).................(lb)   11,350

ADDITIONAL DATA

....
....
....
....

SEMITRAILERS, INSTRUMENT SHOP, 8-TON GROSS

Technical Order: TO 19-25-27.   Parts List:

Manufacturer: Keystone, Model AC-105.

RA PD 309089

Classification: Standard

Purpose: Used by Army Air Forces for repair, calibration and maintenance of aircraft instruments.

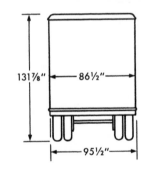

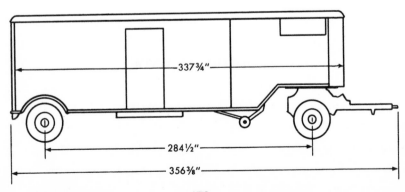

GENERAL DATA

Body type..			
Weight..................	Net......................	(lb)	12,670
	Payload (test equipment).....(lb)		4,214
	Gross.....................	(lb)	16,884
Loading height..................................(in.)			35
Ground clearance.................................(in.)			13
Tires...................	Operating.....................		4
	Ply.........................		12
	Size........................		9.00 x 20
Kingpin to center of axle..........................(in.)			$284\frac{1}{2}$
Brakes..Air			
Towing tractor.......................................			
Shipping dimensions........(cu ft) 2,607.........(sq ft) 237			

ADDITIONAL DATA

....

....

....

....

SEMITRAILER, REFRIGERATOR,
5-TON (10-TON GROSS)

Technical Manuals:

Parts List:

American Body, TM 10-1311;

Hyde, TM 10-1313;

Watson, TM 10-1307.

Manufacturers: American Body and Trailer; Hyde; A. J. Miller; Robbins and Burke Inc.; U. S. Thermo Control Co.; Watson.

RA PD 66398

Classification: Standard

Purpose: Used by Quartermaster Corps to transport perishable food.

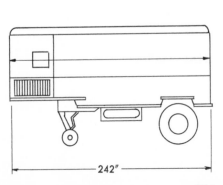
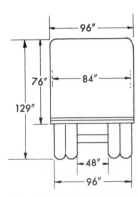

SEMITRAILER, REFRIGERATOR, 5-TON (10-TON GROSS)

GENERAL DATA

Body type....................................Refrigeration

Weight...................Net.......................(lb) 12,150

Payload...................(lb) 10,000

Gross....................(lb) 22,150

Loading height.......................................(in.)

Tires...................Operating................... 4

Ply........................... 10

Size......................... 9.00 x 20

Ground clearance.....................................(in.) 14

Brakes..Air

Towing tractor......................................

Shipping dimensions........(cu ft) 1,763.........(sq ft) 164

ADDITIONAL DATA

....
....
....
....

SEMITRAILERS, MAP REPRODUCTION EQUIPMENT VAN, 10-TON GROSS

Technical Manuals: Parts List:

Manufacturer: Fruehauf Trailer Co.

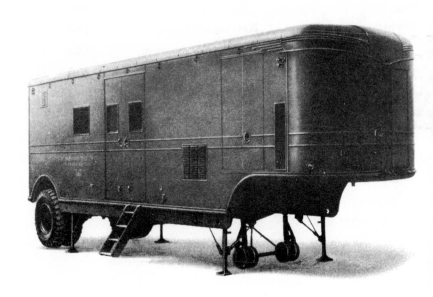

RA PD 309010

Classification: Limited standard

Purpose: Used by Corps of Engineers to transport camera and reproducing equipment.

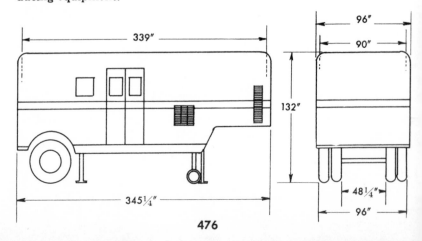

SEMITRAILERS, MAP REPRODUCTION EQUIPMENT VAN, 10-TON GROSS

GENERAL DATA

Body type. . . . . .Van

Weight. . . . . .Gross (with loads). . . . .(lb) 18,000 to
23,500

Ground clearance. . . . .(in.)   12

Fording depth. . . . .(in.)   30

Tread, center to center. . . . .(in.)   70⅜

Tires. . . . . .Operating.   4

Spares.   1

Ply.   14

Size. . . . . .12.00 x 20

Brakes. . . . . .Air

Towing tractor. . . . . .Truck tractor, 4-ton, 4 x 4

Shipping dimensions. . . . .(cu ft) 2,534. . . . .(sq ft) 230

ADDITIONAL DATA

The same basic vehicle outfitted with different equipment is used as: Camera section, 24- x 30-inch; Camera section, 24- x 24-inch; Combination "A"; Combination "B"; Photographic section; Laboratory section; Plate grainer section; Plate process section; Press section, 22- x 29-inch; Press section 20- x 22½-inch.

SEMITRAILER, VAN, 6-TON (10-TON GROSS)

Technical Manuals: American, Dorsey, Kentucky, Strick, Timpte, Utility, Olson, and Carter, TM 9-888; Gramm, TM 10-1217; Highway, TM 10-1381; Trailer Co. of Am., TM 10-1351; Gerstenslager, 10-1315.

Parts List:

Manufacturers: Various.

RA PD 66411

Vehicle illustrated above: Gerstenslager Co.

Classification: Standard

Purpose: To transport general cargo.

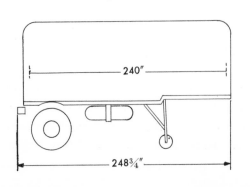

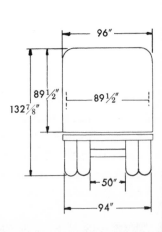

SEMITRAILER, VAN, 6-TON (10-TON GROSS)

GENERAL DATA

Body type.............................Van—wood or steel

Weight	Net (steel)............(lb)	7,450
	Net (wood)............(lb)	7,200
	Payload................(lb)	12,000
	Gross (steel)...........(lb)	19,450
	Gross (wood)..........(lb)	19,200

Loading height.................................(in.)   50

Ground clearance..............................(in.)   16½

Tread...(in.)   72

Tires	Operating....................	4
	Spare........................	1
	Ply.........................	10
	Size.........................	9.00 x 20

Brakes...Air

Towing tractor...............Truck tractor, 4-5 ton, 4 x 4

Shipping dimensions........(cu ft) 1,836.........(sq ft) 165

ADDITIONAL DATA

Similar vehicles manufactured by: American Body and Trailer Co., Dorsey Brothers, Gramm Truck and Trailer Corp., Highway Trailer Co., Kentucky Mfg. Co., Olson Mfg. Co., Strick Co., Timpte Brothers, Trailer Company of America, Carter Mfg. Co., and Utility Trailer Mfg. Co.

SEMITRAILER, CLOTHING REPAIR, 6-TON
(10-TON GROSS)

Technical Manual: Timpte, TM 10-1309.   Parts List: SNL G-591.

Manufacturers: Rivers Body Factory, Timpte Bros.

RA PD 66401

Vehicle illustrated above: Rivers Body Factory

Classification: Standard

Purpose: Used by Quartermaster Corps to provide mobile clothing repair facilities.

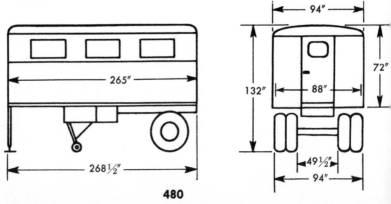

SEMITRAILER, CLOTHING REPAIR, 6-TON
(10-TON GROSS)

GENERAL DATA

Body type..Van
Weight................Net.....................(lb)   8,000

Payload..................(lb) 12,000

Gross....................(lb) 20,000

Loading height......................................(in.)   50
Tires...................Operating....................   4

Ply....................... 10

Size....................... 9.00 x 20

Ground clearance..................................(in.) 14
Brakes..Air
Towing tractor..............Truck tractor, 4-5 ton, 4 x 4
Shipping dimensions.......(cu ft)   ....(sq ft)

ADDITIONAL DATA

....
....
....
....

SEMITRAILER, COMBINATION ANIMAL AND CARGO, 6-TON (10-TON GROSS)

Technical Manuals: Gramm, TM 10-1380; Parts List: SNL G-580
Highway, TM 10-1372.

Manufacturers: Gramm Motor Truck and Trailer Corp., Highway Trailer Co.

RA PD 66399

Classification: Standard

Purpose: To transport eight men and eight horses with equipment for both, including rifle and saddle racks.

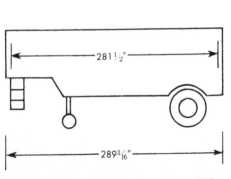

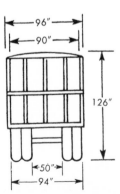

SEMITRAILER, COMBINATION ANIMAL AND CARGO, 6-TON (10-TON GROSS)

GENERAL DATA

Body type.................................Open-top van

Weight..................Net....................(lb)   8,820

                       Payload..................(lb)   12,000

                       Gross....................(lb)   20,820

Loading height......................................(in.)   38

Tires...................Operating....................   4

                       Spare.......................   1

                       Ply.........................   10

                       Size........................   9.00 x 20

Ground clearance..................................(in.)   14

Brakes...Air

Towing tractor...............Truck tractor, 4-5-ton, 4 x 4

Shipping dimensions.......(cu ft)   ....(sq ft)

ADDITIONAL DATA

....
....
....
....

SEMITRAILER, FIELD SHOP REPAIR, 10-TON GROSS, TYPE A-3A

Technical Orders: Parts List:

Manufacturer: Fruehauf Trailer Co.

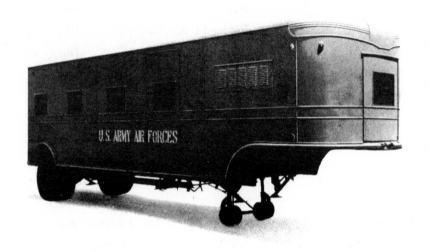

RA PD 309067

Classification: Standard

Purpose: Used by Army Air Forces to provide mobile machine shop facilities.

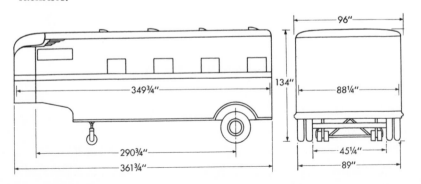

SEMITRAILER, FIELD SHOP REPAIR, 10-TON GROSS, TYPE A-3A

GENERAL DATA

Body type......................................Van

Weight..................Net......................(lb)   9,000

Payload (equipment).......(lb)   8,550

Gross....................(lb)   17,550

Gross (allowable)...........(lb)   29,000

Loading height.....................................(in.)   33

Ground clearance...................................(in.)   17½

Kingpin to center of axle..........................(in.)   290¾

Tires....................Operating....................   4

Ply........................   10

Size........................ 9.00 x 20

Brakes..Air

Towing tractor...............Truck tractor, 4-5 ton, 4 x 4

Shipping dimensions.......(cu ft) 2,692.........(sq ft) 241

(cu ft) (disassembled) 2,258

Weight packed for export............................(lb)   29,000

ADDITIONAL DATA

Equipment includes 4,000 pound derrick (on tractor); 110-volt generating plant; 15,000 pound capacity winch (on tractor); die making machine; 10-inch grinder; 1-inch collet lathe; arbor press; 14-inch drill press; 2 vises; work bench; air compressor; gasoline heater. A full complement of hand tools and utility parts are provided by the using organization.

SEMITRAILER, LAUNDRY, 6-TON (10-TON GROSS)

Technical Manual: TM 10-1217. Parts List: SNL G-584

Manufacturer: Gramm Motor Truck & Trailer Corp.

RA PD 66403

Classification: Standard

Purpose: To provide mobile laundry facilities for use by Quartermaster Corps.

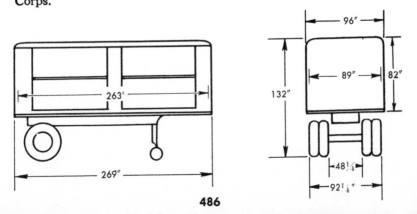

SEMITRAILER, LAUNDRY, 6-TON (10-TON GROSS)

GENERAL DATA

Body type.................................Van laundry

Weight.................Net.....................(lb)   8,000

                Payload..................(lb), 12,000

                Gross....................(lb) 20,000

Loading height....................................(in.)

Tires...................Operating...................   4

                Ply........................   10

                Size........................ 9.00 x 20

Ground clearance.................................(in.)

Brakes...Air

Towing tractor.......................................

Shipping dimensions........(cu ft)   ....(sq ft)

ADDITIONAL DATA

....
....
....
....

SEMITRAILER, MOBILE RECORDS, 6-TON (10-TON GROSS)

Technical Manuals: Parts List: SNL G-592

Manufacturer: Watson Automotive Equipment Co.

RA PD 308967

Classification: Standard

Purpose: To provide mobility for electric accounting machines used in the field.

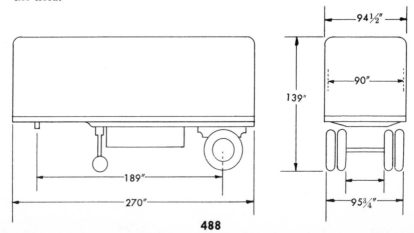

SEMITRAILER, MOBILE RECORDS, 6-TON (10-TON GROSS)

GENERAL DATA

Body type...Van
Weight..................Net......................(lb)   9,000
Payload..................(lb) 12,000
Gross....................(lb) 21,000
Loading height....................................(in.) 49
Ground clearance.................................(in.) $16\frac{1}{2}$
Tread...(in.) 69
Tires.................Operating.....................4
Ply...........................10
Size........................9.00 x 20
Brakes..Air
Towing tractor....................Truck tractor, 4-5 ton, 4 x 4
Shipping dimensions.......(cu ft)   ....(sq ft)

ADDITIONAL DATA

....

....

....

....

SEMITRAILER, LABORATORY, PHOTOGRAPHIC
10-TON GROSS, TYPE N-I, N-2, N-3

Technical Orders: Parts List:

Manufacturer: Fruehauf Trailer Co.

RA PD 309065

Classification: Standard

Purpose: Used by Army Air Forces to process photographic negatives and
print photographs.

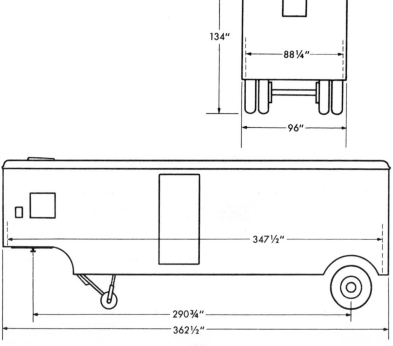

SEMITRAILER, LABORATORY, PHOTOGRAPHIC
10-TON GROSS, TYPE N-I, N-2, N-3

GENERAL DATA

Body type...Van

Weight................*Net (with equipment)......(lb)   10,730

Payload..................(lb)   18,270

Gross...................(lb)   29,000

Loading height...................................(in.)   33

Ground clearance.................................(in.)   17½

King pin to center of axle.........................(in.)   290¾

Tires...................Operating.....................   4

Ply........................   10

Size........................   9.00 x 20

Brakes...Air

Towing tractor...............Truck tractor, 4-5 ton, 4 x 4

Shipping dimensions........(cu ft) 2,699........(sq ft) 241

ADDITIONAL DATA

Contains complete equipment necessary to develop and print photographs, air conditioner, gasoline heater, 110-volt generator driven by a
4-cylinder, air-cooled engine.

*Equipment installed in vehicle weighs approximately 1,730 pounds.

....
....
....

SEMITRAILER, SHOE REPAIR,
6-TON (10-TON GROSS)

Technical Manual: Gerstenslager, TM 10-1315. Parts List: SNL G-569

Manufacturers: The Gerstenslager Co.; Trailmobile Co.

RA PD 66405

Vehicle illustrated above: The Gerstenslager Co., Model W-8120.

Classification: Standard

Purpose: Used by Quartermaster Corps to provide mobile shoe repair facilities.

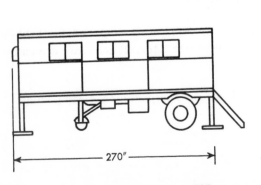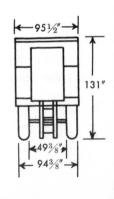

SEMITRAILER, SHOE REPAIR, 6-TON (10-TON GROSS)

GENERAL DATA

Body type.......................................Van

Weight...................Net.........................(lb)   8,400

                      Payload..................(lb)   12,000

                      Gross.....................(lb)   20,400

Loading height....................................(in.)   50

Tires....................Operating.....................   4

                      Ply..........................   10

                      Size......................... 9.00 x 20

Ground clearance..................................(in.)   14

Brakes..Air

Towing tractor................Truck tractor, 4-5 ton, 4 x 4

Shipping dimensions........(cu ft)   ....(sq ft)

ADDITIONAL DATA

. . . .

. . . .

. . . .

. . . .

SEMITRAILER, STERILIZER AND BATH, 6-TON (10-TON GROSS)

Technical Manuals: Strick, TM 10-1397;   Parts List:
                   Hyde, TM 10-1295.

Manufacturers: Gramm Truck and Trailer Corp.; Hyde Corp.; Lufkin
   Foundry and Machine Co.; Strick Co.; Trailmobile.

RA PD 66407

Vehicle illustrated above: Strick.

Classification: Standard

Purpose: To provide mobile facilities for sterilization and bath.

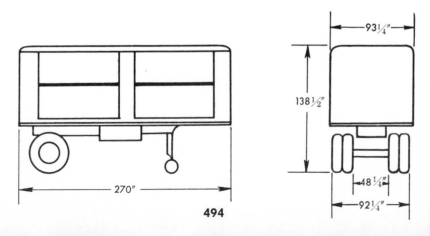

SEMITRAILER, STERILIZER AND BATH, 6-TON (10-TON GROSS)

GENERAL DATA

Body type			Van
Weight	Net	(lb)	9,500
	Payload	(lb)	12,000
	Gross	(lb)	21,500
Loading height		(in.)	49
Tires	Operating		4
	Ply		10
	Size		9.00 x 20
Ground clearance		(in.)	16½
Brakes			Air
Towing tractor		Truck tractor, 4-5 ton, 4 x 4	
Shipping dimensions	(cu ft)	(sq ft)	

ADDITIONAL DATA

. . . .

. . . .

. . . .

. . . .

SEMITRAILER, TECHNICAL SUPPLY, 10-TON GROSS

Technical Orders: Parts List:

Manufacturer: Fruehauf Trailer Co.

RA PD 309063

Classification: Standard

Purpose: Used by Army Air Forces for storage, issue and transportation of aircraft spare parts and accessories.

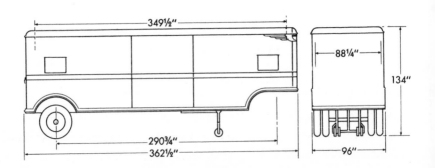

SEMITRAILER, TECHNICAL SUPPLY, 10-TON GROSS

GENERAL DATA

Body type		Van	
Weight	Net	(lb)	9,000
	Payload (racks and shelving)	(lb)	4,250
	Gross	(lb)	13,250
	Gross (maximum allowable)	(lb)	29,000
Loading height		(in.)	30
Ground clearance		(in.)	17½
Tread		(in.)	
Kingpin to center of axle		(in.)	290¾
Tires	Operating		4
	Ply		10
	Size		9.00 x 20
Brakes		Air	
Towing tractor	Truck tractor, 4-5 ton, 4 x 4		
Shipping dimensions	(cu ft) 2,697	(sq ft) 241	
	(cu ft) (disassembled)	1,954	
Weight packed for export		(lb)	29,000

ADDITIONAL DATA

Equipment includes a 110-volt generator driven by a one-cylinder air-cooled engine, storage bins and heating and ventilating equipment. Winch capacity 15,000 lb., located back of cab on tractor.

SEMITRAILER, TEXTILE REPAIR,
6-TON (10-TON GROSS)

Technical Manuals: Carter, TM 10-1213;
Utility, TM 10-1317.

Parts List: SNL G-588
(Utility)
SNL G-534
(Carter)

Manufacturers: Carter Mfg. Co.; Utility Trailer Mfg. Co.

RA PD 66409

Vehicle illustrated above: Carter

Classification: Standard

Purpose: Used by Quartermaster Corps to provide mobile textile repair
facilities.

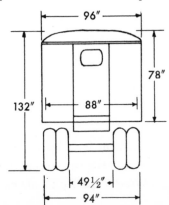

SEMITRAILER, TEXTILE REPAIR, 6-TON (10-TON GROSS)

GENERAL DATA

Body type..Van

Weight...................Net.....................(lb)   8,500

                        Payload..................(lb) 12,000

                        Gross....................(lb) 20,500

Loading height.......................................(in.)   50

Tires....................Operating.....................   4

                        Ply..........................   10

                        Size......................... 9.00 x 20

Ground clearance.......................(minimum) (in.)   14

Brakes..Air

Towing tractor...............Truck tractor, 4-5 ton, 4 x 4

Shipping dimensions........(cu ft)   ....(sq ft)

ADDITIONAL DATA

....

....

....

....

SEMITRAILER, CARGO, 7-TON (10-TON GROSS)

Technical Manual: TM-9-882. Parts List: SNL G-596

Manufacturers: Various

RA PD 308969

Vehicle illustrated above: Highway Trailer. Co.

Classification: Substitute standard

Purpose: To transport general cargo.

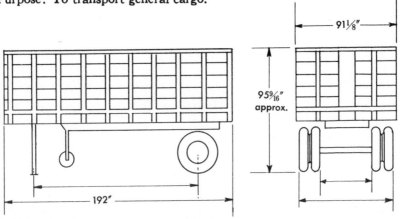

SEMITRAILER, CARGO, 7-TON (10-TON GROSS)

GENERAL DATA

Body type.............................Cargo—wood or steel

Weight	Net, wood	(lb)	5,100
	Net, steel	(lb)	5,500
	Payload	(lb)	14,000
	Gross, wood	(lb)	19,100
	Gross, steel	(lb)	19,500

Loading height...(in.) $48\frac{1}{2}$

Ground clearance......................................(in.) $15\frac{1}{2}$

Tread..(in.) 67

Tires	Operating	4
	Spare	1
	Ply	10
	Size	7.50 x 20

Brakes...Vacuum

Towing tractor.......................Truck, 2½-ton, 6 x 6

Shipping dimensions........(cu ft)   ....(sq ft)

ADDITIONAL DATA

Similar vehicle manufactured by: Carter Mfg. Co.; Edwards Iron Works; Gramm Motor Truck & Trailer Corp.; Hyde Corp.; Kentucky Mfg. Corp.; Lufkin Foundry & Machine Co.; W. C. Nabors Co.; Pointer Willamette Co, and Whitehead & Kales Co.

....

....

....

SEMITRAILER, LOW PLATFORM, 7½-TON (12-TON GROSS)

Technical Manual: TM 10-1228   Parts List: SNL G-600

Manufacturers: American Body and Trailer Co.; Hobbs Mfg. Co.; Lufkin
Foundry & Machine Co.; Steel Products Co.; Truck Engineering Corp.

RA PD 308978

Vehicle illustrated above: Truck Engineering Corp.

Classification: Standard

Purpose:

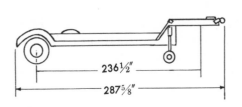

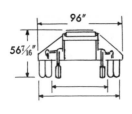

SEMITRAILER, LOW PLATFORM, 7½-TON (12-TON GROSS)

GENERAL DATA

Body type. . . . . .Platform

Weight. . . . . .Net. . . . .(lb)   7,000

Payload. . . . .(lb)   15,000

Gross. . . . .(lb)   22,000

Ground clearance. . . . .(in.)   12

Tread. . . . .(in.)

Tires. .Operating.   4

Spare.   1

Ply.   12

Size. . . . .   9.00 x 15

Brakes. . . . . .Vacuum

Towing tractor. . . . . Truck tractor, 2½-ton, 4 x 2

Shipping dimensions. . . . .(cu ft)   . . . .(sq ft)

ADDITIONAL DATA

. . . .

. . . .

. . . .

. . . .

SEMITRAILER, 13-TON GROSS, K-78

Technical Manuals: Parts List:

Manufacturer: Fruehauf Trailer Co.

Classification: Standard

Purpose: Used by Signal Corps.

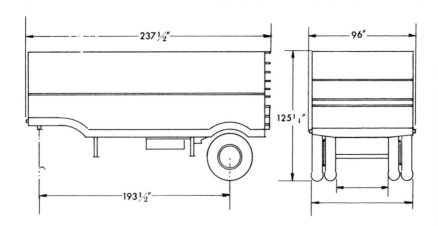

SEMITRAILER, 13-TON GROSS, K-78

GENERAL DATA

Body type. . . . . .Van

Weight. . . . . .Net. . . . .(lb)   9,500

                      Payload. . . . .(lb)   10,000

                      Gross. . . . .(lb)   19,500

Loading height. . . . .(in.)

Ground clearance. . . . .:(in.) $17\frac{1}{2}$

Tread. . . . .(in.)

Tires. . . . . .Operating. 4

                      Ply. 10

                      Size. . . . . 9.00 x 20

Brakes. . . . . .Air

Towing tractor. . . . . .Truck tractor, 5-ton, 4 x 4

Shipping dimensions. . . . .(cu ft) 1,556. . . . .(sq ft)

Weight packed for export. . .(loaded). . . . .(lb)   20,000

ADDITIONAL DATA

No photo available at date of publication.

. . . .

. . . .

. . . .

SEMITRAILER, CARRYALL, 15-TON

Technical Orders: Parts List:

Manufacturer: Trailer Company of America.

RA PD 309050

Classification: Standard

Purpose: Used by Army Air Forces for transporting heavy maintenance vehicles such as mowers, graders, trenchers, rollers and for transportation of supplies and equipment.

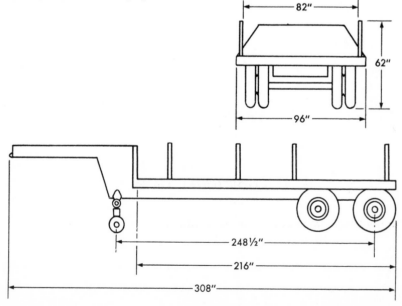

SEMITRAILER, CARRYALL, 15-TON

GENERAL DATA

Body type.....................................Platform

Weight...................Net.......................(lb)   9,210

Payload..................(lb)   30,000

Gross....................(lb)   39,210

Loading height.......................................(in.)   35

Ground clearance..................................(in.)   8

Tread...(in.)

Kingpin to center of bogie............................(in.)   248½

Tires....................Operating......................   8

Ply...........................   10

Size........................ 7.50 x 15

Brakes...Air

Towing tractor...............Truck tractor, 4-5 ton, 4 x 4

Shipping dimensions........(cu ft) 528..........(sq ft) 174

(cu ft) (disassembled).......500

ADDITIONAL DATA

. . . .
. . . .
. . . .
. . . .

SEMITRAILER, FLAT BED, 20-TON, WITH DOLLY

Technical Manuals: See additional data   Parts List:

Manufacturers: Fruehauf Trailer Co., LaCrosse Trailer & Equipment Co.,
Rogers Bros. Co., Timpte Bros.

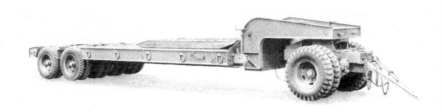

RA PD 309000

Vehicle illustrated above: Fruehauf

Classification: Standard

Purpose: Used by Corps of Engineers to transport heavy equipment.

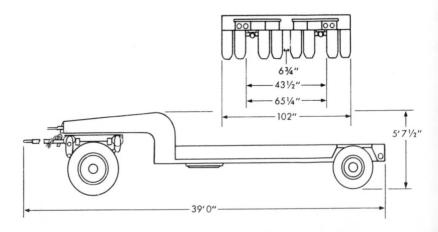

SEMITRAILER, FLAT BED, 20-TON, WITH DOLLY

GENERAL DATA

Body type.................................Full flat bed

		Minimum	Maximum
Weight.................Net (lb).............		12,790	16,700
	Payload (lb)..........	40,000	40,000
	Gross (lb)...........	52,790	56,700
Loading height, empty.........................(in.)		36	40½
Ground clearance............................(in.)		10	
Tread.......................................(in.)			
Tires..................Operating..............		20	
	Spares...7.50 x 20, 9.00 x 20	1	
	Ply...Front 14....Rear 8		
	Size:		
	Front..12.00 x 20, 9.00 x 20		
	Rear.......... 7.50 x 20		

Brakes......................Air and hand parking

Towing tractors...........Truck tractor, 5-6 ton, 4 x 4
6-ton, 6 x 6

Shipping dimensions.......(cu ft) 1,885....(sq ft) 330

ADDITIONAL DATA

Trailers supplied by various manufacturers vary in weight. The figures given are the maximum and minimum values.

Fruehauf Trailer Co., Model CPT-20, TM 5-9034.

LaCrosse Trailer and Equipment Co., Model DF 6.

Rogers Bros. Company, Model LKS-620.

Rogers Bros. Company, Model H-20-L-S-14.

Timpte Bros.

SEMITRAILER, 10-TON PONTON

Technical Manual: TM 5-9006   Parts List:

Manufacturer: Fruehauf Trailer Co.

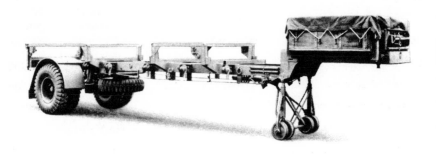

RA PD 309022

Classification: Standard

Purpose: Used by Corps of Engineers to transport ponton bridge equipment.

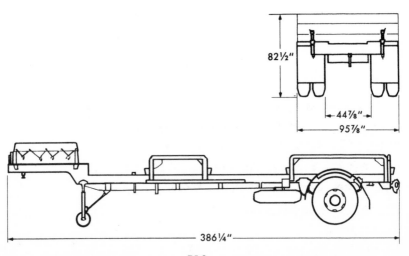

SEMITRAILER, 10-TON PONTON

GENERAL DATA

Body type..Drop frame

Weight...................Net......................(lb)   7,200

                      Payload..................(lb) .18,000

                      Gross....................(lb) 25,200

Loading height.......................................(in.)

Ground clearance...................................(in.)   16

Ground pressure.........................(lbs per sq in.)   45

Tread..(in.)

Tires...................Operating....................   4

                      Spare........................   1

                      Ply...........................   14

                      Size........................12.00 x 20

Brakes..Air

Towing tractor......................................

Shipping dimensions........(cu ft) 1,785.........(sq ft) 257

ADDITIONAL DATA

....

....

....

....

SEMITRAILER, 25-TON PONTON

Technical Manuals: TM 5-9012, TM 5-9014   Parts List:

Manufacturers: Electric Wheel Co.; Fruehauf Trailer Co.; Trailer Company of America.

RA PD 309034

Vehicle illustrated above: Fruehauf Trailer Co.

Classification: Standard

Purpose: Used by Corps of Engineers to transport ponton bridge equipment.

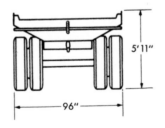

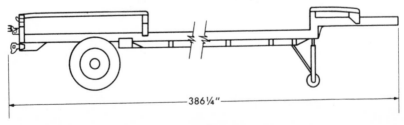

SEMITRAILER, 25-TON PONTON

GENERAL DATA

Body type..................................Drop frame

		Minimum	Maximum
Weight..............Net (lb)...............		7,200	7,660
	Payload (lb)............	10,148	18,000
	Gross (lb)..............	17,808	25,200
Loading height.......................................(in.)			55½
Ground clearance...................................(in.)			16
Ground pressure...........................(lbs per sq in.)			45
Tread..(in.)			
Tires..................Operating....................			4
	Spares.....................			1
	Ply........................			14
	Size........................			12.00 x 20

Brakes...Air

Towing tractor............... Truck tractor, 5-6 ton, 4 x 4

Shipping dimensions.......(cu ft) 1,536.........(sq ft) 257

ADDITIONAL DATA

....

....

....

....

SEMITRAILER, WRECKING, 25-FOOT, TYPE C-2

Technical Orders: Parts List:

Manufacturer: Trailer Co. of America.

RA PD 309046

Classification: Standard

Purpose: Used by Army Air Forces for transporting salvaged and new aircraft; also for general purpose hauling.

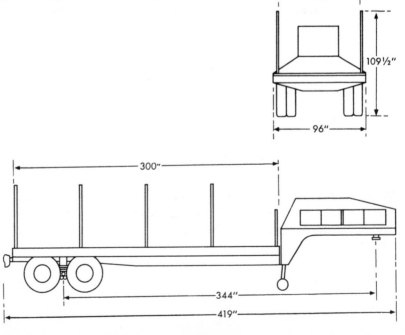

514

SEMITRAILER, WRECKING, 25-FOOT, TYPE C-2

GENERAL DATA

Body type. . . . . .Flat bed

Weight. . . . . .Net. . . . .(lb)   10,850

Payload. . . . .(lb)   25,000

Gross. . . . .(lb)   35,850

Loading height. . . . .(in.)   48

Ground clearance. . . . .(in.)   10

Tread. . . . .(in.)

Tires. . . . . .Operating.   8

Ply. . . . .

Size. . . . . .10.00 x 15

Brakes. . . . . .Air

*Towing tractor. . . . .

Shipping dimensions. . . . .(cu ft) 1,150 . . . .(sq ft) 236

(cu ft) (disassembled). 950

Weight packed for export. . . . .(lb)   10,850

ADDITIONAL DATA

*Towed by the type C-2 wrecking truck tractor. May also be towed by
the standard Army 4-5 ton, 4 x 4 truck tractor (Autocar or Federal)
which is used for towing the AAF type F-2 and type F-2A fuel servicing
semitrailers.

. . . .

. . . .

. . . .

SEMITRAILER, WRECKING, 40-FOOT, 12½-TON, TYPE C-2

Technical Orders: Parts List:

Manufacturer: Trailer Co. of America.

RA PD 309048

Classification: Standard

Purpose: Used by Army Air Forces for transporting salvaged and new aircraft; also for general purpose hauling.

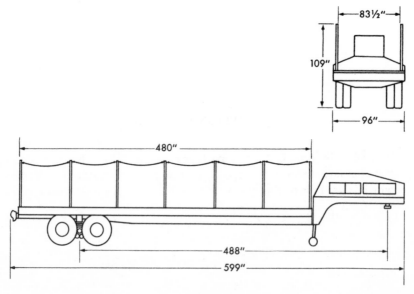

SEMITRAILER, WRECKING, 40-FOOT, 12½-TON, TYPE C-2

GENERAL DATA

Body type..Flat bed

Weight...................Net.........................(lb) 13,790

Payload..................(lb) 25,000

Gross....................(lb) 38,790

Loading height......................................(in.) 48

Ground clearance....................................(in.) 10

Kingpin to center of bogie..........................(in.) 488

Tires....................Operating..................... 8

Ply...........................

Size.........................10.00 x 15

Brakes..Air

*Towing tractor...

Shipping dimensions........(cu ft) 1,727.........(sq ft) 361

(cu ft) (disassembled)......1,500

Weight packed for export............................(lb) 13,790

ADDITIONAL DATA

*Towed by the type C-2 wrecking truck tractor. May also be towed by
the standard Army 4-5-ton, 4 x 4 truck tractor (Autocar or Federal),
which is used for towing the AAF type F-2 and type F-2A fuel servicing
semitrailers.

SEMITRAILER, TANK, WATER, 1,500-GAL.

Technical Manual: TM 5-5000.

Parts List:

Manufacturer: Columbian Steel Tank Co.

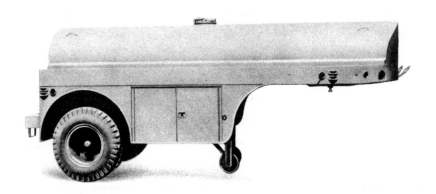

RA PD 309012

Classification: Standard

Purpose: Used by Corps of Engineers to transport and dispense water.

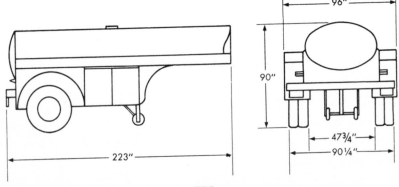

SEMITRAILER, TANK, WATER, 1,500-GAL.

GENERAL DATA

Body type..............Frameless, water tank......(gal)   1,500

Weight................Net.....................(lb)   7,500

                       Payload.................(lb)   12,450

                       Gross...................(lb)   19,450

Loading height......................................(in.)

Ground clearance....................................(in.)   16

Tread..(in.)

Tires..................Operating....................   4

                       Spare.......................   1

                       Ply.........................   10

                       Size........................   9.00 x 20

Brakes.................(Bendix-Westinghouse)......Air

Towing tractor............... Truck tractor, 5-6 ton, 4 x 4

Shipping dimensions........(cu ft) 1,115.........(sq ft)

Weight packed for export...........................(lb)   7,650

ADDITIONAL DATA

Wheelbase (tractor to trailer).........................(in.)   136

....

....

....

SEMITRAILER, FUEL SERVICING, 2,000 GAL., TYPE F-2

Technical Orders: T. O. 19-25-24.   Parts List:

Manufacturer: The Heil Co.

RA PD 309044

Classification: Standard

Purpose: Used by Army Air Forces to transport aircraft engine fuel from distributing points to flying fields, and to service aircraft.

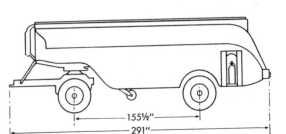 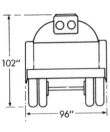

SEMITRAILER, FUEL SERVICING, 2,000 GAL., TYPE F-2

GENERAL DATA

Body type. . . . . Tank

Weight. . . . . .Net. . . . .(lb)   8,485

Payload. . . . .(lb)   12,000

Gross. . . . .(lb)   20,485

Loading height. . . . .(in.)   102

Ground clearance. . . . .(in.)

Kingpin to center of axle. . . . .(in.) $155\frac{1}{2}$

Tires. . . . . .Operating.   4

Ply.   10

Size. . . . . 9.00 x 20

Brakes. . . . . Air

Towing tractor. . . . . .Truck tractor, 4-5 ton, 4 x 4

Shipping dimensions. . . . .(cu ft) 1,628. . . . .(sq ft) 208

ADDITIONAL DATA

Equipped with two gasoline engine driven pumps having a rated capacity (total) of 160 gallons per minute.

. . . .

. . . .

SEMITRAILER, FUEL SERVICING, 2,000 GAL., TYPE F-2A

Technical Order: T.O. 19-25-15

Parts List:

Manufacturer: The Heil Co.

RA PD 309042

Classification: Standard

Purpose: Used by Army Air Forces to transport aircraft engine fuel from distributing points to flying fields, and to service aircraft.

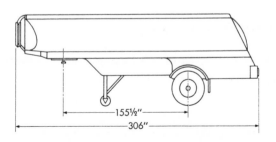

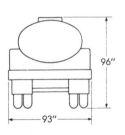

SEMITRAILER, FUEL SERVICING, 2,000 GAL., TYPE F-2A

GENERAL DATA

Body type		Tank	
Weight	Net	(lb)	8,600
	Payload	(lb)	12,000
	Gross	(lb)	20,600
Loading height		(in.)	
Ground clearance		(in.)	
Tread		(in.)	
Kingpin to center of axle		(in.)	155½
Tires	Operating		4
	Ply		10
	Size		9.00 x 20
Brakes		Air	
Towing tractor		Truck tractor, 4-5 ton, 4 x 4	
Shipping dimensions	(cu ft) 1,632	(sq ft) 204	

ADDITIONAL DATA

This vehicle is the same as the type F-2 fuel servicing semitrailer, except that the side compartment hose reels have been eliminated.

SEMITRAILER, FUEL SERVICING, 4,000 GAL., TYPE F-1

Technical Orders: Parts List:

Manufacturer: Standard Steel Works

RA PD 309083

Classification: Standard

Purpose: Used by Army Air Forces to transport aircraft engine fuel from distributing points to flying fields, and to service aircraft.

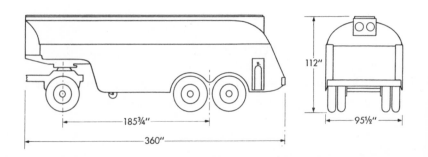

SEMITRAILER, FUEL SERVICING, 4,000 GAL., TYPE F-1

GENERAL DATA

Body type...................................Tank

Weight...................Net....................(lb)   16,440

Payload..................(lb)   24,000

Gross....................(lb)   40,440

Ground clearance..................................(in.)

Tires...................Operating...................   8

Ply........................   12

Size.......................10.00 x 22

Kingpin to center of bogie.........................(in.)   185¾

Brakes..Air

Towing tractor...............Truck tractor, 7½-ton, 6 x 6

Shipping dimensions.......(cu ft) 2,232........(sq ft) 240

ADDITIONAL DATA

Equipped with two gasoline engine driven pumps having a rated capacity (total) of 320 gallons per minute.

. . . .

. . . .

. . . .

SEMITRAILER, FUEL SERVICING, 4,000 GAL., TYPE F-1A

Technical Orders: Parts List:

Manufacturer: Standard Steel Works

RA PD 309081

Classification: Standard

Purpose: Used by Army Air Forces to transport aircraft engine fuel from distributing points to flying fields, and to service aircraft.

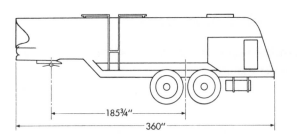

SEMITRAILER, FUEL SERVICING, 4,000 GAL., TYPE F-1A

GENERAL DATA

Body type . . . . Tank

Weight . . . . Net . . . . (lb)   19,676

Payload . . . . (lb)   24,000

Gross . . . . (lb)   43,676

Ground clearance . . . . (in.)

Tread . . . . (in.)

Tires . . . . Operating   8

Ply   12

Size . . . . 10.00 x 22

Kingpin to center of bogie . . . . (in.)   185¾

Brakes . . . . Air

Towing tractor . . . . Truck tractor, 7½-ton, 6 x 6, type F-1

Shipping dimensions . . . . (cu ft) 2,232 . . . . (sq ft) 240

ADDITIONAL DATA

Equipped with two gasoline engine driven pumps having a rated capacity (total) of 320 gallons per minute.

. . . .

. . . .

. . . .

DOLLY, FUEL SERVICING, 1-TON, TYPE D-2

Technical Manuals: Parts List:

Manufacturers: Equipment: The Heil Co.

Trailer: Standard Cargo, 1 Ton.

RA PD 309059

Classification: Standard

Purpose: Used by Army Air Forces to convert commercial gasoline transports to aircraft servicing vehicles as a stand-by unit for refueling pits and for pumping from portable bulk storage.

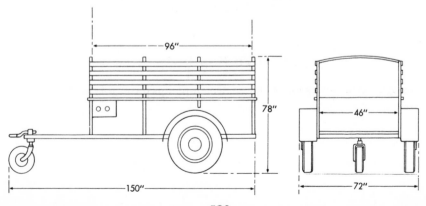

DOLLY, FUEL SERVICING, 1-TON, TYPE D-2

GENERAL DATA

Body type...Cargo

Weight.................Net........................(lb)   1,360

Payload (equipment)........(lb)   1,990

Gross.....................(lb)   3,350

Loading height....................................(in.)   28

Ground clearance.....................................

Tread...

Tires..................Operating....................   2

Ply..........................   10

Size ....7.50 x 20

Brakes..

Towing tractor......................................

Shipping dimensions........(cu ft) 488.............(sq ft) 75

ADDITIONAL DATA

Equipment consists of a fluid segregator, 80 GPM fuel transfer pump, two hose reels with hose and nozzles. Pump is driven by an air-cooled gasoline engine. Basic vehicle is standard 1-ton cargo trailer.

. . . .
. . . .
. . . .
. . . .

DOLLY, TRAILER CONVERTER, FUEL SERVICING, TYPE F-1 OR F-1A

Technical Manuals: Parts List:

Manufacturer: Standard Steel Works.

RA PD 309087

Classification: Standard

Purpose: Used by the Army Air Forces to convert F-1 and F-1A fuel servicing semitrailer to full trailer so it can be towed by any Army prime mover.

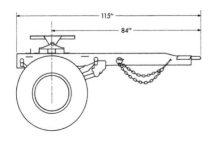

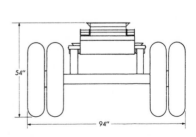

DOLLY, TRAILER CONVERTER, FUEL SERVICING, TYPE F-1 OR F-1A

GENERAL DATA

Body type...

Weight................Net......................(lb)   2,300

                        Payload.................(lb)

                        Gross...................(lb)

Loading height.....................................(in.) $53\frac{1}{2}$

Ground clearance..................................(in.)

Tires.................Operating....................   4

                     Ply..........................   12

                     Size........................10.00 x 22

Brakes..

Towing tractor...........Truck tractor, $7\frac{1}{2}$-ton.....6 x 6

Shipping dimensions.......(cu ft) 250..........(sq ft)

ADDITIONAL DATA

....

....

....

....

DOLLY, TRAILER CONVERTER, FUEL SERVICING, TYPE F 2 OR F 2A

Technical Manuals: Parts List:

Manufacturers:

RA PD 309085

Classification: Standard

Purpose: Used by the Army Air Forces to convert instrument semitrailer to full trailer so that it can be towed by any Army prime mover.

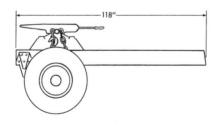
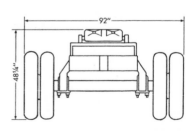

DOLLY, TRAILER CONVERTER, FUEL SERVICING, TYPE F 2 OR F 2A

GENERAL DATA

Body type..

Weight..................Net.....................(lb)   2,550

Payload..................(lb)   15,000

Gross...................(lb)   17,550

Loading height.......................................(in.)   48½

Ground clearance...................................(in.)

Tires...................Operating....................   4

Ply.........................   10

Size........................   9.00 x 20

Brakes..

Towing tractor...

Shipping dimensions.......(cu ft)   ....(sq ft)

ADDITIONAL DATA

....

....

....

....

DOLLY, TRAILER CONVERTER, WRECKING, TYPE C-2

Technical Manuals: Parts List:

Manufacturer: Trailer Company of America.

RA PD 309073

Classification: Standard

Purpose: Used by Army Air Forces to convert semitrailer to full trailer so it can be towed by any Army prime mover.

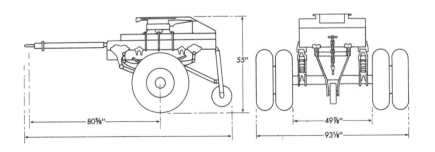

DOLLY, TRAILER CONVERTER, WRECKING, TYPE C-2

GENERAL DATA

Body type...

Weight.................... Net.................... (lb)   2,485

                          Payload................ (lb)   14,000

                          Gross.................. (lb)   16,485

Loading height.................................... (in.)   55

Ground clearance................................. (in.)

Tread.. (in.)

Tires.................... Operating....................   4

                          Ply.........................   12

                          Size....................... 10.00 x 15

Brakes...

Towing tractor............. Truck tractor wrecker, type C-2

Shipping dimensions........ (cu ft) 256.......... (sq ft)

ADDITIONAL DATA

. . . .

. . . .

. . . .

. . . .

DOLLY, TRAILER CONVERTER, TECHNICAL SUPPLY, FIELD SHOP AND INSTRUMENT SHOP

Technical Orders: Parts Lists:

Manufacturer: Fruehauf Trailer Co.

RA PD 309079

Classification: Standard

Purpose: Used by Army Air Forces to convert a semitrailer to a full trailer (4-wheel).

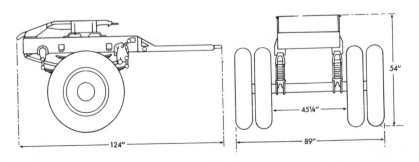

DOLLY, TRAILER CONVERTER, TECHNICAL SUPPLY, FIELD SHOP AND INSTRUMENT SHOP

GENERAL DATA

Body type...			
Weight...................	Net......................	(lb)	2,760
	Payload..................	(lb)	16,000
	Gross...................	(lb)	18,760
Loading height..................................		(in.)	
Ground clearance...............................		(in.)	17½
Tread..		(in.)	
Tires..................	Operating...................		4
	Ply........................		10
	Size.......................		9.00 x 20
Brakes.......................................	Air		
Towing tractor..................... Truck, 4-5 ton, 4 x 4			
Shipping dimensions........(cu ft) 364...........(sq ft) 69			
	(cu ft) disassembled........202		

ADDITIONAL DATA

. . . .

. . . .

. . . .

. . . .

DOLLY, 2-WHEEL, D.T., PONTON

Technical Manual: TM 5-9016   Parts List:

Manufacturer: Electric Wheel Co.

RA PD 309004

Classification: Standard

Purpose: Used by Corps of Engineers to convert semitrailer into four-wheel trailer.

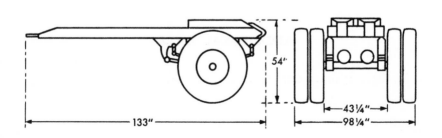

DOLLY, 2-WHEEL, D.T., PONTON

GENERAL DATA

Body type...Dolly

Weight...................Net......................(lb)   3,600

                       Payload..................(lb)

                       Gross....................(lb)

Loading height, empty.............................(in.)   54

Ground clearance..................................(in.) $18\tfrac{11}{16}$

Tread..(in.) $70\tfrac{3}{4}$

Tires...................Operating.....................   4

                       Ply.........................   14

                       Size........................12.00 x 20

Brakes...Air

Towing tractor....................................

Shipping dimensions........(cu ft) 425...........(sq ft) 94

ADDITIONAL DATA

33-inch rigid-mounted semiautomatic fifth wheel.

....

....

....

DOLLY, PROPELLER, TYPE C-1A

Technical Manuals: Parts List:

Manufacturer: General Bronze Corp.

RA PD 309061

Classification: Standard

Purpose: Used by Army Air Forces to transport 3- or 4-blade propellers up to 14 feet in diameter.

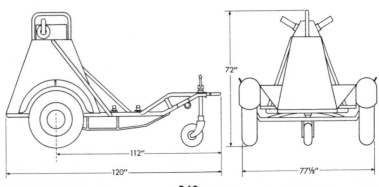

DOLLY, PROPELLER, TYPE C-1A

GENERAL DATA

Body type. . . . . Special

Weight. . . . . Net. . . . . (lb)   1,207

Payload. . . . . (lb)   1,200

Gross. (lb)   2,407

Loading height. . . . . (in.)   70

Ground clearance. . . . .

Tread. . . . .

Tires. . . . . Operating.   2

Ply.   6

Size. . . . .   6.50 x 16

Brakes. . . . .

Towing tractor. . . . . Any Army truck

Shipping dimensions. . . . . (cu ft) 420. . . . . (sq ft)

ADDITIONAL DATA

. . . .

. . . .

. . . .

. . . .

NOMENCLATURE	Vehicle classification (see par. 3, AR 850-15)	MAINTENANCE				STORAGE AND ISSUE			Page Number
		Parts Procurement		Third Echelon and Higher		Vehicle	Maintenance Parts		
		Chassis	Body	Chassis	Body		Chassis	Body	
Signal Corps									
Truck, 1/2-ton, 4 x 2, telephone maintenance	SE	Ord	SC de to Ord	Ord	Ord	SC	Ord	Ord	
Truck, 1/2-ton, 4 x 4, light maintenance and installation K-50	SE	Ord	SC de to Ord	Ord	Ord	SC	Ord	Ord	170
Truck, 3/4-ton, 4 x 4, light maintenance and installation K-50	SE	Ord	SC de to Ord	Ord	Ord	SC	Ord	Ord	170
Truck, 1 1/2-ton, 4 x 4, K-18	SE	Ord	SC de to Ord	Ord	Ord	SC	Ord	Ord	
Truck, 1 1/2-ton, 4 x 2, telephone maintenance and construction w/w	SE	Ord	SC de to Ord	Ord	Ord	SC	Ord	Ord	
Truck, 1 1/2-ton, 4 x 4, combination stake and platform, K-33	SE	Ord	Ord	Ord	Ord	SC	Ord	Ord	202
Truck, 1 1/2-ton, 4 x 4, combination stake and platform, K-54	SE	Ord	SC de to Ord	Ord	Ord	SC	Ord	Ord	202
Truck, 1 1/2-ton, 4 x 4, earth borer and pole setter, K-44	SE	Ord	Ord	Ord	Ord	SC	Ord	Ord	208
Truck, 1 1/2-ton, 4 x 4, panel delivery, K-51	SE	Ord	Ord	Ord	Ord	SC	Ord	Ord	216
Truck, 1 1/2-ton, 4 x 4, panel delivery, K-70	SE	Ord	Ord	Ord	Ord	SC	Ord	Ord	
Truck, 1 1/2-ton, 4 x 4, telephone construction and maintenance wo/w, K-42	SE	Ord	SC de to Ord	Ord	Ord	SC	Ord	Ord	218
Truck, 1 1/2-ton, 4 x 4, telephone construction and maintenance w/w, K-3	SE	Ord	SC de to Ord	Ord	Ord	SC	Ord	Ord	218
Truck, 2 1/2-ton, 4 x 2, telephone construction	SE	Ord	SC de to Ord	Ord	Ord	SC	Ord	Ord	
Truck, 2 1/2-ton, 6 x 6, van, K-53	SE	Ord	SC	Ord	Ord	SC	Ord	Ord	272
Truck, 2 1/2-ton, 6 x 6, van, K-57	SE	Ord	SC	Ord	Ord	SC	Ord	Ord	274
Truck, 2 1/2-ton, 6 x 6, van, K-59	SE	Ord	SC	Ord	Ord	SC	Ord	Ord	
Truck, 2 1/2-ton, 6 x 6, van, K-60	SE	Ord	SC	Ord	Ord	SC	Ord	Ord	274
Truck, 2 1/2-ton, 6 x 6, van, K-61	SE	Ord	SC	Ord	Ord	SC	Ord	Ord	
Trailer, 1/4-ton, 2-wheel, telephone cable splicer, K-38	SP	Ord	Ord	Ord	Ord	SC	Ord	Ord	384
Trailer, 1/2-ton, 2-wheel, mobile communication, K-19	SP	Ord	Ord	Ord	Ord	SC	Ord	Ord	392
Trailer, 1-ton payload, 2-wheel, house, K-29	SP	SC	SC	Ord	Ord	SC	Ord	Ord	
Trailer, 1-ton payload, 2-wheel, cargo, K-52	SE	Ord	SC de to Ord	Ord	Ord	SC	Ord	Ord	394
Trailer, 1-ton payload, 2-wheel, cargo, K-63	SE	Ord	SC de to Ord	Ord	Ord	SC	Ord	Ord	394
Trailer, 1-ton payload, 2-wheel, pigeon loft, PG-45	SP	SC	SC	Ord	Ord	SC	Ord	Ord	
Trailer, 1 1/2-ton payload, 2-wheel, photographic, K-45	SP	SC	SC	Ord	Ord	SC	Ord	Ord	398

Item									Page
Trailer, 1½-ton payload, 4-wheel, K-65	SP	SC de to Ord	SC de to Ord	Ord	Ord	SC	Ord	Ord	402
Trailer, 2-ton payload, 2-wheel, telephone construction and pole hauling, K-36	SP	Ord	Ord	Ord	Ord	SC	Ord	Ord	410
Truck, 4-5 ton, 4 x 4, tractor, K-32	GP	Ord	SC de to Ord	Ord	Ord	SC	Ord	Ord	
Truck, 4-5 ton, 4 x 4, van, K-30	SE	Ord	SC de to Ord	Ord	Ord	SC	Ord	Ord	
Truck, 4-5 ton, 4 x 4, van, K-31	SE	Ord	SC de to Ord	Ord	Ord	SC	Ord	Ord	
Truck, 5-6 ton, 4 x 4, van, K-30	SE	Ord	SC de to Ord	Ord	Ord	SC	Ord	Ord	
Truck, 5-6 ton, 4 x 4, van, K-31	SE	Ord	SC de to Ord	Ord	Ord	SC	Ord	Ord	
Truck, 5-6 ton, 4 x 4, van, K-62	SE	Ord	SC de to Ord	Ord	Ord	SC	Ord	Ord	
Truck, 6-ton, 6 x 6, van, K-56	SP	Ord	SC	Ord	Ord	SC	Ord	Ord	402
Trailer, 6-ton gross, 4-wheel, house type, K-35	SP	SC	SC	Ord	Ord	SC	Ord	Ord	434
Trailer, 4-ton payload, 2-wheel, antenna mount, K-64	SP	SC	SC	Ord	Ord	SC	Ord	Ord	434
Trailer, 4-ton payload, 2-wheel, antenna mount, K-22	SP	SC	SC	Ord	Ord	SC	Ord	Ord	436
Trailer, 4-ton payload, 4-wheel, antenna mount, K-28	SP	SC	SC	Ord	Ord	SC	Ord	Ord	
Trailer, 4-ton payload, 4-wheel, K-39	SP	SC	SC	Ord	Ord	SC	Ord	Ord	
Trailer, 4-ton payload, 4-wheel, K-40	SP	SC	SC	Ord	Ord	SC	Ord	Ord	
Trailer, 4-ton payload, 4-wheel, K-41	SP	SC	SC	Ord	Ord	SC	Ord	Ord	
Trailer, 4-ton payload, 4-wheel, K-49	SP	SC	SC	Ord	Ord	SC	Ord	Ord	420
Trailer, 4-ton payload, 4-wheel, van, K-34	SP	SC	SC	Ord	Ord	SC	Ord	Ord	404
Trailer, 5-ton payload, 4-wheel, K-58	SP	SC	SC	Ord	Ord	SC	Ord	Ord	
Trailer, 5-ton payload, 4-wheel, K-76	SP	SC	SC	Ord	Ord	SC	Ord	Ord	
Trailer, 5-ton payload, 2-wheel, K-37, telephone construction combination cable hauler	SP	SC de to Ord	SC de to Ord	Ord	Ord	SC	Ord	Ord	418
Trailer, 10-ton gross, 4-wheel, antenna mount and operating cab, K-75	SP	SC	SC	Ord	Ord	SC	Ord	Ord	438
Truck, 5-ton payload, 4-wheel, K-77	SP	SC	SC de to Ord	Ord	Ord	SC	Ord	Ord	404
Semitrailer, 1½-ton payload, van, K-55	SP	SC de to Ord	SC	Ord	Ord	C	Ord	Ord	460
Semitrailer, 4-ton payload, 2-wheel, antenna mount, K-71	SP	SC	SC	Ord	Ord	SC	Ord	Ord	468
Semitrailer, 6-ton gross, 2-wheel, K-67	SP	SC	SC de to Ord	Ord	Ord	SC	Ord	Ord	470
Semitrailer, 7-ton gross, K-72	SP	SC de to Ord	SC	Ord	Ord	SC	Ord	Ord	504
Semitrailer, 13-ton gross, K-78	SP	SC	SC	Ord	Ord	SC	Ord	Ord	
Quartermaster Corps									
Truck, 2½-ton, 6 x 6, sales commissary	SE	Ord	QMC de to Ord	Ord	Ord	QMC	Ord	Ord	494
Truck, 5-ton, 4 x 2, refrigerator	SE	Ord	QMC de to Ord	Ord	Ord	QMC	Ord	Ord	480
Semitrailer, 10-ton gross, 2-wheel, sterilizer and bath	SP	QMC	QMC	Ord	Ord	QMC	Ord	Ord	486
Semitrailer, 10-ton gross, 2-wheel, clothing repair	SP	QMC	QMC	Ord	Ord	QMC	Ord	Ord	492
Semitrailer, 10-ton gross, 2-wheel, laundry	SP	QMC	QMC	Ord	Ord	QMC	Ord	Ord	498
Semitrailer, 10-ton gross, 2-wheel, shoe repair	SP	QMC	QMC	Ord	Ord	QMC	Ord	Ord	
Semitrailer, 10-ton gross, 2-wheel, textile repair	SP	QMC	QMC	Ord	Ord	QMC	Ord	Ord	

NOMENCLATURE	Vehicle classification (see par. 3, AR 850-15)	MAINTENANCE				STORAGE AND ISSUE			Page Number
		Parts Procurement		Third Echelon and Higher		Vehicle	Maintenance Parts		
		Chassis	Body	Chassis	Body		Chassis	Body	
Semitrailer, 10-ton gross, 2-wheel, refrigerator	SP	QMC	QMC	Ord	Ord	QMC	Ord	Ord	474
Semitrailer, 15-ton gross, 2-wheel, refrigerator	SP	QMC	QMC	Ord	Ord	QMC	Ord	Ord	474
Chemical Warfare Service									
Truck, 1½-3-ton, 4 x 4, bus body	SE	Ord	Ord	Ord	Ord	CWS	Ord	Ord	
Apparatus, decontaminating, power-driven, M-3-A-1 (chassis 2½-ton, 6 x 6)	SE	Ord	CWS	Ord	CWS**	CWS	Ord	CWS**	240
Truck, chemical service M1 (chassis 2½-ton, 6 x 6)	SE	Ord	Ord	Ord	CWS**	CWS	Ord	Ord	250
Truck, crane, swinging boom, M-1 (chassis 4-ton, 6 x 6, SWB)	SE	Ord	CWS	Ord	Ord	CWS	Ord	Ord	286
Trailer, chemical handling, M-2, 4-ton payload, 4-wheel	SP	CWS	CWS	Ord	Ord	CWS	Ord	Ord	416
Trailer, chemical service, M-1 (4-ton payload, 4-wheel)	SP	CWS	CWS	Ord	Ord	CWS	Ord	Ord	416
Tractor, crane (wheeled)	SP	CWS	CWS	Ord	Ord	CWS	Ord	Ord	
Medical Corps									
Truck, 2½-ton, 6 x 6, surgical	SE	Ord	Med de to Ord	Ord	Ord	Med	Ord	Ord	270
Corps of Engineers									
Trailer, 2-ton tandem axle searchlight	SP	Engr	Engr	Engr	Engr	Engr	Engr	Engr	408
Trailer, full, flat bed, 8-ton	SP	Engr	Engr	Ord	Ord	Engr	Ord	Ord	426
Trailer, full, flat bed, 16-ton	SP	Engr	Engr	Ord	Ord	Engr	Ord	Ord	428
Trailer, full, low bed, 20-ton	SP	Engr	Engr	Ord	Ord	Engr	Ord	Ord	430
Trailer, 2-wheel, utility, pole type, 2½-ton, types I, II, III, IV, and V	SP	Engr	Engr	Ord	Ord	Engr	Ord	Ord	414
Trailer, platform, low bed, 60-ton	SP	Engr	Engr	Ord	Ord	Engr	Ord	Ord	444
Trailer, fire pumper, 2-wheel, 500 gpm, class 1000	SE	Ord	Ord	Ord	Ord	Engr	Ord	Ord	446
Trailer, fire crash, 2-wheel, high pressure, class 1010	SE	Ord	Engr	Ord	Ord	Engr	Ord	Ord	
Searchlight, 24-inch, complete with power plant, trailer-mounted	SP	Engr	Engr	Engr	Engr	Engr	Engr	Engr	538
Welding equipment, electric arc, 300 amp., trailer-mounted	SP	Engr	Engr	Engr	Engr	Engr	Engr	Engr	538
Dolly, 2-wheel, dt, ponton	SP	Engr	Engr	Ord	Ord	Engr	Ord	Ord	538

**Ordnance stores parts for maintenance of engine of power-driven decontaminating apparatus.

Item	Type								Page
Power plant, trailer-mounted, 5 kw	SP	Engr	Engr	Engr	Engr	Engr	Engr	Engr	510
Semitrailer, ponton, 10-ton	SP	Engr	Engr	Ord	Ord	Engr	Ord	Ord	512
Semitrailer, ponton, 25-ton	SP	Engr	Engr	Ord	Ord	Engr	Ord	Ord	508
Semitrailer, flat bed with dolly, 20-ton	SP	Engr	Engr	Ord	Ord	Engr	Ord	Ord	518
Tank, water, semitrailer, mounted, 1,500-gallon	SP	Engr	Engr	Ord	Ord	Engr	Ord	Ord	476
Reproduction equipment, camera section, 24 x 30, semi-trailer mounted, 10-ton, w/van body	SP	Engr	Engr	Ord	Ord	Engr	Ord	Ord	476
Reproduction equipment, combination section A, semi-trailer mounted, 10-ton, w/van body	SP	Engr	Engr	Ord	Ord	Engr	Ord	Ord	476
Reproduction equipment, combination section B, semi-trailer mounted, 10-ton, w/van body	SP	Engr	Engr	Ord	Ord	Engr	Ord	Ord	476
Reproduction equipment, camera section, 24 x 24 semi-trailer mounted, 10-ton, w/van body	SP	Engr	Engr	Ord	Ord	Engr	Ord	Ord	476
Reproduction equipment, photographic section, semi-trailer mounted, 10-ton, w/van body	SP	Engr	Engr	Ord	Ord	Engr	Ord	Ord	476
Reproduction equipment, plate grainer section, semi-trailer mounted, 10-ton, w/van body	SP	Engr	Engr	Ord	Ord	Engr	Ord	Ord	476
Reproduction equipment, plate process section, semi-trailer mounted, 10-ton, w/van body	SP	Engr	Engr	Ord	Ord	Engr	Ord	Ord	476
Reproduction equipment, laboratory section, semitrailer, mounted, 10-ton, w/van body	SP	Engr	Engr	Ord	Ord	Engr	Ord	Ord	476
Reproduction equipment, press section, 20 x $22\frac{1}{2}$, semi-trailer mounted, 10-ton, w/van body	SP	Engr	Engr	Ord	Ord	Engr	Ord	Ord	476
Reproduction equipment, press section, 22 x 29, semi-trailer mounted, 10-ton, w/van body	SP	Engr	Engr	Ord	Ord	Engr	Ord	Ord	476
Reproduction equipment, camera section, 24 x 24, semi-trailer mounted, $2\frac{1}{2}$-ton, w/van b dy	SP	Engr	Engr	Ord	Ord	Engr	Ord	Ord	462
Reproduction equipment, press section, 17 x 19, semi-trailer mounted, 10-ton, w/van body	SP	Engr	Engr	Ord	Ord	Engr	Ord	Ord	462
Crane, gasoline, engine driven, truck-mounted, $\frac{3}{8}$-cubic yard bucket (chassis 6-ton, 6 x 6)	SE	Ord	Engr	Engr	Engr	Engr	Ord	Engr	304
Truck, powered, fire, crash, class 135	SE	Ord	Engr	Engr	Engr	Engr	Ord	Engr	186
Truck, 6-ton, 6 x 6, 4b, bridge construction	SE	Ord	Engr	Engr	Engr	Engr	Ord	Engr	302
Compressor, air, gasoline engine driven, truck-mounted, 105 CFM, $2\frac{1}{2}$-ton, 6 x 6	SE	Ord	Engr	Engr	Engr	Engr	Ord	Engr	238
Auger, earth, gasoline engine powered, motorized M-2, $1\frac{1}{2}$-ton, 4 x 4	SE	Ord	Engr	Engr	Engr	Engr	Ord	Engr	206
Distributor, bituminous, truck-mounted, 800-gallon, 4-ton, 6 x 6	SE	Ord	Engr	Engr	Engr	Engr	Ord	Engr	296
Shop, motorized, general purpose, $2\frac{1}{2}$-ton, 6 x 6	SE	Ord	Engr	Engr	Engr	Engr	Ord	Engr	268

NOMENCLATURE	Vehicle classification (see par. 3, AR 850-15)	MAINTENANCE Parts Procurement Chassis	Body	Third Echelon and Higher Chassis	Body	STORAGE AND ISSUE Vehicle	Maintenance Parts Chassis	Body	Page Number
Shop, motorized, emergency repair, ¾-ton, 4 x 4	SE	Ord	Engr	Ord	Ord	Engr	Ord	Ord	168
Shop, motorized, electrical repair, 2½-ton, 6 x 6	SE	Ord	Engr	Ord	Engr	Engr	Ord	Engr	268
Shop, motorized, machine shop, light, 2½-ton, 6 x 6	SE	Ord	Engr	Ord	Engr	Engr	Ord	Engr	268
Shop, motorized, machine shop, heavy, 2½-ton, 6 x 6	SE	Ord	Engr	Ord	Engr	Engr	Ord	Engr	268
Shop, motorized, small tool repair, 2½-ton, 6 x 6	SE	Ord	Engr	Ord	Engr	Engr	Ord	Engr	268
Shop, motorized, tool and bench, 2½-ton, 6 x 6	SE	Ord	Engr	Ord	Engr	Engr	Ord	Engr	268
Distributor, water, truck, mounted, 1,000 GM 4-ton, 6 x 6	SE		Engr	Ord	Engr	Engr	Ord	Engr	288
Tank, bituminous supply steel, truck-mounted, 800-gallon, 4-ton, 6 x 6	SE	Ord	Engr	Ord	Engr	Engr	Ord	Engr	296
Water purification unit, mobile, 2½-ton, 6 x 6	SE	Ord	Engr	Ord	Engr	Engr	Ord	Engr	276
Reproduction equipment camera section, 24 x 24, 4-ton, 6 x 6, standard truck chassis w/van body	SE	Ord	Engr	Ord	Engr	Engr	Ord	Engr	292
Reproduction equipment laboratory section, motorized, 2½-ton, 6 x 6, standard truck chassis, w/van body	SE	Ord	Engr	Ord	Engr	Engr	Ord	Engr	256
Reproduction equipment map lay-out section, motorized, 2½-ton, 6 x 6, standard truck chassis, w/van body	SE	Ord	Engr	Ord	Engr	Engr	Ord	Engr	256
Reproduction equipment photographic section, motorized, 2½-ton, 6 x 6, standard truck chassis, w/van body	SE	Ord	Engr	Ord	Engr	Engr	Ord	Engr	256
Reproduction equipment, plate grainer section, motorized, 2½-ton, 6 x 6, standard truck chassis, w/van body	SE	Ord	Engr	Ord	Engr	Engr	Ord	Engr	256
Reproduction equipment, plate process section, motorized, 2½-ton, 6 x 6, standard truck chassis, w/van body	SE	Ord	Engr	Ord	Engr	Engr	Ord	Engr	256
Reproduction equipment, press section, 20 x 22½, motorized, 4-ton, 6 x 6, standard truck chassis, w/van body	SE	Ord	Engr	Ord	Engr	Engr	Ord	Engr	292
Reproduction equipment, press section, 20 x 29, motorized, 4-ton, 6 x 6, standard truck chassis, w/van body	SE	Ord	Engr	Ord	Engr	Engr	Ord	Engr	292
Reproduction equipment, camera section, 24 x 24, motorized, 2½-ton, 6 x 6, standard truck chassis, w/van body	SE	Ord	Engr	Ord	Engr	Engr	Ord	Engr	256
Reproduction equipment, press section, 20 x 22½, motorized, 2½-ton, 6 x 6, standard truck chassis, w/van body	SE	Ord	Engr	Ord	Engr	Engr	Ord	Engr	256
Truck, powered, fire pumper, class 500 (500 gpm)	SE	Ord	Engr	Ord	Engr	Engr	Ord	Engr	186
Truck, powered, fire pumper, class 525 (500 gpm)	SE	Ord	Engr	Ord	Engr	Engr	Ord	Engr	186
Truck, powered, fire pumper, type A, oversea, class 325	SE	Ord	Engr	Ord	Engr	Engr	Ord	Engr	186

Item	Service								Page
Truck, powered, fire, brush, class 300 (300 gpm)	SE	Ord	Engr	Ord	Engr	Engr	Ord	Engr	186
Truck, powered, fire, crash, class 110 (Co. 2)	SE	Ord	Engr	Ord	Engr	Engr	Ord	Engr	186
Truck, powered, fire, crash, class 125	SE	Ord	Engr	Ord	Engr	Engr	Ord	Engr	
Compressor, air, motorized, chassis 1½-ton to 3-ton, 4 x 4	SE	Ord	Engr	Ord	Engr	Engr	Ord	Engr	
Truck, 2½-ton, 6 x 6 earth auger	SE	Ord	Engr	Ord	Engr	Engr	Ord	Engr	326
Truck, 5-6-ton, 4 x 4 tractor ponton	SE	Ord	Engr	Ord	Ord	Engr	Ord	Ord	326
Truck, 5-6-ton, 4 x 4 tractor, topographical	SE	Ord	Engr	Ord	Engr	Engr	Ord	Ord	
Truck, powered, fire, class 155, 5-ton, 6 x 6	SE	Ord	Engr	Ord	Engr	Engr	Ord	Engr	
Truck, powered, fire crash, 7½-ton, 6 x 6	SP	Engr	Ebgr	Ord	Engr	Engr	Ord	Engr	
Army Air Forces									
Trailer, fuel servicing, type A-2-A-220-gallon (airborne)	SP	AAF	AAF	AAF	AAF	AAF	AAF	AAF	454
Trailer, fuel servicing, 600-gallon, A-1 and A-3, 2-wheel	SP	AAF	AAF	AAF	AAF	AAF	AAF	AAF	452–454
Trailer, 2-wheel, office	SP	AAF	AAF	Ord	Ord	AAF	Ord	Ord	
Trailer, laboratory, photo type A-1, 2-wheel	SP	AAF	AAF	AAF	AAF	AAF	AAF	AAF	440
Trailer, laboratory, photo type A-2, 2-wheel	SP	AAF	AAF	AAF	AAF	AAF	AAF	AAF	442
Truck, 1½-ton, 4 x 4, field lighting, J-3, J-4, J-5	SE	Ord	AAF	Ord	AAF	AAF	Ord	AAF	210–212
Truck, 1½-ton, 4 x 4, turret trainer, E-5	SE	Ord	AAF	Ord	AAF	AAF	Ord	AAF	220
Truck, 2½-ton, 4 x 4, oil servicing, type L-1	SE	Ord	AAF	Ord	AAF	AAF	Ord	AAF	232
Truck, 2½-ton, 6 x 6, oil servicing, 600-gallon, L-2	SE	Ord	AAF	Ord	AAF	AAF	Ord	AAF	258
Truck, 2½-ton, 6 x 6, fuel servicing, or oil, 750-gallon, F-3	SE	Ord	AAF	Ord	AAF	AAF	Ord	AAF	254
Truck, 7½-ton, 6 x 6, fuel servicing (tractor) F-1	SP	AAF	AAF	Ord	AAF	AAF	Ord	AAF	328
Truck, 7½-ton, 6 x 6, wrecking, C-2 (tractor)	SP	AAF	AAF	Ord	AAF	AAF	Ord	AAF	330
Dolly trailer converter, fuel servicing, 2-wheel, type F-2 or F-1A	SP	AAF	AAF	AAF	AAF	AAF	AAF	AAF	530
Dolly trailer converter, fuel servicing, 2-wheel, type F-2 or F-2A	SP	AAF	AAF	AAF	AAF	AAF	AAF	AAF	532
Dolly trailer, technical supply, field shop and instrument shop	SP	AAF	AAF	AAF	AAF	AAF	AAF	AAF	536
Dolly trailer, wrecking, C-2, 2-wheel	SP	AAF	AAF	AAF	AAF	AAF	AAF	AAF	534
Semitrailer, 2-wheel, 10-ton gross, field shop repair, type A-3	SP	AAF	AAF	AAF	AAF	AAF	AAF	AAF	484
Semitrailer, 2-wheel, fuel servicing, 2,000-gallon, F-2 or F-2A	SP	AAF	AAF	AAF	AAF	AAF	AAF	AAF	520–522
Semitrailer, 2-wheel, 6-ton payload, instrument shop	SP	AAF	AAF	AAF	AAF	AAF	AAF	AAF	472
Semitrailer, 2-wheel, 10-ton gross, photo laboratory, types N-1-2-3	SP	AAF	AAF	AAF	AAF	AAF	AAF	AAF	490
Semitrailer, 2-wheel, 10-ton gross, technical supply	SP	AAF	AAF	AAF	AAF	AAF	AAF	AAF	496
Semitrailer, 4-wheel, 15-ton payload, carry-all	SP	AAF	AAF	AAF	AAF	AAF	AAF	AAF	506

| | | MAINTENANCE | | | | STORAGE AND ISSUE | | | |
NOMENCLATURE	Vehicle classification (see par. 3, AR 850-15)	Parts Procurement Chassis	Parts Procurement Body	Third Echelon and Higher Chassis	Third Echelon and Higher Body	Vehicle	Maintenance Parts Chassis	Maintenance Parts Body	Page Number
Semitrailer, 4-wheel, fuel servicing, 4,000-gallon, F-1 or F-1A	SP	AAF	AAF	AAF	AAF	AAF	AAF	AAF	524–526
Semitrailer, 4-wheel, 10-ton gross, oxygen generator	SP	AAF	AAF	AAF	AAF	AAF	AAF	AAF	516
Semitrailer, 4-wheel, wrecking, 40-foot, type C-2	SP	AAF	AAF	AAF	AAF	AAF	AAF	AAF	514
Semitrailer, 4-wheel, wrecking, 25-foot, type C-2	SP	AAF	AAF	AAF	AAF	AAF	AAF	AAF	
Tractor, medium (track-laying), high speed, M-2, prime mover	SP	Ord	Ord	AAF	AAF	AAF	AAF	AAF	344
Tractor, crane, medium (track-laying), 6-ton, T-1, prime mover	SP	Ord	Ord	AAF	AAF	AAF	AAF	AAF	
Tractor, medium (track-laying), 2-ton crane, T-1, prime mover	SP	Ord	Ord	AAF	AAF	AAF	AAF	AAF	

Ordnance Department

NOMENCLATURE	Vehicle classification (see par. 3, AR 850-15)	Parts Procurement Chassis	Parts Procurement Body	Third Echelon and Higher Chassis	Third Echelon and Higher Body	Vehicle	Maintenance Parts Chassis	Maintenance Parts Body	Page Number
Ambulance, metropolitan	SP	Ord	Ord	Ord	Ord	Ord	Ord	Ord	358
Ambulance, ½-ton, 4 x 4	SE	Ord	Ord	Ord	Ord	Ord	Ord	Ord	354
Ambulance, ¾-ton, 4 x 4	SE	Ord	Ord	Ord	Ord	Ord	Ord	Ord	356
Ambulance, 1½-ton, 4 x 2 field	SE	Ord	Ord	Ord	Ord	Ord	Ord	Ord	360
Bus, passenger, 25-passenger	GP	Ord	Ord	Ord	Ord	Ord	Ord	Ord	364
Bus, passenger, 40-passenger	GP	Ord	Ord	Ord	Ord	Ord	Ord	Ord	368
Bus, passenger, 33-passenger	GP	Ord	Ord	Ord	Ord	Ord	Ord	Ord	362
Bus, sedan, converted, 15-passenger	GP	Ord	Ord	Ord	Ord	Ord	Ord	Ord	366
Bus, commercial type, 20- to 29-passenger	GP	Ord	Ord	Ord	Ord	Ord	Ord	Ord	370
Bus, semitrailer, converted, 40- to 45-passenger	GP	Ord	Ord	Ord	Ord	Ord	Ord	Ord	16–23
Cars, armored, all types	C	Ord	Ord	Ord	Ord	Ord	Ord	Ord	24
Cars, scout	C	Ord	Ord	Ord	Ord	Ord	Ord	Ord	372
Cars, 5-passenger light sedan	GP	Ord	Ord	Ord	Ord	Ord	Ord	Ord	374
Cars, 5-passenger medium sedan	GP	Ord	Ord	Ord	Ord	Ord	Ord	Ord	26–45
Carriages, half-tracks, all types	C	Ord	Ord	Ord	Ord	Ord	Ord	Ord	46–87
Carriages, self-propelled, artillery, all types	C	Ord	Ord	Ord	Ord	Ord	Ord	Ord	380
Scooters, all types	GP	Ord	Ord	Ord	Ord	Ord	Ord	Ord	136
Truck, ¼-ton, 4 x 4, cargo	GP	Ord	Ord	Ord	Ord	Ord	Ord	Ord	6
Truck, ¼-ton, 4 x 4, amphibian	SP	Ord	Ord	Ord	Ord	Ord	Ord	Ord	

Ord	Ord	Ord	Ord	Ord	Ord	Ord	Class	Ord	Truck	Page
Ord	Ord	Ord	Ord	Ord	Ord	Ord	SE	Ord	Truck, 1/2-ton, 4 x 2, ammunition	140
Ord	Ord	Ord	Ord	Ord	Ord	Ord	GP	Ord	Truck, 1/2-ton, 4 x 2, canopy express	138
Ord	Ord	Ord	Ord	Ord	Ord	Ord	GP	Ord	Truck, 1/2-ton, 4 x 2, carry-all	
Ord	Ord	Ord	Ord	Ord	Ord	Ord	GP	Ord	Truck, 1/2-ton, 4 x 2, C. S. & P.	144
Ord	Ord	Ord	Ord	Ord	Ord	Ord	GP	Ord	Truck, 1/2-ton, 4 x 2, panel delivery	142
Ord	Ord	Ord	Ord	Ord	Ord	Ord	GP	Ord	Truck, 1/2-ton, 4 x 2, pick-up	
Ord	Ord	Ord	Ord	Ord	Ord	Ord	GP	Ord	Truck, 1/2-ton, 4 x 2, sedan, delivery	146
Ord	Ord	Ord	Ord	Ord	Ord	Ord	GP	Ord	Truck, 1/2-ton, 4 x 4, carry-all	148
Ord	Ord	Ord	Ord	Ord	Ord	Ord	SE	Ord	Truck, 1/2-ton, 4 x 4, command-reconnaissance w & wo/w	150
Ord	Ord	Ord	Ord	Ord	Ord	Ord	SE	Ord	Truck, 1/2-ton, 4 x 4, emergency repair	152
Ord	Ord	Ord	Ord	Ord	Ord	Ord	GP	Ord	Truck, 1/2-ton, 4 x 4, panel delivery	224
Ord	Ord	Ord	Ord	Ord	Ord	Ord	SE	Ord	Truck, 1 1/2-3-ton, 4 x 4, automotive repair, M-2	154
Ord	Ord	Ord	Ord	Ord	Ord	Ord	GP	Ord	Truck, 1/2-ton, 4 x 4, pick-up, w & wo/w	156
Ord	Ord	Ord	Ord	Ord	Ord	Ord	GP	Ord	Truck, 1/2-ton, 4 x 4, radio	
Ord	Ord	Ord	Ord	Ord	Ord	Ord	GP	Ord	Truck, 3/4-ton, 4 x 2, panel delivery	160
Ord	Ord	Ord	Ord	Ord	Ord	Ord	GP	Ord	Truck, 3/4-ton, 4 x 2, pick-up	162
Ord	Ord	Ord	Ord	Ord	Ord	Ord	GP	Ord	Truck, 3/4-ton, 4 x 4, carry-all	164
Ord	Ord	Ord	Ord	Ord	Ord	Ord	GP	Ord	Truck, 3/4-ton, 4 x 4, command, w & wo/w	166
Ord	Ord	Ord	Ord	Ord	Ord	Ord	SE	Ord	Truck, 3/4-ton, 4 x 4, emergency repair	168
Ord	Ord	Ord	Ord	Ord	Ord	Ord	GP	Ord	Truck, 3/4-ton, 4 x 4, weapons carrier, w & wo/w	172
Ord	Ord	Ord	Ord	Ord	Ord	Ord	GP	Ord	Truck, 1 1/2-ton, 4 x 2, canopy express	174
Ord	Ord	Ord	Ord	Ord	Ord	Ord	GP	Ord	Truck, 1 1/2-ton, 4 x 2, pick-up	176
Ord	Ord	Ord	Ord	Ord	Ord	Ord	SE	Ord	Truck, 1 1/2-ton, ammunition body	
Ord	Ord	Ord	Ord	Ord	Ord	Ord	GP	Ord	Truck, 1 1/2-ton, 4 x 2, canopy express	182
Ord	Ord	Ord	Ord	Ord	Ord	Ord	GP	Ord	Truck, 1 1/2-ton, 4 x 2, cargo	180
Ord	Ord	Ord	Ord	Ord	Ord	Ord	GP	Ord	Truck, 1 1/2-ton, 4 x 2, combination stake and platform	178
Ord	Ord	Ord	Ord	Ord	Ord	Ord	GP	Ord	Truck, 1 1/2-ton, 4 x 2, dump	184
Ord	Ord	Ord	Ord	Ord	Ord	Ord	SE	Ord	Truck, 1 1/2-3-ton, 4 x 4, machine shop, M-4	224
Ord	Ord	Ord	Ord	Ord	Ord	Ord	SE	Ord	Truck, 1 1/2-ton, 4 x 2, explosives	
Ord	Ord	Ord	Ord	Ord	Ord	Ord	GP	Ord	Truck, 1 1/2-ton, 4 x 2, panel delivery	188
Ord	Ord	Ord	Ord	Ord	Ord	Ord	SP	Ord	Truck, 1 1/2-ton, 4 x 2, refuse collector, G-W	
Ord	Ord	Ord	Ord	Ord	Ord	Ord	SP	Ord	Truck, 1 1/2-ton, 4 x 2, pick-up	190
Ord	Ord	Ord	Ord	Ord	Ord	Ord	GP	Ord	Truck, 1 1/2-ton, 4 x 2, recruiting	
Ord	Ord	Ord	Ord	Ord	Ord	Ord	GP	Ord	Truck, 1 1/2-ton, 4 x 2, tractor	314
Ord	Ord	Ord	Ord	Ord	Ord	Ord	SE	Ord	Truck, 1 1/2-ton, 4 x 4, bomb service, M-6	194
Ord	Ord	Ord	Ord	Ord	Ord	Ord	GP	Ord	Truck, 1 1/2-ton, 4 x 4, cargo w & wo/w	196
Ord	Ord	Ord	Ord	Ord	Ord	Ord	SP	Ord	Truck, 1 1/2-ton, 4 x 4, C. O. E., S. & P. Body, 15-feet	200
Ord	Ord	Ord	Ord	Ord	Ord	Ord	SP	Ord	Truck, 1 1/2-ton, 4 x 4, C. S. & P.	198
Ord	Ord	Ord	Ord	Ord	Ord	Ord	GP	Ord	Truck, 1 1/2-ton, 4 x 4, dump w & wo/w	204
Ord	Ord	Ord	Ord	Ord	Ord	Ord	GP	Ord	Truck, 1 1/2-ton, 4 x 4, panel delivery	214

| | | MAINTENANCE | | | | STORAGE AND ISSUE | | | |
NOMENCLATURE	Vehicle classification (see par. 3, AR 850-15)	Parts Procurement Chassis	Parts Procurement Body	Third Echelon and Higher Chassis	Third Echelon and Higher Body	Vehicle	Maintenance Parts Chassis	Maintenance Parts Body	Page Number
Truck, 1½-ton, 4 x 4, tractor	GP	Ord	Ord	Ord	Ord	Ord	Ord	Ord	316
Truck, 1½-ton, 6 x 6, cargo and personnel carrier	GP	Ord	Ord	Ord	Ord	Ord	Ord	Ord	222
Truck, 1½-ton, 4 x 4, artillery, repair, M-2 and M-1	SE	Ord	Ord	Ord	Ord	Ord	Ord	Ord	224
Truck, 1½-ton, 4 x 4, instrument repair, M-1	SE	Ord	Ord	Ord	Ord	Ord	Ord	Ord	224
Truck, 1½-ton, 4 x 4, small arms repair, M-1	SE	Ord	Ord	Ord	Ord	Ord	Ord	Ord	224
Truck, 1½-ton, 4 x 4, spare parts, M-2	SE	Ord	Ord	Ord	Ord	Ord	Ord	Ord	224
Truck, 1½-ton, 4 x 4, tank maintenance, M-1	SE	Ord	Ord	Ord	Ord	Ord	Ord	Ord	224
Truck, 2½-ton, 4 x 2, ammunition	SP	Ord	Ord	Ord	Ord	Ord	Ord	Ord	
Truck, 2½-ton, 4 x 2, canopy express	GP	Ord	Ord	Ord	Ord	Ord	Ord	Ord	226
Truck, 2½-ton, 4 x 2, cargo	GP	Ord	Ord	Ord	Ord	Ord	Ord	Ord	
Truck, 2½-ton, 4 x 2, chassis only	GP	Ord	Ord	Ord	Ord	Ord	Ord	Ord	228
Truck, 2½-ton, 4 x 2, C. S. & P.	GP	Ord	Ord	Ord	Ord	Ord	Ord	Ord	230
Truck, 2½-ton, 4 x 2, dump	GP	Ord	Ord	Ord	Ord	Ord	Ord	Ord	
Truck, 2½-ton, 4 x 2, explosives	SE	Ord	Ord	Ord	Ord	Ord	Ord	Ord	318
Truck, 2½-ton, 4 x 2, tank, 1,000-gallon, fuel and oil	SP	Ord	Ord	Ord	Ord	Ord	Ord	Ord	
Truck, 2½-ton, 4 x 2, tank, 1,000-gallon, water	SP	Ord	Ord	Ord	Ord	Ord	Ord	Ord	
Truck, 2½-ton, 4 x 2, tractor	SE	Ord	Ord	Ord	Ord	Ord	Ord	Ord	
Truck, 2½-ton, 4 x 2, utility w/hoist and buckets	GP	Ord	Ord	Ord	Ord	Ord	Ord	Ord	
Truck, 2½-ton, 4 x 2, van	SP	Ord	Ord	Ord	Ord	Ord	Ord	Ord	320
Truck, 2½-ton, 4 x 2, load packer	SE	Ord	Ord	Ord	Ord	Ord	Ord	Ord	322
Truck, 2½-ton, 4 x 4, tractor	GP	Ord	Ord	Ord	Ord	Ord	Ord	Ord	234
Truck, 2½-ton, 6 x 4, tractor	GP	Ord	Ord	Ord	Ord	Ord	Ord	Ord	8
Truck, 2½-ton, 6 x 4, cargo w/and wo/w	GP	Ord	Ord	Ord	Ord	Ord	Ord	Ord	
Truck, 2½-ton, 6 x 6, amphibian	SE	Ord	Ord	Ord	Ord	Ord	Ord	Ord	242
Truck, 2½-ton, 6 x 6, artillery repair, M-9	SE	Ord	Ord	Ord	Ord	Ord	Ord	Ord	246
Truck, 2½-ton, 6 x 6, automotive repair, M-8	GP	Ord	Ord	Ord	Ord	Ord	Ord	Ord	248
Truck, 2½-ton, 6 x 6, cargo, LWB w/and wo/w	GP	Ord	Ord	Ord	Ord	Ord	Ord	Ord	252
Truck, 2½-ton, 6 x 6, cargo, SWB w/and wo/w	SP	Ord	Ord	Ord	Ord	Ord	Ord	Ord	260
Truck, 2½-ton, 6 x 6, cargo, C.O.E. 15-foot body wo/w	GP	Ord	Ord	Ord	Ord	Ord	Ord	Ord	260
Truck, 2½-ton, 6 x 6, dump, LWB w/and wo/w	SP	Ord	Ord	Ord	Ord	Ord	Ord	Ord	260
Truck, 2½-ton, 6 x 6, electrical repair, M-18	GP	Ord	Ord	Ord	Ord	Ord	Ord	Ord	
Truck, 2½-ton, 6 x 6, instrument repair, M-10	SE	Ord	Ord	Ord	Ord	Ord	Ord	Ord	
Truck, 2½-ton, 6 x 6, machine shop, M-16	SE	Ord	Ord	Ord	Ord	Ord	Ord	Ord	

Item	Class							Page
Truck, 2½-ton, 6 x 6, small arms repair, M-7	SE	Ord	Ord	Ord	Ord	Ord	Ord	260
Truck, 2½-ton, 6 x 6, spare parts	SE	Ord	Ord	Ord	Ord	Ord	Ord	260
Truck, 2½-ton, 6 x 6, stock rack	GP	Ord	Ord	Ord	Ord	Ord	Ord	262
Truck, 2½-ton, 6 x 6, tank, gasoline, 750-gallon	SE	Ord	Ord	Ord	Ord	Ord	Ord	264
Truck, 2½-ton, 6 x 6, tank, water, 700-gallon	SE	Ord	Ord	Ord	Ord	Ord	Ord	266
Truck, 2½-ton, 6 x 6, tool and bench, M-13	SE	Ord	Ord	Ord	Ord	Ord	Ord	260
Truck, 2½-ton, 6 x 6, welding, M-12A1	SE	Ord	Ord	Ord	Ord	Ord	Ord	260
Truck, 2½-ton, 6 x 6, instrument bench, M-23	SE	Ord	Ord	Ord	Ord	Ord	Ord	260
Truck, 4-ton, 6 x 6, cargo	GP	Ord	Ord	Ord	Ord	Ord	Ord	284
Truck, 4-ton, 6 x 6, cargo, LWB	GP	Ord	Ord	Ord	Ord	Ord	Ord	282
Truck, 4-ton, 6 x 6, wrecker, w/winch	SE	Ord	Ord	Ord	Ord	Ord	Ord	294
Truck, 4-ton, 6 x 6, dump	GP	Ord	Ord	Ord	Ord	Ord	Ord	290
Truck, 4-5-ton, 4 x 4, tractor	GP	Ord	Ord	Ord	Ord	Ord	Ord	324
Truck, 5-ton, 4 x 2, ammunition	SP	Ord	Ord	Ord	Ord	Ord	Ord	298
Truck, 5-ton, 4 x 2, cargo	GP	Ord	Ord	Ord	Ord	Ord	Ord	300
Truck, 5-ton, 4 x 2, C. S. and P.	GP	Ord	Ord	Ord	Ord	Ord	Ord	
Truck, 5-ton, 4 x 2, dump	GP	Ord	Ord	Ord	Ord	Ord	Ord	
Truck, 5-ton, 4 x 2, explosives	SE	Ord	Ord	Ord	Ord	Ord	Ord	
Truck, 5-ton, 4 x 2, tractor	GP	Ord	Ord	Ord	Ord	Ord	Ord	326
Truck, 5-6-ton, 4 x 4, tractor, w/w	GP	Ord	Ord	Ord	Ord	Ord	Ord	306
Truck, 6-ton, 6 x 6, prime mover, w/w	GP	Ord	Ord	Ord	Ord	Ord	Ord	302
Truck, 7½-ton, 6 x 6, prime mover, w/w	SP	Ord	Ord	Ord	Ord	Ord	Ord	332
Truck, 8-ton, 6 x 4, tractor	SE	Ord	Ord	Ord	Ord	Ord	Ord	312
Truck, 10-ton, 6 x 6, heavy wrecker, M-1	SP	Ord	Ord	Ord	Ord	Ord	Ord	132
Truck and trailer, 40-ton, wheeled, tank recovery, T-21	GP	Ord	Ord	Ord	Ord	Ord	Ord	382
Trailer, ¼-ton, 2-wheel, cargo, amphibian	SP	Ord	Ord	Ord	Ord	Ord	Ord	388
Trailer, ½-ton, 2-wheel, van, public address	GP	Ord	Ord	Ord	Ord	Ord	Ord	390
Trailer, ¾-ton, 2-wheel, cargo	GP	Ord	Ord	Ord	Ord	Ord	Ord	390
Trailer, 1-ton, 2-wheel, cargo	SE	Ord	Ord	Ord	Ord	Ord	Ord	400
Trailer, 1-ton, 2-wheel, 250-gallon, water	SP	Ord	Ord	Ord	Ord	Ord	Ord	396
Trailer, 1-ton, 2-wheel, 2-horse van	SP	Ord	Ord	Ord	Ord	Ord	Ord	
Trailer, 1½-ton, 4-wheel, recruiting	SP	Ord	Ord	Ord	Ord	Ord	Ord	450
Trailer, armored, 2-wheel, M-8	SP	Ord	Ord	Ord	Ord	Ord	Ord	448
Trailer, bomb, M-5	SP	Ord	Ord	Ord	Ord	Ord	Ord	
Trailer, plotting room, M-4	GP	Ord	Ord	Ord	Ord	Ord	Ord	422–424
Trailer, 6-ton, Athey, track-laying	GP	Ord	Ord	Ord	Ord	Ord	Ord	432
Trailer, 20-ton, Athey, track-laying	GP	Ord	Ord	Ord	Ord	Ord	Ord	
Semitrailer, 6-ton gross, 2-wheel, cargo	GP	Ord	Ord	Ord	Ord	Ord	Ord	
Semitrailer, 6-ton gross, 2-wheel, dump	GP	Ord	Ord	Ord	Ord	Ord	Ord	
Semitrailer, 6-ton gross, 2-wheel, stake and platform	GP	Ord	Ord	Ord	Ord	Ord	Ord	466

NOMENCLATURE	Vehicle classification (see par. 3, AR 850-15)	Parts Procurement Chassis	Parts Procurement Body	Third Echelon and Higher Chassis	Third Echelon and Higher Body	Vehicle	Maintenance Parts Chassis	Maintenance Parts Body	Page Number
		MAINTENANCE				STORAGE AND ISSUE			
Semitrailer, 6-ton gross, 2-wheel, van	GP	Ord	Ord	Ord	Ord	Ord	Ord	Ord	464
Semitrailer, 2-wheel, combination animal and cargo	GP	Ord	Ord	Ord	Ord	Ord	Ord	Ord	482
Semitrailer, 7-ton (PL), 10-ton gross, cargo	GP	Ord	Ord	Ord	Ord	Ord	Ord	Ord	500
Semitrailer, 10-ton gross, 2-wheel, van	GP	Ord	Ord	Ord	Ord	Ord	Ord	Ord	478
Semitrailer, 10-ton gross, 2-wheel mobile record unit	SE	Ord	Ord	Ord	Ord	Ord	Ord	Ord	488
Semitrailer, 12-ton gross, 2-wheel low platform	SP	Ord	Ord	Ord	Ord	Ord	Ord	Ord	502
Semitrailer, 16-ton gross, 4-wheel tandem, van	GP	Ord	Ord	Ord	Ord	Ord	Ord	Ord	
Tanks, all types	C	Ord	Ord	Ord	Ord	Ord	Ord	Ord	88-125
Tractor, crane, 1-ton, M-1	SP	Ord	Ord	Ord	Ord	Ord	Ord	Ord	340
Tractor, light (track-laying)	SP	Ord	Ord	Ord	Ord	Ord	Ord	Ord	
Tractor, medium (track-laying)	SP	Ord	Ord	Ord	Ord	Ord	Ord	Ord	
Tractor, heavy (track-laying)	SP	Ord	Ord	Ord	Ord	Ord	Ord	Ord	
Motorcycles, solo, chain driven, 45 cubic inches	GP	Ord	Ord	Ord	Ord	Ord	Ord	Ord	376
Motorcycles, solo, shaft drive	GP	Ord	Ord	Ord	Ord	Ord	Ord	Ord	
Motorcycles, w/side car, chain driven	GP	Ord	Ord	Ord	Ord	Ord	Ord	Ord	378

$$\begin{bmatrix} \text{(A. G. 300.7—(9 July 43))} \\ \text{(O. O. 461/43922 misc. (12 July 42))} \end{bmatrix}$$

BY ORDER OF THE SECRETARY OF WAR:

G. C. MARSHALL,
Chief of Staff.

OFFICIAL:
J. A. ULIO,
Major General,
The Adjutant General.

DISTRIBUTION: C & H (1)

TANK, MEDIUM, M4, AND
TANK, MEDIUM, M4 (105-MM HOW.)

Armament: One Gun, 75-mm, M3, or one Howitzer, 105-mm, T8; two Guns, machine, cal. .30 M1919A4 (flexible); one Gun, machine, cal. .50, HB, M2; one Gun, submachine, cal. .45 M1928A1.

Ammunition: 97 rounds, 75-mm or 68 rounds, 105-mm; 300 rounds, cal. .50; 600 rounds, cal. .45; 6,250 rounds, cal. .30; 12 hand grenades.

For further information see pages 106-107.

NOTES

NOTES